A SYSTEMATIC REGIONAL GEOGRAPHY
A Post-Matriculation Course

VOLUME III

A WORLD SURVEY
FROM THE HUMAN ASPECT

A SYSTEMATIC REGIONAL GEOGRAPHY
A Post-Matriculation Course

Volume 1
THE BRITISH ISLES

Volume 2
EUROPE

Volume 3
A WORLD SURVEY—
FROM THE HUMAN ASPECT

UNIVERSITY OF LONDON PRESS, LTD.

A SYSTEMATIC
REGIONAL GEOGRAPHY
A Post-Matriculation Course

VOLUME III
A WORLD SURVEY
FROM THE HUMAN ASPECT

by
J. F. UNSTEAD, M.A., D.Sc.

*Formerly Professor of Geography in the
University of London*

*With Numerous Maps and
Diagrams Specially Prepared
and other Illustrations*

UNIVERSITY OF LONDON PRESS, Ltd.
WARWICK SQUARE, LONDON, E.C.4

First Printed 1948

X763915342

AGENTS OVERSEAS

AUSTRALIA AND NEW ZEALAND
AND SOUTH SEA ISLANDS
>W. S. SMART, P.O. Box 120,
>> SYDNEY, N.S.W.
>*Showroom :* 14, York Street.

CANADA
>CLARKE, IRWIN & Co., Ltd.,
>> 480–486, University Avenue, TORONTO.

EGYPT AND SUDAN
>DINO JUDAH NAHUM,
>> P.O. Box 940, CAIRO.
>*Showroom :* 44, Sharia Sherif Pasha.

FAR EAST (including China and Japan)
>DONALD MOORE,
>> 22, Orchard Road, SINGAPORE.

INDIA
>ORIENT LONGMANS, Ltd.,
>> BOMBAY : Nicol Road.
>> CALCUTTA : Chittaranjan Avenue.
>> MADRAS : Mount Road.

SOUTH AFRICA
>H. B. TIMMINS, P.O. Box 94, CAPE TOWN.
>*Showroom :* 58–60, Long Street.

6002057213

Printed in Great Britain for the UNIVERSITY OF LONDON PRESS, LTD.,
by HAZELL, WATSON AND VINEY, LTD., The Printing Works, Aylesbury

PREFACE

THE aim of this book is to present a broad view of the way in which man lives upon the earth, and to show how men and their environments have influenced each other. It is written with special reference to the needs of students preparing for or pursuing courses in Universities and Training Colleges, in order to set out the general pattern of natural conditions and human life over the globe, and thus to provide a framework for more detailed studies either of geographical regions or of man's activities.

A general view, or framework, of this kind is necessary, whether it be systematically attempted as here, or whether it be gradually and perhaps fragmentarily acquired, as is sometimes the case. Yet the scope is so great that within the limits of a single volume it is well to give most of the available space to those matters which appear, to the writer, of greatest importance. At the present time, it is clear that many of the compelling problems which face mankind are so bound up with geographical factors that people gain greatly by understanding their connection ; this is one of the main contributions which geography can make to education.

A pitfall, however, must be avoided : one may unconsciously allow prejudice or partisanship to distort an objective and scientific view. Hence I have tried to explain the social, economic and political problems without putting forward policies for their solution where these are still in dispute. Similarly I have tried to avoid judgments about the thoughts and actions of peoples, except where standards are now commonly accepted by informed opinion.

The scheme of the survey is indicated on the Contents page, and only a few points need be added. In Part I there is a concise examination of the geographical background of man's life and activities, with brief preliminary indications of the ways in which natural conditions have important influences on mankind. In Part II the human developments include those of the evolution of man himself, and of his ideas, modes of life and work,

v

political organizations and present difficulties ; in this part fuller account is taken of the mutual interaction of human and natural factors.   In Part III there is a systematic synthesis of the particular human and physical elements which characterize the major geographical regions, leading to an examination of the extent to which man has by now succeeded in constituting " one world.".

Material not usual in a geographical textbook has been introduced in several connections.   Among these may be mentioned a series of charts, with accompanying text, showing the seasonal rhythms which characterize natural conditions and human activities in each type of geographical region.   Also the chapter on the distribution of population and its problems contains sections on the present trends towards increase or decrease, and on the comparative standards of living in the various States. Further, the next two chapters represent an attempt to mark out and describe the " Cultural Regions " of the world, using the term " cultural " in its widest sense ; here I felt special difficulty in realizing and in stating the ideas and ideals of the peoples, for I have had to allow for the tendency towards prejudice natural to one habituated to European, and particularly to British, modes of thought and sources of information.   For this reason I have considered it wise to adopt a general rule to say the best one honestly can about what to us are alien conceptions and actions.

The great changes brought about by the Second World War in political, social and economic conditions have been taken into account as far as possible at this time, but they are still proceeding, and it will be necessary for readers to amplify or modify some of the statements in this book by facts obtained from current publications.

My special thanks are due to Professor C. B. Fawcett who read and discussed the typescript of this book and at all stages of its preparation generously gave his advice and assistance, and to Miss G. H. Savory, B.A., for the preparation of the Index. Thanks are also due to the Director of the Courtauld Institute of Art, the Librarian and Map Curator of the Royal Geographical Society and the Secretary of the Royal Anthropological Institute for their aid in obtaining, and permission to use, the photographs of racial types of man and characteristic dwellings and architecture.

J. F. U.

February, 1948.

CONTENTS

PART I

NATURAL CONDITIONS

PART II

HUMAN DEVELOPMENTS

PART III

GEOGRAPHICAL SYNTHESES

LIST OF MAPS AND DIAGRAMS

LIST OF PLATES

NOTE ON MAPS

THE maps showing the distribution of various phenomena over the world as a whole are constructed so as to give the most important regions, from the human point of view, with as little distortion, and at the same time on as large a scale, as the shape and size of a page allow. The projection on which these maps are drawn is one by Eckert[1] which is area-true, showing all areas in their correct sizes in relation to one another; the distortion which is inevitable in all maps includes in this case a progressive exaggeration of east-west distances, and a corresponding diminution of north-south distances, towards the poles. When the polar areas are omitted, as here, this projection distorts the marginal areas of the maps less than is the case in the more commonly adopted Mollweide and Sinusoidal projections. Also, to enable the continental areas to be shown as large as possible, the maps are centred upon Long. 30° E. and the oceanic areas on the margins are cut off.

These maps deal with most aspects of geography, but the available space has been used mainly to supplement those commonly found in atlases; it is assumed that an atlas will be constantly used with this book.

[1] Published, with an explanation of the construction and a discussion of the use, as Entwurf VI in *Petermann, Mitteilungen*, 1906.

NOTE ON THE USE OF THE NAME "INDIA"

THE greater part of this book was set up in type before the Independence of India Act of 1947 converted the Empire of India into the two Dominions of India and Pakistan, as explained at the end of Chapter XVIII.

The name " India " has had to be retained in the text where it refers to the whole area which has generally been understood by this term, e.g. in the accounts of the relief and structure, the climatic conditions, the long-past incursions of racial groups, the present types of agriculture, and the total population as it is considered in Chapter XIX. In the chapter on Colonies and Commonwealth, however, the distinction between the Dominions of India and Pakistan is pointed out, and the two States are shown separately in the diagrams of Areas and Populations of the most populous States on p. 272.

If the new political organization proves permanent, it may be well to reserve the name " India " only for the one State, and to substitute the phrase " the Indian sub-continent " when referring to the region as a whole, but the traditional usage of the term " India " in the present volume should not cause misunderstanding.

PART I
NATURAL CONDITIONS

CHAPTER I
THE RELIEF OF THE LANDS

General Introduction.—From the human aspect we may regard geography as the study of " the earth as the home of man," but we must interpret this phrase with some care.

In considering " man " we must take into account the fact that there are marked differences between different peoples of the world. There are a number of racial groups of mankind, which differ from one another in some of their physical and physiological characteristics. Men differ, too, in the ways in which they have developed culturally, e.g. in such matters as languages, religions, social organizations and forms of government ; they have learnt various methods of supplying their needs, and their particular occupations are bound up with strongly contrasted modes of life.

In considering the earth as the " home " of these differing peoples, we must think of it as providing them with the materials for their houses and their household equipment ; we must also see how the available materials and even the forms of the houses and equipment are affected by the climatic conditions and the vegetation of the regions in which the various peoples live. Similarly we must study how the earth gives opportunities, and perhaps encouragement or discouragement, for men to undertake particular kinds of work. Thus, in agriculture the climate and soil conditions are very important factors ; mining can be carried on only where there are useful mineral deposits, and these depend upon the structure of the earth's crust below the surface ; many occupations are affected greatly by the relief of the earth's surface—the situation and form of lowland plains, upland plateaus and highland masses.

Even man himself is affected by his " home." For example, in equatorial regions the bodily characteristics of Negroes show special adaptations which withstand the heat and moisture ; in other regions the mental energy of people is stimulated by certain climates and lessened by others. Further, the movements of racial groups, and also of peoples with particular forms of cultural development, have been influenced by natural conditions : they have been encouraged to migrate into some regions by the relatively low relief of the intervening land, by the course of rivers, by suitable climate and soils, or by desired forms of natural vegetation. On the contrary, they have been barred from other regions by highlands or seas, by the direct hindrance of climatic conditions, by the lack of plant life or even by its very exuberance.

A consideration of such factors shows that a study of the broad features of the earth's surface is the necessary preliminary to a study of the life and work of man.

The Relief of the Lands.—More than two-thirds of the earth's crust is covered by the water of the oceans, and beneath the surface of the water the relief is so marked that the ocean depths are greater than the height of any mountains above sea-level. Nevertheless the shape and elevations of the continents have a far greater influence on human geography.

Because of the projection on which the map of world relief on p. 4 is drawn, the relative areas of the highlands, etc., are accurately indicated, but their shape and directions can be truly realized only upon a globe.

The Highland Regions.—Under this term are included regions which exceed 3,000 feet over considerable areas.

The Circum-Pacific Highlands.—On a globe it may be seen that around the Pacific Ocean is a broken rim of highlands. In North America is the Cordillera region of the west, formed partly by ranges, e.g. the Rocky Mountains, the Cascade Mountains, the Sierra Nevada and the Sierra Madre, and partly by high plateaus and basins which are bounded by these and other ranges. Farther south, broken mountain masses rise from Central America and the West Indian Islands. Then, after a narrow break at the Isthmus of Panama, in the west of South America rises the great Cordillera region of the Andes ; this is narrower than that of North America but is similarly composed of mountain ranges and of high plateaus and basins. In both North and South America very considerable areas are more than 6,000 feet high, while in South America some of the plateaus rise to over 12,000 feet, and in both continents the culminating peaks exceed 20,000 feet.

In later chapters we shall trace in some detail the consequences of the height and situation of these Cordillera. Here it may be pointed out that, partly because of low temperatures at high altitudes and partly because some of the ranges shut off sea-winds and cause interior areas to be desert or semi-desert, the Cordillera prevent great parts of the west of North and South America from being the homes of any large numbers of people. Further, they bar easy movement between the eastern parts of the continents and the Pacific coasts.

Yet the influence of these highlands depends to a considerable extent upon their latitude. Their effects in making some areas too cold and in keeping out moisture-bearing winds from others are most marked in mid-latitudes, i.e. outside the Tropics. On the contrary, in inter-tropical latitudes the altitude modifies the great heat which is harmful to man's health and hinders his activity. Also, where people have utilized the rain and snow which fall on the ranges for irrigating the interior plateaus and basins, as in Mexico, the United States and parts of the Andes, agriculture is carried on ; it was on this basis that, many centuries ago, a civilization developed upon the Mexican plateau and a still earlier one in the Andean region. (To appreciate these influences of relief, in connection with situation, upon the distribution of population at the present time, compare the map on p. 4 with that on p. 295.)

On the other side of the Pacific Ocean are also mountain masses whose general direction is more or less north-south and which together form a highland boundary to the ocean. On this side of the Pacific, however, the highland rim is broken into relatively short mountain chains which rise abruptly from the greatest ocean depths and appear as festoons of islands off the coasts of Asia, in the East Indian Archipelago and in New Zealand ; also, in the eastern parts of the continents of Asia and Australia there are other mountain ranges which border the ocean or the seas between the islands and mainland. These mountain areas are less continuous and also of lower elevation than the Cordillera of the Americas ; only a few relatively small areas exceed 6,000 feet in height. Hence, in these parts of the world human settlements and movements are not restricted by the relief as they are on the opposite side

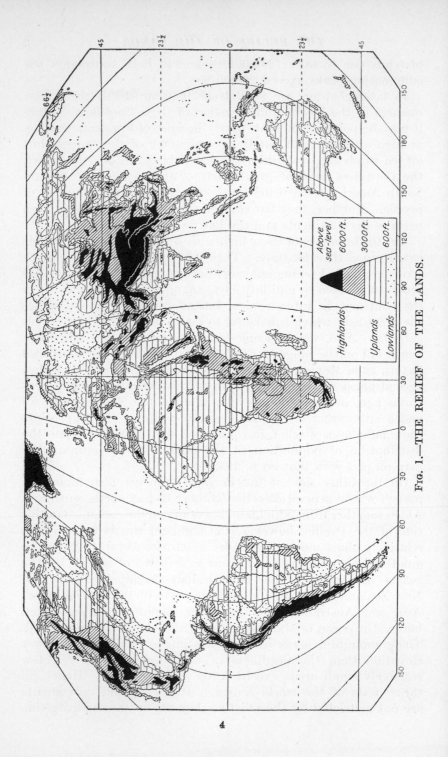

Fig. 1.—THE RELIEF OF THE LANDS.

Above
sea-level
6000 ft.
3000 ft.
600 ft.

Highlands
Uplands
Lowlands

of the Pacific Ocean ; the mountains do not prevent sea-winds bringing moisture to the lands, and between the ranges there are no unproductive and scantily populated areas. Indeed, the groups of islands have served again and again as stepping-stones for migrations and settlements of peoples.

The Mid-World Highlands.—From Central Asia westward to the Atlantic Ocean in the neighbourhood of the Mediterranean Sea stretch a series of mountains and plateaus which are some-times termed the mid-world highlands because they lie between the northern and southern parts of the Old World. By far the most outstanding mass is the Tibetan Plateau, exceeding 12,000 feet in elevation, and bordered on the south by the Himalayan ranges from which rise some of the highest points of the globe, including Mount Everest and others over five miles in height. At the western end of the Tibetan Plateau is the highland of the Pamirs, " the roof of the world," and from this highland north-eastward run the Tian Shan and other moun-tains which bound the plateaus of Turkistan and Mongolia. Together with Tibet, these mountains, high plateaus and basins form " High Asia," the core of the Asiatic continent.

Shut off from sea-winds, the interior plateaus and basins of High Asia are dry and in winter are intensely cold ; they can support but little life of any kind. Moreover, the whole high-land region, together with the ranges which curve southward from Tibet through Indo-China, has formed a barrier to human movements and intercourse which has had the greatest effect on the history of mankind. The peoples of the Far East have developed physical and cultural characteristics which set them quite apart from those of India, who have evolved under very different conditions, while both these great groups of mankind are contrasted in many ways with the inhabitants of the lands of Europe and Asia which lie west and north-west of High Asia.

Westward from the Pamirs run several series of curving mountain ranges which have a common characteristic of branching out from one another and then drawing together again to enclose basin-shaped areas. First, and linked to High Asia by the Hindu Kush Mountains, there is the Iranian Plateau bordered by high ranges. Next, spreading westward from the Armenian Mountains which adjoin the Caucasus, is the less elevated Anatolian Plateau of Asia Minor. From the break which separates Asia Minor from Europe, the curving moun-

tain chains continue westward to the Atlantic Ocean ; in Europe
they form arcs in the Balkan, Carpathian, Alpine, Apennine
and Iberian regions, and in North-west Africa they comprise
the ranges of the Atlas Lands. In this part of the mid-world
belt of highlands, however, while the ranges bound some plateau
areas, as in the Balkan and Iberian Peninsulas and in the Atlas
Lands, elsewhere they enclose lower basins, either in the form
of lowlands, e.g. the Plains of Hungary and Lombardy, or
depressions so deep that they have been invaded by the waters
and form the Mediterranean and adjoining seas.

In this western portion of the mid-world belt of highlands,
the ranges and the elevated plateaus are but poorly populated.
In the neighbourhood of the Mediterranean Sea, however, the
relatively small areas of habitable land in the river valleys,
and those which lie between the mountains and the sea, have
been the homes of people who, though by no means great in
number, have developed highly in successive civilizations.
From this region streams of cultural influence have gone out
to all parts of the world of man.

The Arabian-African Highlands.—Adjoining the mid-world
belt at the eastern end of the Mediterranean region, another
great zone of highlands extends southward. It begins as a
narrow belt in Syria and broadens in western Arabia. Then it is
broken by the valley which is covered by the waters of the Red
Sea and separates Asia from Africa. On the African side it rises to
the Highland of Abyssinia, and thence is continued southward
by the East African Plateau until the area of highland widens
to include almost all Africa south of the Congo Basin, together
with part of the detached mass of Madagascar. From the
point of view of human geography, this southward-trending
highland belt is significant as having provided a bridge of
habitable land across the equatorial region with its damp heat
and dense forests which are so hostile to man.

Isolated Highland Areas.—In the far north and the far south
of the globe are two large isolated highland masses : the island
of Greenland in Arctic latitudes and the continent of Antarctica.
In Greenland small coastal lowlands have served, together with
similar areas in Iceland, as stepping-stones across the North
Atlantic Ocean between Europe and America, but until recent
years Antarctica has lain entirely beyond the world of man.

In several parts of the world there are other areas exceeding

3,000 feet in height, but most of these are not of great extent. Here attention can be drawn only to the Guiana Highlands to the north, and to the Brazilian Highlands to the south, of the Amazon Basin in South America ; perhaps these might be best regarded as the culminating parts of more extensive uplands with a general elevation of between 600 and 3,000 feet. The same is true of the smaller highlands in Scandinavia, the Appalachian region in North America, and other areas to which the term " mountains " is commonly applied.

Upland and Lowland Regions.—The areas below 3,000 feet provide homes for by far the greater part of the world's population. Except in the hottest and coldest latitudes and in some arid regions, the lowlands (below 600 feet) offer opportunities for agriculture, the main support of mankind. The uplands (between 600 and 3,000 feet) are also in many cases agricultural lands, and in some instances they have mineral and forest resources which have attracted settlers. A useful distinction can sometimes be drawn between the uplands and lowlands, but elsewhere they merge into one another, and in some parts of the world the difference in height has relatively little influence on the human geography. The uplands and lowlands may therefore be considered together.

Eurasia.—From several points of view Europe and Asia are but parts of one land-mass which it is convenient to name Eurasia. In the Eurasian area an important distinction exists between the lands (less than 3,000 feet high) on the northern side of the mid-world belt of highlands, and those of similarly low altitude in southern and eastern Asia.

In the northern region of Eurasia, from the Atlantic shores to the mountains near the Pacific coast of Siberia, stretches a very large area over which, although it is partly upland and partly lowland, the relief is so slight that it is essentially an enormous plain ; over this great region human movements suffer almost no hindrance. Most of it is less than 600 feet above sea-level, but there are uplands on its margins, e.g. in the west of the British Isles and in Scandinavia, and between the northern Eurasian lowland and the mid-world and circum-Pacific highlands. In eastern Europe there are also areas which rise to just over 600 feet, but the great plain which stretches across central Europe and western Siberia is broken only by one important elevation, viz. the Ural Mountains, and these exceed 3,000 feet only in small areas.

In the west of this Eurasian plain lives one of the greatest groups of population in the world (see the map on p. 295). The fact that there is but a small population in the Asiatic part of the region is due to climatic causes, viz. the aridity of Turkistan and the long, cold winter of Siberia.

South of the mid-world belt of highlands in Asia are two regions below 3,000 feet. The first is in Syria, Arabia and Mesopotamia, where aridity has prevented the existence of any large populated areas except where irrigation has reclaimed the desert near the rivers Tigris and Euphrates. The second region lies south of the highest part of High Asia and comprises the lowlands of northern India and the plateau of the Deccan ; except in north-western India where rain is lacking, these lands yield sustenance for a population which numbers almost four-fifths that of Europe or of the Far East.

In eastern Asia are a number of very important lowlands and uplands situated among the circum-Pacific highlands, and between these highlands and the ocean. In the basins of the Chinese rivers and on the Japanese islands, these lower lands support the greatest concentration of humanity on the globe. (Refer again to the map on p. 295, and note the table of population on p. 298.)   So shut off are the people of the Far East by the ocean on the one side and by High Asia and the mountains of Indo-China on the other, that their civilization for thousands of years proceeded along different lines from that of the West ; only quite recently has it been greatly affected by influences brought over long sea-routes from Europe and America.

East Indies and Australia.—As in the Far East, so in the East Indies the scattered lowlands and uplands which lie between the sea and the highlands are capable of supporting large numbers of people. On the contrary, although Australia is mainly a great area of lowland or upland, the position of this continent on the globe gives most of it such unfavourable climatic conditions that the greater part is almost uninhabited.

New Zealand is another instance in which a small area of lowland lies between highlands and the sea but is so climatically favoured that it could support a relatively large population for its size ; in this case, however, the region is so far from the lands which were early civilized that its possibilities have not yet been fully developed and its population is at present small.

Africa.—With the exception of the Atlas Highlands, the huge mass of North Africa is almost entirely a plateau of moderate altitude, although small parts of it rise to over 3,000 feet. As in Australia, so here the extent to which the land is habitable depends on its world position. Between the dry desert of the Sahara and the unhealthy, hot and wet forests of the Congo Basin lies the grassland of the Sudan, and in this region men have been able to migrate and to settle in considerable numbers. Of very great importance is the narrow valley of the Nile ; fertilized by the waters of the river, this valley was one of the cradles of civilization, and irrigation has now made it an extraordinarily densely populated strip within the belt of desert. The southern part of the African continent is mainly highland, but there are upland and lowland areas where the climate determines the value for mankind.

South of the Sahara, Africa has been for many centuries the home of the Negroes who have occupied most of the habitable areas. They have had a considerable degree of isolation from other races by the ocean surrounding the area on all sides except the north, where the belt of desert cuts it off from Eurasia. Their dominion was effectively checked only when Europeans by-passed the barrier of the Sahara by learning to navigate distant seas.

South America.—As was stated above, the areas in the Guiana and Brazilian Highlands exceeding 3,000 feet are the culminating parts of great plateaus which have a general altitude between 600 and 3,000 feet.

The Guiana Plateau, situated almost on the Equator, rises steeply on the west from the lowlands of the Orinoco and Amazon river basins and slopes down more gently eastward to the Atlantic coastal plain. The Brazilian Plateau, on the contrary, rises steeply on its eastern side from a very narrow coastal lowland and forms a broad upland sloping gradually westward to the lowlands of the Amazon basin and the rivers which drain to the La Plata estuary.

Much of the rest of South America east of the Andes consists of vast plains which have a threefold arrangement : in the centre are the great Amazon Lowlands ; to the north are the Llanos of the Orinoco Basin ; southward stretch the lands drained by the rivers leading to the La Plata and, still farther to the south, those running directly to the Atlantic Ocean.

The effect of these features of the relief of South America upon the human geography varies according to their world position. In the inter-tropical area, i.e. as far south as the Tropic of Capricorn, the climate of the lowlands is either directly inimical to man or it promotes the growth of natural vegetation of no great value as a food supply. The most productive areas are the eastern parts of the Brazilian Plateau which have the advantage of sea-winds from the Atlantic ; on these uplands the tropical climate is modified and around Rio de Janeiro there is a fairly dense population.

In the extra-tropical areas, south of the Tropic of Capricorn, the lower lands of South America have a climate relatively favourable to man, and here wide areas have been opened up to occupation, especially in the Pampa region round the La Plata estuary.

On the Pacific side of the Andean Highlands are but narrow coastal lowlands ; on these, men have settled in considerable numbers only in specially favourable conditions.

North America.—Apart from the Western Cordillera, the greater part of this continent is lowland or upland ; the only exceptions are relatively small culminating areas above 3,000 feet in the Appalachian Uplands region of the Eastern States and in the continuation of the same line of upland farther to the north-east in Canada. Moreover, although the map shows a distinction between the uplands and lowlands at the 600 feet contour line, there is seldom any important change at this level ; between the Western Cordillera and the Appalachian Uplands there are certain areas which stand up markedly from the rest of the country, but over vast expanses the prevailing impression is that of great plains. In this central belt of the continent, from the Arctic archipelago southward to the sub-tropical (i.e. almost tropical) coasts of the Gulf of Mexico, there is no serious barrier either to the movement of man or to the sweep of winds—sometimes bitterly cold from the north and sometimes swelteringly hot from the south.

The extent to which the vast areas of lowland and upland are productive, and therefore habitable, is a matter of climate due to world position. In north-eastern Canada, as in Siberia, the long, cold winter is a hindrance, and drought is a handicap in the western interior near the Cordillera ; nevertheless, there is great and varied production over large regions.

The aboriginal " American Indians " made little use of the resources, but the utilization of the possibilities went on rapidly after the settlement of Europeans along the eastern coasts two or three centuries ago. Now this part of the continent has become densely populated, and North America as a whole, with its wide lowlands and uplands, has become one of the most important homes of mankind.

Land and Sea Hemispheres.—The map printed below [1] shows a circle bounding the " land hemisphere "—the half of the globe which contains the maximum amount of land surface.

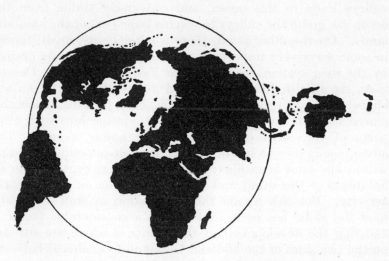

FIG. 2.—THE LAND HEMISPHERE.

This hemisphere includes practically all the great continental mass of Eurasia which together with Africa forms the " Mainland " of the globe ; it includes also all North America and a considerable part of South America. With adjoining islands these areas comprise more than five-sixths of the total land surface. The other half of the globe is the " water hemisphere," in which the only lands are the southern part of South America, the East Indies, Australia, the islands of the Pacific region and Antarctica. Excluding this ice-capped plateau and the similarly uninhabitable highland of Greenland, nearly nine-tenths of the land area of the globe is situated in the land hemisphere.

[1] For this map and the suggestion of the names " Mainland " and " Midland Ocean " I am indebted to Professor C. B. Fawcett.

The map brings out the important fact that the two great continental groups, the Mainland and the Americas respectively, face one another across the Atlantic—the " Midland Ocean " ; moreover, from the northern part of the Midland Ocean only its much smaller extension of the Arctic Sea separates Eurasia from North America.

By comparing this map with one in an atlas showing the river systems, it will be seen that the drainage both of the Mainland and of the Americas is largely towards the Midland Ocean ; therefore much of the traffic going down the rivers or their valleys leads to this ocean, and conversely traffic from this ocean can go up the valleys to reach a large part of the habitable lands.   On the other hand, there is a relatively small, though in some ways very important, area of the land-masses drained by the river systems leading to the Pacific and Indian Oceans.

As the British Isles are situated in the Midland Ocean and almost in the centre of the land hemisphere, they are favourably placed from the point of view of their relationships with other parts of the earth considered as the home of man.   This advantage is seen to be the greater when it is pointed out that within the land hemisphere are about 94 per cent. of the inhabitants of the world and almost the whole of its industrial activity.   For this reason the distribution of land and water over the globe has been, and still is, a considerable factor in assisting the development of the countries which are situated on the two sides of the Midland Ocean and are almost half-way between the Arctic and Equatorial regions.

Maritime and Continental Regions.—Land areas which do not extend very far from the ocean differ in several important respects from those which are remote from sea influences. For instance, the maritime regions are more influenced by ocean winds, which tend to increase the rainfall and also to modify the heat of summer and the cold of winter.   Moreover, maritime regions are more easily reached by people travelling by water, and therefore many of them have in the past been settled by sea-farers, and in some cases by those from several distant regions.   Further, commerce is in general more easily carried on in maritime areas than in the heart of continents.   In all these respects Europe offers a contrast between its west and centre which are distinctly maritime and its east which is more continental ; the two regions are marked off from one another by a line drawn southward from North Cape through the Gulf of Bothnia and the east of the Baltic Sea, the Vistula Basin and the Carpathian Mountains to the Danube mouth.

On the Atlantic side of this line is the maritime area of " Peninsular Europe," so named because it consists of peninsulas, viz. Scandinavia, the main peninsula of Central and Western Europe, and the Mediterranean peninsulas in the south, together with the British and other islands. On the continental side of the dividing line is Eastern Europe, named also " Trunk Europe " because it forms part of the great trunk of Eurasia.

In later chapters it will be seen that these two regions are broadly distinguished by different climates and different types of natural vegetation. In its human geography, Peninsular Europe has been greatly influenced by the settlement of civilized peoples from the Mediterranean area, by the early adoption of the Roman form of Christianity, and by the first developments of modern agriculture, industry and commerce. In contrast, Trunk Europe suffered from frequent incursions by Asiatic peoples, adopted Christianity in connection with the Greek or Orthodox Church, and developed on modern economic lines in quite recent years.

Considering the whole of Eurasia, it may be regarded as comprising a markedly continental " Heartland " bordered by several " Coastlands " or maritime areas.[1] The Heartland may be thought of as including Trunk Europe and extending eastward and south-eastward across all Central Asia; i.e. it includes both the lowlands and uplands now within the Union of Soviet Socialist Republics (U.S.S.R.) and also much of the highlands and interior basins of the Asiatic part of the mid-world mountain systems (see Fig. 3 on p. 14). Around this Heartland are the maritime areas : on the west is fertile Peninsular Europe ; on the south-west is the relatively dry region now often called the " Middle East " ; on the south-east and east are the Monsoon coastlands of India and China where abundant rain is brought from the Indian and Pacific Oceans ; on the north is a less clearly marked transition to the inhospitable

---

[1] The term " Heartland " as applied to central Eurasia was used by Sir Halford Mackinder in the work entitled *Democratic Ideals and Reality,* in which he expressed his view about the way in which the contrasting characteristics of this region and its marginal " Coastlands " affected the course of history over many centuries. As Sir Halford Mackinder employed the term " Heartland," however, its limits differ somewhat from those of the region referred to under this name in the present book.

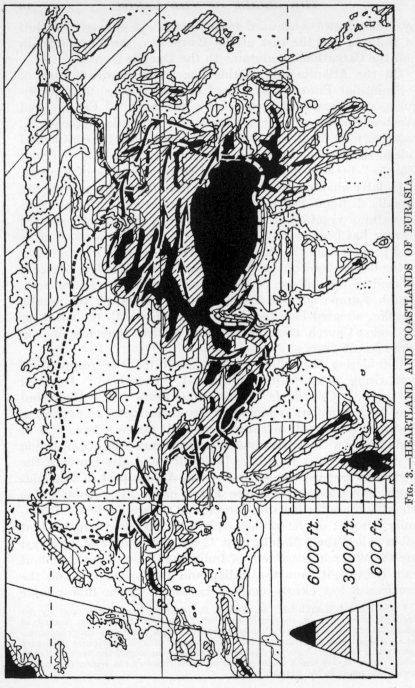

Fig. 3.—HEARTLAND AND COASTLANDS OF EURASIA.

Note.—The heavier broken line is the boundary between the Heartland and the more fertile Coastlands : the lighter broken line in northern Eurasia suggests the transition to the inhospitable Arctic area. The arrows show the main routes by which the horsemen of the Heartland invaded the Coastlands.

Arctic margin where only in summer is the sea open for communications and for the coastal peoples to obtain from it much of their food supply.

Within the Heartland there is generally little rain, and in winter there is bitter cold ; because of these conditions much of the area is a rather poor grassland, and for long ages the people got their living from flocks and herds of grazing animals, using horses to transport themselves and their few belongings from place to place in search of pasture. Their numbers were restricted, even in normal times, by the food supply ultimately dependent upon the rainfall which determined the amount of grass. When in severe winters snow turned to thick sheets of ice over the grazing-grounds, or in spring and summer the rains failed, the animals died and the people suffered.

At long intervals such disasters assumed catastrophic dimensions in the Heartland. Then the nomads looked to the maritime regions where rain from the sea and rivers from the mountains might still fertilize the earth, and where men had already learnt to cultivate the soil, to practise crafts, to form cities and States, to build ships and to carry on commerce. From the interior the horsemen, driven by famine, inspired by hardy and warlike leaders and attracted by the wealth of the Coastlands, swept across the lowlands to Europe or crossed the passes of the highlands to India or to China. Sometimes they were checked, but again and again they overwhelmed the rich settlements and threatened the civilizations of the west, the south and the east. Yet the invaders, though they might seize power in the kingdoms and empires, tended in time to become absorbed among the more numerous sedentary folk of the Coastlands ; with lessened vigour, their dynasties were destroyed by fresh waves of conquest from the Heartland.

Such in broadest outline was a rhythm, the " Pulse of Asia," by which physical conditions of the earth's surface influenced the history of mankind during a time when some of the essential characters of the civilization of the present age were formed.[1]

[1] *The Pulse of Asia* is the name of a book by Ellsworth Huntington, to some extent overlapping the work of Sir Halford Mackinder. In this book, Ellsworth Huntington first developed his special theory about the climatic conditions and climatic changes which he regarded as " the geographical basis of history," affecting not only Eurasia but also Africa and even North America.

CHAPTER II
STRUCTURAL REGIONS

The Geological Eras.—Just as the history of a nation affects the present life of its people, so the history of the movements and changes in the rocks forming the crust of the earth affects the present conditions of the surface. Geologists divide this history into several great eras. The earliest are the Pre-Cambrian (or Archæan); during these eras life first appeared in its primordial form. The successive eras are named according to the stages of development of the life forms whose remains can be traced in the rocks: there is the Palæozoic, i.e. " old life " era ; the following is the Mesozoic or " middle life " era ; the next is the Cainozoic or " new life " era, also known as Tertiary because it is the third of the main life eras ; the present is the Quaternary era. The time covered by these eras is measured in hundreds of millions of years (see table opposite). Because of the changes which the rocks have gone through during this vast period, it is convenient to group the resultant structural regions, shown in the map on p. 18, according to their age as well as according to their general form.

Types of Rock.—An important element in geological structure is the nature of the rock which forms the surface or underlies it. One very widespread class of rock is the sedimentary, consisting of material which was laid down by running water or wind upon a land area, or has settled down under water upon the beds of seas or oceans. This material usually occurs in the form of strata deposited one above another. The sedimentary rocks include fine-grained clays and shale, coarse-grained sands, pebbles, chalk and other limestones formed by organisms which lived in the sea, or strata comprising the remains of vegetable matter, e.g. coal and lignite. Frequently the sedimentary rocks are of comparatively loose texture and some, especially clays, have relatively little power of resistance to erosive agents, such as rain and streams, which may wear them away. Very recently formed sedimentary rocks are the alluvial deposits consisting of mud and silt dropped by rivers in their

16

GEOLOGICAL		EARTH HISTORY	LIFE HISTORY	YEARS AGO
ERAS	PERIODS			
Quaternary	Recent		Civilized man	6,000
			Homo sapiens	100,000
	Pleistocene	Ice Age	Genus homo	500,000
Tertiary or Cainozoic	Pliocene	Alpine revolution	Sub-man	1,000,000
			Higher apes	50,000,000
	Miocene		Evolution of mammals, birds and flowering plants to modern types	
	Oligocene			
	Eocene			
Mesozoic	Cretaceous		Deciduous trees	
			Mammals	150,000,000
	Jurassic		Toothed birds	
	Triassic		Giant reptiles	
Palæozoic	Permian	Hercynian revolution	Reptiles Insects	
	Carboniferous		Conifers	250,000,000
			Amphibians	
	Devonian	Caledonian revolution	Tree ferns	
	Silurian Ordovician Cambrian		Land plants Fish Sea shelled-life	500,000,000
Pre-Cambrian (Archæan)		Charnian revolution	Primitive sea life	600,000,000

Note.—The numbers of years are merely approximate estimates

flood plains and deltas ; lowlands of such deposits are shown as " Alluvial Plains " in the map of structural regions.

Another main class of rock is known as igneous ; this originated in the cooling and solidifying of material which existed in molten form beneath the earth's surface. When the rock cooled in the depths, slowly and under pressure, it became crystalline and hard, e.g. granite ; if later the overlying layers were

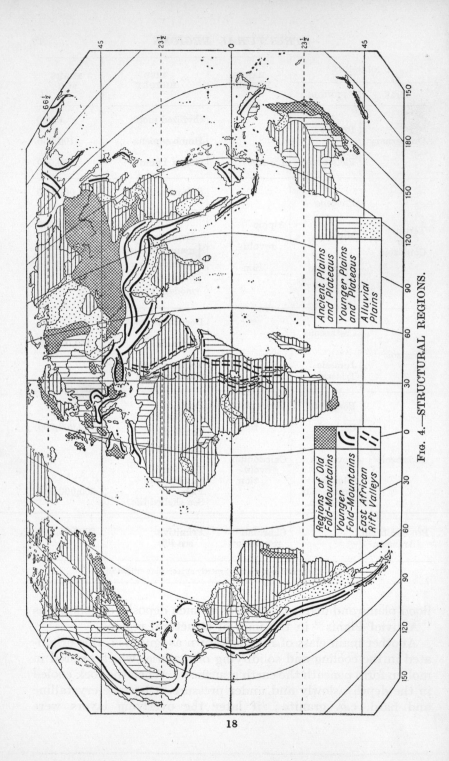

Fig. 4.—STRUCTURAL REGIONS.

Ancient Plains and Plateaus

Younger Plains and Plateaus

Alluvial Plains

Regions of Old Fold-Mountains

Younger Fold-Mountains

East African Rift Valleys

removed by denudation, the igneous rock might remain as a very resistant mass at the surface.

When the material was forced up in still molten form through vents or cracks to the surface, it there cooled more rapidly and the resultant igneous rock, called eruptive, became less crystalline and less resistant than that cooled in the depths. One example is the lava which flows down the sides of volcanoes ; it weathers fairly rapidly and may form an unusually fertile soil. Another example of eruptive igneous rock is seen in the sheets of basalt forced out through long fissures of the earth's crust ; such sheets have sometimes been piled one upon another to form plateaus. This is the origin of the basalt areas in the north-west of the Deccan of India, the basins of the Columbia and Snake rivers in the Western Cordillera of North America, and the great lava flows of the East African Plateaus ; these and other areas of like origin are shown in the map on p. 24.

A third main class is composed of the metamorphic, i.e. changed, rocks. These, like many igneous rocks, are crystalline, but they have been formed by previously existing sedimentary strata or igneous masses being subjected to great heat or changes of pressure in the course of disturbances in the crust of the earth. Some disturbances resulted in layers being lowered to great depths and there fused by the heat. Others caused rocks to be folded and crumpled, to be thrust above one another or even forced into one another ; these movements, also, brought about fusing of the rock material. When this again solidified, the rocks were changed to a crystalline state ; thus, sandstones have been metamorphosed into resistant quartzites, limestones into marble, clays into slates, and granite and other rocks into gneiss. Metamorphic rocks have often been formed within mountain masses, and when overlying layers were worn away they have been exposed as belts of quartzites, gneiss, etc. ; they are so resistant that further denudation has resulted in their standing up as ridges above the surrounding country.

Pervious and Impervious Strata.—There is an important distinction between pervious rocks, including chalk and other limestones and some sandstones, which allow water to percolate through them, and impervious rocks, such as clay and crystalline rocks, through which water cannot pass. Where the surface of the earth consists of a pervious stratum, rain water may sink down until it is held up by an impervious layer and the pervious stratum may then become saturated by ground water ; where only the lower part of the ground is saturated by water, its upper limit is known as the water-table (see the diagram below).

If wells are sunk below the water-table, water may be pumped to the surface. When the strata are bent downwards into the form known as a syncline, the water lying in a pervious layer above the impervious stratum collects in the hollow and can be reached by a surface-water well. In some cases, beneath the impervious stratum there lies another pervious layer, and within this a lower mass of water may accumulate from a distant catchment-area, and is subject to considerable pressure.

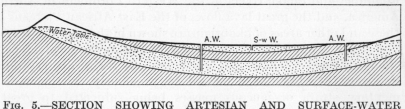

FIG. 5.—SECTION SHOWING ARTESIAN AND SURFACE-WATER WELLS.

Note.—Surface-water well marked S-w W.   Artesian wells marked A. W.   The impervious strata are lined; in the pervious strata the spaces which may be saturated by ground-water are dotted.   In this section, as in practically all sections shown in books, the vertical scale has to be greatly exaggerated in comparison with the horizontal scale.

If a boring is made through the impervious stratum to the underlying water this may be forced up by the pressure and form a gushing or flowing well. A structure of this kind is known as an artesian basin, and the well is also called artesian. Later, when the pressure is relieved, pumping may be needed to bring up the water. In such artesian basins, water may percolate from great distances, even from a rainy to a dry region, as in the interior of Australia ; thus the arrangement of the rocks underlying the surface may determine whether or not man may make his home in a particular area.

Also, surface-water from the topmost layer may be contaminated by drainage, whereas water from the distant catchment-area is filtered by its passage through the pervious stratum and forms a more hygienic drinking supply; here again, subterranean structures affect the conditions of man's life.

Structural Regions.—The earth may be divided into regions, in each of which the crust is formed of rocks of certain classes (e.g. they may be mainly ancient igneous and metamorphic masses, or mainly recent sedimentary strata) and in which these rocks are arranged in a characteristic way—perhaps contorted during long-past mountain-forming disturbances, or perhaps remaining in a generally horizontal or merely tilted position. Such structural regions are shown in the map on p. 18, and are there grouped into types.

Younger Fold-Mountains.—This label is given in the structural map to the regions which were the last to suffer great earth-movements. These disturbances took place mainly in the Tertiary era, and the folded mountains then produced are sometimes referred to as the Tertiary mountain systems. As the Alps were produced by these disturbances the series is called the Alpine revolution. (Again see table on p. 17.)

Along very extensive but relatively narrow belts of the earth's crust, the rocks were folded and upraised in a most complicated manner, and to such an extent that they formed very high mountain regions; at the same time lower strata were metamorphosed into a crystalline and resistant state. During the two- or three-score millions of years since these mountains were formed, they have been exposed to much wearing by weather, streams and ice, and have therefore been carved into a very marked relief of ridges, peaks and valleys, while at the same time their general elevation has been reduced. (See the diagram on p. 22.) Nevertheless, broadly speaking they form most of the highest parts of the earth's surface, as may be seen by comparing the regions of younger fold-mountains on p. 18 with those of highlands on p. 4. Besides the contortions which the rock layers suffered at this period, they were often faulted, i.e. fractured or fissured, and great masses were forced up on one side of the faults and lowered on the other, with accompanying earthquakes of great violence. Hence in addition to the up-folded areas, many blocks were up-tilted or were upraised to a plateau form. (See diagram on p. 29.) Elsewhere molten material was forced out through vents, and volcanoes or sheets of lava were built up; some of these are shown in the map on p. 24.

The complicated structure and relief of the Tertiary fold-mountains, together with their altitude, accounts for the way in which they act as barriers to the movements of mankind. On the other hand, geological structures associated with these

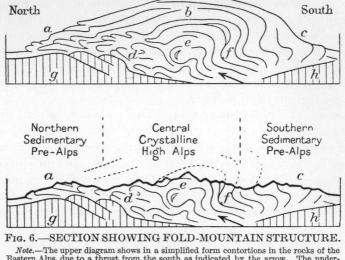

FIG. 6.—SECTION SHOWING FOLD-MOUNTAIN STRUCTURE.

Note.—The upper diagram shows in a simplified form contortions in the rocks of the Eastern Alps, due to a thrust from the south as indicated by the arrow. The underlying platform, *g* and *h*, is dislocated ; the lower sedimentary rocks, *d*, *e*, and *f*, are metamorphosed into crystalline sheets ; the upper sedimentary strata, *a*, *b*, and *c*, are thrust northward.

The lower diagram shows the present structure after great denudation. In the central zone the crystalline sheets are exposed, and in the northern zone the sedimentary strata are left widely separated from their counterparts in the south.

younger fold-mountains have led to the occurrence of mineral wealth, and thus attracted people to these areas.

The Circum-Pacific Fold-Mountains.—A comparison of the relief and structural maps shows that there is a circum-Pacific belt of the younger fold-mountains which corresponds with the circum-Pacific highlands, particularly closely in the Western Cordillera regions of North and South America, in the north-eastern part of Siberia, in the chains of islands off the Asiatic coasts, in the East Indian Archipelago and in New Zealand. In some parts the circum-Pacific fold-mountains have a structure similar to that of the Alps shown in the section above, while in other parts there are upraised and tilted block-mountains ; elsewhere great lava flows form interior plateaus.   It should be noted also that the West Indian islands correspond to a curve of the Tertiary fold-mountains ; the islands do not all rise high above sea-level, but they are the highest parts of sub-marine mountain chains ; the connection is shown in the shallowness of the sea between each island and its neighbours on either side.   Similarly the festoons of islands off Eastern Asia and the lines of islands in the East Indian Archipelago are parts of submerged mountain chains.

The Mid-World Fold-Mountains.—The second great group of younger fold-mountains coincides generally with the mid-world series of highlands. It is linked with the circum-Pacific group in the East Indies area through the Malay Peninsula and Burma ; thence it continues westward in curves in and around the Tibetan, Iranian and Anatolian regions to Europe. On the northern side of the Mediterranean Sea it shows itself in the great arcs of the Balkan, Carpathian, Alpine and Apennine mountains, and in some of the ranges of the Iberian Peninsula. At the southernmost point of Spain, the fold-mountains have suffered a slight break which has allowed the sea to penetrate and to form the narrow and shallow Strait of Gibraltar ; thence the line is continued in Africa eastward through the Atlas Lands to another break between Tunis and Sicily. Thus the western basin of the Mediterranean Sea is seen to be one of several areas which are alike in being surrounded by high fold-mountains although they differ in their actual altitude.

Although the mountains were formed many millions of years ago, the weakness of the earth's crust in their neighbourhood still shows itself by occasional outpourings of molten material through volcanic vents, and by earthquake shocks when the solid rocks are displaced along the lines of faults. The connection between these phenomena and the Tertiary folds can be seen by comparing the map on p. 18 with that on p. 24. The latter map shows that most of the volcanoes which have been active within recent times are within the areas of younger fold-mountains. It may be noted that among the ways in which volcanoes may affect man is that their outpourings in many cases weather to fertile soils ; a striking example is found in Java, which is of exceptional fertility for tropical latitudes partly because of its numerous volcanoes.

The same map shows the areas in which earthquake shocks have been either frequent or severe within recent times. Here, too, the relation to the Tertiary fold-mountain systems is clear although the earthquakes are felt over areas wider than the actual fold-mountain belts. It is scarcely necessary to refer to the disastrous effects upon human beings which are associated with this feature of the structure of the earth's crust.

Old Fold-Mountains.—Long before the Tertiary era, two other systems of mountain-forming disturbances occurred which are of importance to present-day geography, viz. the

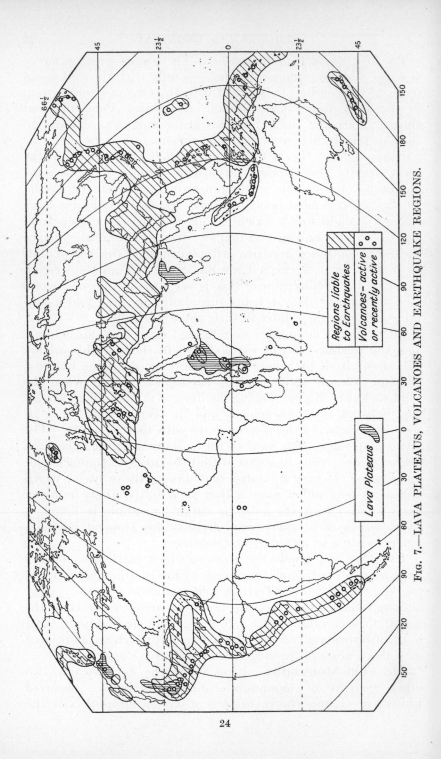

FIG. 7.—LAVA PLATEAUS, VOLCANOES AND EARTHQUAKE REGIONS.

Regions liable to Earthquakes

Volcanoes— active or recently active

Lava Plateaus

" Hercynian " foldings which took place in the last part of the Palæozoic era, and the " Caledonian " foldings of the middle part of the same era ; these names refer to two areas of Europe in which the effects of these systems of foldings are seen.

The *Hercynian* disturbances took place over large parts of the world, including central Europe. Here great mountain ranges were formed which might be compared with the Alps of the Tertiary era, but in the immense periods of time which followed they were worn down so that even their highest and most resistant parts were little above sea-level ; thus they became peneplains, i.e. almost plains, over which the rivers slowly meandered without further cutting power. Then, when the Tertiary disturbances came, some of the areas were upraised, either by dislocations which split them along fault-lines and forced some blocks above others, or by the general uplift of a region. The rivers then ran more rapidly from the raised areas to the sea, and eroded belts of country where the less resistant rocks formed the surface ; hence the more resistant belts stood above the general level of the uplands as higher ridges whose direction coincided with that of the original mountain ranges.

One such upraised massif forms the Harz Mountains of Germany, and from the old name of this district, Hercynia, the term Hercynian has been adopted and applied to the earth movements of the late Palæozoic era, and also to the structural regions folded at that period. (The term Variscan is sometimes used to denote the foldings here named Hercynian.) In Europe the Hercynian areas have the general elevation of uplands ; again compare the maps of relief and structure. They include the uplands of the Pennines in Britain, those of central Europe, others nearer the Mediterranean region and the relatively low Donetz Plateau of southern Russia.

Farther east in Eurasia, the Hercynian areas show themselves in more continuous relief features, some of which reach considerably greater heights. There are the Ural Mountains and the mountains and plateaus of High Asia north of the Tertiary fold system. In China, a belt of Hercynian highlands runs eastward from High Asia, including the Tsin Ling Mountains which almost exactly divide the basin of the Hwang Ho in north China from the basin of the Yangtze Kiang in central China, and mark an important difference in the climate of the two regions.

In Australia, the long belt of uplands and highlands on the eastern side belongs to the same group of old fold-mountains ; in South Africa the system is represented only in the south of the province of the Cape of Good Hope, where the ranges and plateaus have a general east-west direction.

In North America, a long Hercynian belt runs through the Appalachian region in the United States north-eastward to the Maritime Provinces of Canada, and ends in Newfoundland.

The rocks involved in the Hercynian foldings in many cases have mineral deposits, of which coal and iron are the most important. Hence the Hercynian areas are associated to a considerable extent with mining and manufactures, commerce and the growth of towns and cities ; this is particularly true of the industrial areas in Great Britain and other countries of Peninsular Europe, in the Soviet territories of Trunk Europe and Siberia, and in the United States of America.

The *Caledonian* foldings have had a somewhat similar geological history. The original mountains were long ago worn down to peneplains, and the present relief is mainly due to the uplift of great masses along the lines of faults at the time of the Tertiary disturbances.

The foldings are called Caledonian because their effects are now seen in Scotland. Here the Highlands and the Southern Uplands were raised on either side of the lower Hercynian belt of Central Scotland. Much of Ireland is also a part of the same Caledonian region, while a larger part is seen in north-western Scandinavia. It is because of the structural connection, and the similar geological history, of the Scottish and Norwegian Highlands that there are so many similarities in the physical conditions and also in the human geography of these two regions. Only one more area of the Caledonian type can be mentioned, viz. the high portion of the Brazilian Plateau.

Ancient Plains and Plateaus.—A considerable part of the world's surface consists of plains or plateaus which have not suffered any considerable amount of mountain-folding during the whole span of the main life eras : they are the " rigid masses " of the earth's crust, and in them the great disturbances since Pre-Cambrian times have had their main effect in causing fracturing and associated vertical and horizontal shifts.

In Europe there is the " Baltic Shield," so called because its hollowed surface-form is somewhat like that of a shallow inverted shield, with a centre in which lies the northern part of the Baltic Sea. It is also known as Fenno-Scandia because it forms the sub-soil of Finland and the south-eastern part of Scandinavia. Because it has remained almost undisturbed over such an immense time, its once irregular surface has been worn down to a peneplain and the region is a lowland with but slight relief. The once deep-seated metamorphic rocks are now exposed over most of the area, and there are also igneous masses at the surface. In these rocks mineral deposits were formed and mining is one of the more important occupations of the people of the region. As a whole, the shield slopes very gradually to the south-east, and the rigid mass disappears below sedimentary strata which cover it in north-western Russia.

In North America, the " Canadian Shield " or " Laurentian Shield " is the counterpart of the Baltic Shield. There are a number of similarities between the regions, of which the following may be noted : the rather low relief and the exposure of wide areas of metamorphic rock ; the occurrence of valuable ores and the consequent importance of mining ; the hollow in the central part, covered in the Canadian Shield by the waters of Hudson Bay ; the gradual slope towards the centre of the continent until the ancient rocks disappear below those of the younger plains.

In the far north, most of the Arctic archipelago and Greenland belongs to the same rigid mass ; but these portions have been separated by fractures and the invasion of oceanic waters, while Greenland has been upraised to a highland plateau.

In Asia there is, in the far north, the main " Siberian Shield," which is exposed in its rather higher eastern part but has been covered by alluvium in the lower western part of the region ; a smaller area occurs in the north-east of Siberia. In the Far East, there is the rigid mass known as the Chinese Table ; this appears in two main portions which are separated by the old fold-mountains of the Tsin Ling Mountains and by the alluvial plains of the Hwang Ho and the Yangtze Kiang. The Siberian and Chinese rigid masses have varied and great mineral deposits, but these have only recently been systematically prospected as the peoples and governments had not previously realized their economic importance ; now, however, the mineral resources will doubtless be developed with comparative rapidity.

In the south of Asia, there are two more ancient plateau

areas, and these may best be grouped with others of similar or more southerly latitudes. The Deccan or " Indian Table " and the Syrian-Arabian Plateau are regarded as being parts of what was once a single huge land-mass, including also almost all of Africa together with Madagascar, at least the greater part of Australia, much of South America, and what is now the great plateau of Antarctica. The whole has been given the name of " Gondwanaland," and certainly there is a marked correspondence in the structure of all these regions. There is much dispute among geologists, however, as to how this great " southern continent " of the past was broken up and how the parts have come to occupy their present positions.

The mineral resources of " Gondwanaland " are characteristic ; e.g. from the fragments of this ancient land mass are obtained practically all the world's supply of diamonds, more than half the gold including that from all the really deep gold-mines, and five out of the seven important sources of manganese—a key metal in the smelting of iron ore for the production of steel.

Considering this southern group of rigid masses as a whole, we may note that in several parts the plateau areas drop steeply towards the bordering Indian and South Atlantic Oceans in almost unbroken coastlines. In other parts the areas descend relatively gently to interior lowlands where they are covered by later rocks ; e.g. in south-west Asia there are the alluvial lowlands of Mesopotamia and northern India, and in South America are those of the Amazon and La Plata rivers.

It may also be noted that the plateau form of these rigid masses in inter-tropical latitudes has several effects on the human geography, including the possibility of settlement and movement mentioned earlier. In this connection, one aspect of the African continent may be further indicated. Its great rivers—Nile, Niger, Congo and Zambezi—all drop over edges of the tableland structure in falls which prevent navigation, and in consequence people going from the sea inland up the rivers are checked after a relatively short distance. This was one factor which prevented the penetration and exploration of much of Africa for centuries, so that it long remained the " dark continent " ; even more recently the commercial development of large regions was hindered by the same characteristic of the build of this continent.

The East African Rift-Valleys.—Africa also gives the most striking examples of another structural feature, viz. the rift-valley. In many parts of the world, faults have occurred parallel to one another and a strip of the earth's crust has been let down between them and formed a rift-valley ; an alternative explanation is that the outer areas have been raised up above the central strip. The structure of a rift-valley is illustrated in the diagram opposite. In nature it is more complicated : the two sides are usually not so symmetric ; the " steps," if they exist, are worn ; the surface of the plateau is eroded. The section in the foreground shows that in this plateau, but it is by no means always the case, the rocks were once folded ; as the surface of the contorted area has been levelled off, the area must have been worn down to a peneplain before it was raised to a plateau.

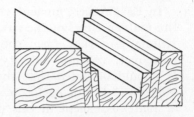

FIG. 8.—BLOCK-PLATEAU AND RIFT-VALLEY STRUCTURE.

Central Scotland is one of many rift-valleys, but the greatest of them form a continuous series which splits the ancient land-mass in Syria and continues southwards through more than 50° of latitude. Refer back to the map on p. 18.

In the northern part the rift includes the valley of the river Jordan and the Dead Sea. Then the general direction changes and the great trench widens where its floor is covered by the waters of the Red Sea ; at the south-eastern end of this stretch, it is met by another trough which runs at right angles and allows the waters of the Indian Ocean to penetrate in the Gulf of Aden between the Arabian Peninsula and the " Horn " of East Africa. In this part of its course the great rift-valley is flooded so that it affords an almost continuous sea-way between the Indian Ocean and the Mediterranean Sea ; here the relatively short Suez Canal sufficed to complete the passage for world commerce. Farther south, it was the uplifting of the earth's crust on both sides of the valley which formed the great plateaus of East Africa, and provided habitable areas, even for White people, across Equatorial latitudes.

The formation of the rifts was part of the Tertiary earth movements (although mountain-folding did not take place in this part of the world) and it was accompanied by much

eruption of molten material. The map on p. 24 shows the great
lava-flows which have occurred from Abyssinia far to the south ;
here, as elsewhere, a fertile soil has developed from the eruptive
rock and in this case waters which feed the Nile have taken the
rich soil-material into the far-distant valley and delta of Egypt.
In the Deccan, too, basaltic outpourings occurred at about
the same period near the faulted edge of the west coast.

In East Africa, ancient volcanic cones were heaped up upon
the plateau edges of the rift-valleys, and in Mounts Kenya and
Kilimanjaro they form the highest points of the continent ;
moreover, volcanic activity has continued into recent times.
It should be noted that the map on p. 24 shows that recent
volcanoes do not occur in any of the areas of ancient plains
or plateaus except in this one instance of the margins of the
African rift-valleys ; the same distribution may be observed
as regards recent earthquakes, save for the case of the Chinese
Table which lies between the recent fold-mountain belts of
Tibet and the Pacific coasts.

Younger Plains and Plateaus.—In several large areas the
ancient rocks, both of the rigid masses and of the older fold-
mountains, have been lowered sufficiently to be covered by
water in which later strata were deposited. Although since
that time these areas have generally been but little disturbed,
they have been again raised relatively to the level of the sea ;
they have thus become dry land and now form the regions
labelled " Younger Plains and Plateaus " on the structural map.

Thus in the case of England, the older rocks of the Welsh
and Pennine Uplands dip eastward below the plain of south-
eastern England which is formed of younger limestones, chalk,
sandstones and clays. These strata are of unequal power of
resistance to weathering and stream action, and frequently
the more resistant limestones and sandstones stand up above
the easily worn clays. Where the strata are tilted, the resistant
layers form plateaus which have a gentle dip-slope in the
direction of the tilt, and a scarped edge or escarpment over-
looking low belts formed from the less resistant layers ; in this
way a scarp-land type of landscape is frequently developed,
as in south-eastern England (see Fig. 9). In central Europe,
broken masses of the Hercynian type lie beneath a covering of
later sediments, from which they emerge in several areas. In
eastern Europe the Baltic Shield dips down under the northern

part of the great plain of Russia, of which the surface is mainly formed of nearly horizontal strata.

Although the younger sedimentary layers in south-eastern England and in central Europe generally have relatively little mineral wealth, there are in some parts coal and ores in the underlying Hercynian platform (again see Fig. 9). Where these coal or iron deposits occur near the outcrop of the visible Hercynian massifs they may not be far from the surface and can be mined, but farther from the outcrops they may be at such depths that it does not pay to sink deep shafts to reach them. Therefore over much of these younger plains and plateaus agriculture is the chief occupation ; at some places,

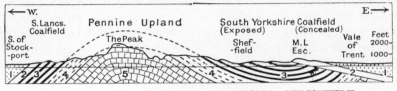

FIG. 9.—SECTION SHOWING COALFIELD STRUCTURE.

Note.—The productive Coal Measures (3) lie above the lower Carboniferous strata (4 and 5), and have been worn away from the central part of the Pennine Upland up-folded in the Hercynian disturbances. The coalfields are therefore found on each side of the Pennines ; they are exposed near the Upland, but farther away are hidden under younger rocks. Magnesian Limestone (2) is more resistant than the sands and clays of the Vale of Trent, above which it forms a westward-facing escarpment (M. L. Esc.).

however, mining and consequently manufacturing have developed and led to the growth of great populations.

Similar conditions exist in North America. The Canadian Shield sinks westward and southward beneath the more recent plains and plateaus of the interior of the continent, while in the southern part of the Hercynian area the older rocks of the Appalachian Upland disappear beneath the younger sedimentary strata of the Atlantic coastal plain on the one side and the Mississippi lowland on the other. In North America, as in Europe, minerals in the older rocks are mined beneath the adjoining parts of the younger plains.

In Africa the main areas of the younger plains and plateaus occur on the margins, in several parts where the older rocks have been overlain by the more recent ones. In Australia the younger sedimentary strata form low plateaus and plains adjoining the rigid masses of the western tableland and also between this and the older fold-mountains of the east ; it is the broad down-folds of these younger layers which bring the water of the artesian wells from the coastal regions to the arid interior.

CHAPTER III

MINERAL RESOURCES

BRIEF references in the preceding chapter suggested that one of the chief ways in which the structure of the earth's crust has an influence upon human geography is in determining the position and the amount of mineral deposits. If the present is the " Age of Steel "—and of machines—it is clear that the occurrence of iron ore for steel-making, and of coal and oil by which machines are worked, is of exceptionally great importance ; the broad distribution of these minerals will be considered in the following paragraphs. There are, moreover, a number of other minerals which play an important part in industry and commerce, or as fertilizers for agriculture ; among such minerals are tin, copper, lead, zinc, aluminium, platinum, mercury, manganese, nickel, salt, potash and phosphates. Others have had a great attraction for people because of the value, perhaps largely fictitious, which has been placed upon them, e.g. gold, silver and precious stones. In recent years pitchblende, from which radium and uranium are extracted, has become of great importance.

Coal.—The map on p. 242 illustrates the distribution of coal in a general manner, showing only the areas in which coal is largely worked at the present time and not those in which there are unused resources ; this distinction applies also to the other mineral workings entered on this map and that on p. 243.

To explain the reasons for the distribution of coal and its relation to the structural regions, it is necessary to summarize the conditions under which the deposits have been formed. They have been derived from the carbon in the tissues of swamp vegetation, mainly of the Carboniferous, i.e. coal-bearing, period of the Palæozoic era. Great thicknesses of plant remains were accumulated when swamp areas gradually sank down and permitted successive layers of vegetation to be formed one above another ; also, these layers were frequently separated by strata of limestone, sandstone or clays where for a time the sinking proceeded more rapidly and the areas were depressed below water-level. As vegetable life had not developed to any great degree on the land until about the middle of the Palæozoic era, rocks formed before that time cannot be coal-bearing (refer to the table on p. 17) ; similarly, coal cannot occur in igneous rocks or those of the metamorphic class in which vegetable matter must have been destroyed by the heat.

The next development in the formation of coal was the gradual disappearance from the plant tissues of water and gases, the change being increased by pressure and moderately high temperatures when the strata were buried and perhaps contorted below the surface. As this process continued, the vegetable matter went through successive stages in which were formed peat, lignite or brown coal, bituminous or soft coal, and finally anthracite. The more valuable kinds of coal have been generally formed from the vegetation of the Palæozoic era, for the process has usually not gone so far in vegetation of the more recent Mesozoic and Tertiary eras ; from strata of these times the coal is mainly of the softer kind or lignite with a lower heating capacity.

Where the strata have been subjected to folding, the quality of the coal is generally greater. Other effects also follow, c.g. where much denudation has occurred, the upfolds or anticlines tend to be worn away first and any coal they may have contained is lost ; on the contrary, the downfolds or synclines may remain longer and the coal deposits may be preserved.

After this summary of the formation of coal it may be noted how the deposits are related to the various types of structural regions. The " ancient plains and plateaus," which date back to the first part of the Palæozoic era, or earlier, are without this mineral. Occasionally, however, it must be noted that where, as in the Chinese Table, the margins of the rigid mass were later sufficiently depressed for swamp vegetation to have been formed upon them, and were subsequently buried beneath other strata, the upper part of the tabular structure may be coal-bearing.

The " old fold-mountains " of the Hercynian type were formed after the Carboniferous period, and in their synclines have been preserved many of the most productive seams of coal, both anthracitic and bituminous. The " younger plains and plateaus " may contain coals of Mesozoic or Tertiary age in their strata, and lignites are fairly widely distributed in these regions ; moreover, where Hercynian-folded rocks are preserved beneath more recent layers, coal-mining may be carried on in the younger plains provided the seams are not at too great a depth.   Similarly, coal may occur beneath alluvial deposits but the surface conditions would not bear witness to the fact, and these regions are typically non-mining areas.

Finally, the " young fold-mountains " may have included strata containing vegetable remains, but the formation of coal would occur only where the degree of heating and pressure was enough, but not too much ; also, the seams would be destroyed after much contortion and denudation, and in fact coal is only exceptionally found and worked in these regions.

The broad distribution of coal-mining may therefore be summarized as follows.   In Europe the Hercynian massifs, both where they are exposed and where they lie just below the surface of the younger plains, are extremely productive ; from Wales and the Pennines on the west, through the coalfields of north France and Belgium, the Ruhr and Silesia, to the Donetz plateau on the east is one of the two great coal-mining belts of the world.   Smaller fields are found in the Hercynian area of the Ural Mountains.

North America has the other great coal-mining belt of the world ; it is situated in and adjoining the Hercynian folded region from the Southern Appalachians to Pennsylvania, with a relatively small area in Nova Scotia.   Great amounts are also mined from the rocks of the Carboniferous period which underlie the plains of the interior on both sides of the Mississippi river. Only a little coal is obtained from the margins and valleys of the younger fold-mountains of the Western Cordillera in the United States and Canada.

Asia has in all probability very great reserves, but the workings are limited because it is only recently that the machine age, which originated in Europe and developed in North America, has penetrated into that continent.   Coal-mining is now carried on in four structural regions of Asia : the Hercynian areas of southern Siberia ; the upper and later-formed layers of the Siberian Shield, and of the Chinese Table from Manchuria to southern and western China ; the fold-mountain district of southern Japan ; the north-east margin of the Deccan Plateau.

It will be noted that all these large resources of coal lie in the northern hemisphere, and indeed north of the Tropic of Cancer. By contrast, the tropical zone of the world is practically without this form of mineral wealth, for coal is almost lacking from the areas which formed part of the ancient " Gondwanaland " and from the fold-mountain regions which lie between the Tropics. South of the Tropic of Capricorn there are only two important coal-mining areas, viz. in New South Wales in the Hercynian fold-mountain region of eastern Australia, and in Natal and the Transvaal on the eastern margin of the rigid mass of South Africa.

In estimating the importance of coal it must be realized that in addition to its use as a fuel and as a source of mechanical power, it supplies many by-products ; with these, applied chemistry produces dyes, drugs, insecticides, perfumes, flavourings, and the now wide range of plastics including containers of various kinds, furniture, perspex and nylons.

The preponderance of the coal resources of the world in the middle latitudes of the northern hemisphere, with the aid they give to industrial and commercial development in this zone, is one of the principal causes of the existence of the great populations in this zone ; moreover, for a long time to come this distribution of coal will work with other factors, particularly the favourable climatic conditions, to retain in these regions a large proportion of the world's inhabitants.

Oil.—The distribution of mineral oil, petroleum, is very different from that of coal, as can be seen by noting on the map on p. 242 how seldom the symbols for these two forms of mineral fuel occur in the same locality. The key to the distribution of petroleum lies, of course, in the mode of its formation and its relation to the geological structures.

Petroleum is derived from the remains of plants, such as seaweeds, which lived in shallow salt or brackish water, or from the remains of minute plants and animals which lived in deeper waters of the sea. The organic material was buried in sediments, and in the course of time was changed by slow chemical action or by bacteria into bubbles of gas and globules of oil, while water was also accumulated. The pressure of overlying rocks would drive the gas and the liquids through pervious strata, and in some cases these products would escape from the surface ; if, however, they were trapped by overlying impervious rocks they would collect into " pools " below ground. This might occur in up-folded strata, and the gas would then rise as far in the anticline as the overlying im-

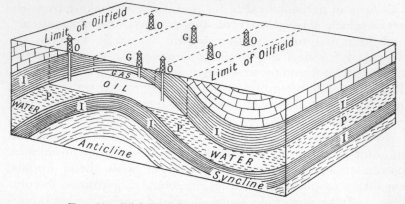

Fig. 10.—BLOCK DIAGRAM OF AN OILFIELD.

Note.—P = Pervious Stratum.   I = Impervious Strata.   O = Oil-yielding wells.   G = Gas-yielding wells in central belt of field.

pervious stratum would permit, while the oil would collect below it and the heavier water would occupy the remaining space in the pervious layer (see the diagram above).

There are therefore two essential conditions for the existence of oilfields. The first is that organic remains of the particular type must have been deposited in large quantities and have been subject to slow bacterial and chemical changes. As this condition may be satisfied in sedimentary rocks, and especially in those of the Tertiary era, oilfields may be found in areas underlain by these rocks ; on the contrary, the igneous and metamorphic rocks cannot contain oil, and oilfields are very exceptional in the regions marked as rigid masses of the earth's crust and in the areas of the older fold-mountains.

The second condition is that after its formation the oil must be preserved and become accessible to man. This would not be the case after mountain-folding which involves violent contortions, metamorphism and frequent faulting of the strata, as in structures of the Alpine type. On the other hand, undisturbed horizontal strata would not give the desired anticlines for storage. The most favourable conditions are the relatively gentle foldings found on the margins of more highly contorted mountain ranges, i.e. in the foothills and foreland areas, as shown in the section opposite.

Thus the most common distribution of oilfields is in the regions adjoining the " younger fold-mountains " and in warped sedimentary strata of the " younger plains."

The structure of oilfields affects also the way in which they are utilized. When wells are sunk through the roof of impervious rock to the stratum in which the gas and oil are trapped, these may at first be forced up by the pressure of the water but later they must be pumped to the surface. The supply of gas may be exhausted first, but sooner or later the oil, too, must fail. As the liquid oil can move along the underground belt of oil-bearing rock, wells sunk to this at any point get a share, and the greater the number of wells the sooner must the total oil supply be exhausted. If several companies have rights in one field, there tends to be a race to put down borings and the whole oilfield may soon cease to yield. In this respect there is a marked contrast with a coalfield, in which the expectation of economic life is far longer.

Also, there has been a great rush to find and exploit new fields, especially in view of the development of many uses for petroleum. The crude oil is refined to yield a series of products, including aviation spirit, petrol for the commoner types of internal-combustion engine, heavier oil for Diesel engines, fuel for boilers of steam engines, kerosene or lamp oil, heavy lubricating oils, wax and asphalt. Fuel oil has a heating value about half as much again as that of coal, and it is much more easily transported and fed into engines ; hence its effective competition with the older source of power, especially for naval and mercantile shipping. In addition, scientific research has made petroleum a base for the manufacture of synthetic rubber, various plastics, explosives and many other chemicals, while " natural gas," which is commonly obtained in association with the oil, also has a high fuel value and is an important raw material in the production of synthetic rubber.

Because of the many uses of oil, demand in recent years has grown enormously, but in some parts the supply has tended

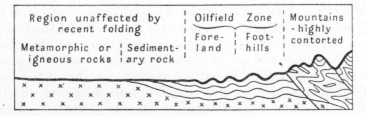

FIG. 11.—SECTION SHOWING SITUATION OF AN OILFIELD.

to exceed the demand ; production has so increased that in certain States laws have been passed to limit the amount obtained.   In spite of attempts to keep conditions fairly steady, there have been great changes in the distribution of the production of oil : some areas have already been practically exhausted ; others have had their lives prolonged by much deeper borings which have tapped hitherto untouched strata ; still other areas have been discovered to be oil-bearing and have been developed.   Hence, besides drawing attention to the chief oil workings of the present time, some notes must be added on their probable, or at least possible, reserves.

North America possesses great supplies of oil and natural gas, and the United States has a production far exceeding that of any other country.   In North America a large proportion of the oil and gas comes either from the immediate vicinity of the younger fold-mountains of the Western Cordillera, especially in California, or from the younger plains of the interior which adjoin these mountains in Kansas, Oklahoma and Texas.   The margins of the Western Cordillera region also yield considerable quantities of oil in Mexico and much smaller amounts in Canada, while another oilfield of the United States occurs on the northern shores of the Gulf of Mexico.   On the eastern side of the continent is a petroliferous belt along the western margin of the Appalachian region ;   this was once important but now has relatively little oil.

There are two reasons for the enormous present production of the United States ; one is the extent of its resources and the other is the thoroughness with which they have been investigated and utilized.   The result is that, in the opinion of geologists, more than half the total supplies have already been obtained and that a decline in the rate of production must soon set in.   Realization of a probable shortage in the U.S.A. has stimulated the American oil interests to acquire fields in other lands ; there has in fact been a world-wide " scramble for oil," not only among several powerful companies of the United States but also among those representing other countries which require much oil and are anxious about their future supplies.

South America is an important producer.   The distribution of the fields is simple, for they are almost all associated with the Andean fold-mountains, especially in the northern portion which swings round eastward to join the partially submerged ranges of the West Indies. At this point the British island of Trinidad has oil, besides the famous " pitch lake " from which asphalt is obtained. On the South American mainland, the chief production of petroleum comes from Venezuela, while Colombia, Peru and Ecuador have smaller resources. In the southern part of the continent, Argentina has some oil, including a supply from the plains of Patagonia east of the Andes.

In *Eurasia* and the *East Indies* there are a considerable number of oilfields connected with the younger fold-mountain systems. The circum-Pacific belt yields petroleum in Sakhalin and Japan ; much greater amounts come from the East Indian Archipelago, and there are fields also in Burma.

The central part of the mid-world fold-mountain belt is very important, ranking among the most productive petroleum regions of the globe ; it includes two groups of oilfields. The first group consists of those on both sides of the Caucasus mountains, and these have greatly aided the relatively recent industrial development of the U.S.S.R. The second group includes the " Middle East " oilfields of the Iranian Plateau and near the Persian Gulf ; this group is likely to increase its yields in the future. Adjoining the European part of the mid-world belt of fold-mountains there are the oilfields of Rumania and Poland on the outer side of the curve of the Carpathian Mountains, and there are small areas in Austria and Albania.

To the south of the younger fold-mountains of Europe and Asia, viz. in the continents of Africa and Australia, there are no considerable oil resources. Indeed, in the main, the areas included in the past " Gondwanaland," as well as the other regions of the " rigid mass " type, lack this form of mineral wealth. An apparent exception to the general rule is found in Egypt where oil occurs by the coast of the Gulf of Suez, but here the petroleum has been formed in sedimentary strata overlying the ancient rocks.

North of the Eurasian belt of younger fold-mountains there are several scattered oilfields, of which the most productive are in the U.S.S.R., e.g. in the Hercynian fold-mountain areas of the Urals and Southern Siberia, while some recently discovered pools are in the Ukraine. Apart from the Russian fields, there is but a relatively small production of oil in the industrial States of the Old World ; hence, the countries of Peninsular Europe are dependent upon imported supplies.

The question of the rate of the exhaustion of the world's supply of mineral oil is much discussed ; in some countries the reserves are being rapidly depleted, though elsewhere new or deeper sources are being discovered and utilized. Yet it seems most probable, and indeed almost certain, that the large-scale use of petroleum is but a passing phase in the evolution of industry and commerce. As a source of mechanical power coal will have a more enduring value to the countries possessing considerable reserves ; in this connection it may be noted that fuel for engines using either heavy or light oil can be obtained from coal.

Iron.—Of the many metals which are extracted from ores found in the earth's crust, iron is by far the most widely used. It is employed both in a more or less pure form, and also as the basis for numerous steels produced by dissolving carbon, chromium, nickel, manganese, tungsten, vanadium, molybdenum or other metals in molten iron, to obtain special qualities. For example, the " stainless steel " familiar in domestic use is produced by the addition of chromium, and for industrial purposes there is nickel-steel, a peculiarly tough combination of nickel and steel, while manganese-steel is remarkably hard ; again, " high-speed " steel, which is used for cutting-tools in rapidly turning lathes because it does not become soft at high temperatures, is a compound of steel, chromium and tungsten.

With the multitudinous uses of iron and its alloys, it is fortunate that workable ores of iron are more abundant than those of any other metal. As iron compounds are very widely distributed in the earth's crust and the metal has been concentrated into useful ore deposits, by several natural processes, valuable ironfields exist in several classes of rocks and in most types of structural region.

From the point of view of human geography, we must make a distinction between the present workings and the resources hitherto unused. Whether iron deposits have been utilized or not depends on several factors. (1) The composition of the ore itself. Some ores have a high iron content, above 70 per cent., while others with less than 30 per cent. of iron are generally not worth working ; some ores have been difficult to smelt because they contain impurities such as phosphorus or sulphur while others, on the contrary, have lime which makes them almost " self-fluxing," i.e. not needing the addition of lime in the smelting process. (2) The situation of the ore. Some deposits are deep and need mining, but others can be quarried in shallow, open workings. (3) The geographical location of the ore. Nearness to coal greatly encourages utilization, for it reduces the cost of transporting the bulky ore ; also easy transport to areas where iron is used is an important factor.

In North America the United States are fortunate in their possession of valuable and easily utilized iron ores ; the most productive deposits in the whole world are in the crystalline rocks of the Laurentian Shield south and west of Lake Superior, and the ores can be cheaply transported by the Great Lakes to the neighbourhood of the North Appalachian coalfields. Other important North American deposits are in the vicinity of the belt of older fold-mountains on the east of the continent. Here they are worked close to coal in Alabama at the southern end of the Appalachian area, in Pennsylvania in the Northern Appalachians, and in Newfoundland at the northern extremity of the Hercynian system. Canada, rich in several forms of mineral wealth, has but a small share in the valuable iron ores of the Laurentian Shield near the Great Lakes. See map on p. 243.

Europe has at present an even greater production of iron than North America. In the Hercynian fold-mountain areas, iron ores were formed in fairly close association with coal, and this situation encouraged their exploitation, and in some cases led to their virtual exhaustion, e.g. in the British Isles and in Germany. Greater amounts of iron ore occur in some of the limestones which form part of the younger plains adjacent to the coal deposits of western Europe ; in England most of the iron now comes from a limestone belt east of the Pennines and in the east Midlands, while the greatest reserves of the continent are in similar deposits in Lorraine. In this latter case, the occurrence of the ore had a serious influence on political and military events, for Lorraine is part of the long-disputed border-land of France and Germany. After Germany had defeated France in 1870 the part of Lorraine in which the iron outcrops at the surface was demanded by the victors, for it was not till later that scientists discovered that the main part of the deposits lay at a rather greater depth on the French side of the boundary, and that new methods of smelting made them of unexpected value. When the Germans were defeated in 1918 all the country containing the ore-bearing strata was reclaimed by

France, except the smaller portion belonging to Belgium and Luxembourg.

In the Baltic Shield are considerable amounts of iron ore ; the greatest deposits are in Sweden, within the Arctic Circle, but their unfavourable situation is partially offset by their high quality and by the fact that even in winter they can be exported through the always ice-free port of Narvik, in Norway. The younger fold-mountains are not in general rich in iron ores, but the western part of the mid-world belt has deposits of value to European industries. These deposits are situated around the western basin of the Mediterranean Sea, notably in the Cantabrian Mountains and in the south of Spain, in the Atlas Lands of north-west Africa, in the island of Elba off the coast of Italy, and in the Austrian Alps.

The U.S.S.R. has great productive resources in the Hercynian regions of southern Russia and the Ural Mountains, and also in the old fold-mountain areas of Siberia. Other Asiatic deposits occur in areas of the rigid mass type in Manchuria and China Proper. There are also considerable supplies of iron ore in parts of " Gondwanaland " ; e.g. in the north-east of the Deccan in India, in the eastern Transvaal, and in South Australia.

Several of the workings already indicated have great reserves still untouched, and in looking forward to the future other resources hitherto entirely unutilized must be considered. There is no sign of the world's supply of iron being exhausted, especially if account is taken of the possibility of developments which may make easier the working of difficult ores, and improvements in transport which may give access to them.

Gold.—As a further illustration of the influence of the structure of the earth's crust upon mankind, there is space to consider only the occurrence of one more mineral, viz. gold.

Gold has far less practical utility than several other metals, and much of the present production is employed only as a monetary reserve kept by banks. Nevertheless, from the time of the earliest civilizations it has exerted an extraordinary attraction upon people, and to win it men have gone to remote regions, braved dangers and toiled—often with little return.

Probably the most striking example of the connection between the occurrence of this metal and human geography is given by the history of the exploitation of Central and South America. Almost immediately after the discovery of the New World by

Columbus in 1492, the search for gold became the main aim of the Spaniards, and thereby one of the chief factors leading to the conquest of much of the western hemisphere ; some of the long-enduring effects of this conquest by Spain, as contrasted for example with the settlement of other European peoples farther north in America, will be given in later chapters. We note here only that South America and Mexico remained the chief source of the gold supply of the world until well into the nineteenth century, when for a time Russia took the first place.

The modern period of gold production began in the middle of the nineteenth century with the discovery of gold in California, and from that time onward there has been a series of " gold rushes " which have increased the supply far beyond that of earlier times. The gold was found here in the form of " placer " deposits brought down as grains of metal in the gravel of streams from the Sierra Nevada mountains, and for its extraction it needed but a pick, shovel and washing-pan. The immediate yield was enormous, but the Californian goldfields experienced the fate which overtook most of those which were the scenes of later gold rushes ; the yield soon fell off as most of the alluvial deposit was worked out, and then the gold had to be traced up the streams to its sources in veins or lodes in the bedrock of the mountains. To extract the gold from lodes in the rock is far more difficult than to work placers in the stream beds ; it involves mining, the use of machinery for crushing the ore, and the employment of chemical processes, and often needs much capital as well as labour. The amount of gold obtained at this stage of the exploitation of a field is commonly less than that at the first rush, but it tends to remain fairly constant for a considerable period.

Meanwhile, the gold-seekers in the exhausted alluvial districts may have had to turn to other occupations in the neighbourhood, such as farming ; it has several times happened that the discovery and mining of gold have led people to a hitherto undeveloped region and thus paved the way to its use along different, and more permanent, lines. On the other hand, the miners who could no longer work placer deposits sometimes went to lode-mining and sometimes took part in another rush to a newly opened goldfield at a distance.

A few years after the Californian discoveries there were similar happenings in the eastern part of Australia ; here

mining began in 1851, produced enormous amounts of gold for
a few years, and then steadily declined. In the case of Australia, the opening up of another gold-bearing region in the
deserts of the western plateau in 1886 led to a second period of
great production.

At about the same time North America also saw another
gold rush ; this took place in the far north-west, i.e. in the
Klondyke district of Alaska belonging to the United States
and in the Canadian portion of the Western Cordillera.

Other consequences followed the discovery of gold in the
Transvaal in South Africa in 1885. The great series of auri-
ferous reefs which stretch for about 70 miles in the Witwaters-
rand district are a " rich man's field " and needed capitalists
as well as miners to develop them. After the discovery, the
city of Johannesburg quickly sprang up on the almost empty
veldt, railways were built to it and commerce developed. The
Boer farmers could not, or would not, adapt their State and its
laws to the new conditions ; the British Government intervened
on behalf of the newcomers, and ultimately there ensued the
Boer war by which the Transvaal was incorporated into the
British Empire. The discovery announced in 1946 of valuable
deposits in the Orange Free State, south-west of those of the
Transvaal, may be of special importance to the Union of South
Africa, as its prosperity largely depends upon gold.

Other fields have developed during the present century, e.g.
in central Canada, though accompanied by less spectacular
developments than in the past. The location of the principal
workings at the present time are shown on the map on p. 243,
which should be compared with the map of structural regions.

Although fragments of gold are washed some distance from
their sources, its original formation is associated with that of
the crystalline rocks, igneous or metamorphic, which have
cooled and solidified below the surface, and have become
accessible by later denudation. Hence the goldfields are in the
structural regions of the rigid mass type or in fold-mountains
where crystalline rocks have been exposed.

Thus a number of important gold-workings occur in the
areas belonging to the ancient " Gondwanaland." The most
productive gold-yielding district in the world is still that of the
Union of South Africa, and not far away are the mines of
Southern Rhodesia, while farther north in Africa are others in

the Congo Basin and the Gold Coast. Across the Indian Ocean are the gold-producing regions of the Deccan in India and those of the western plateau of Australia. (The present yields of Victoria, New South Wales and Queensland in eastern Australia are so small that they are omitted from the map showing the principal workings.) The South American fragments of " Gondwanaland " are gold-bearing in Guiana and eastern Brazil, but the amounts obtained at the present time are small.

In respect of its production of gold, the Laurentian Shield of North America comes next to the South African region, the most important district being situated north-east of Lake Huron on the borders of Ontario and Quebec. Another important gold district in North America is the Black Mountains of the United States, where crystalline rocks are thrust up through the younger strata of the western plains. The remaining fields of the continent are in or adjoining the fold-mountains of the Western Cordillera from Alaska in the north to Mexico in the south. In South America, too, the Western Cordillera still yield gold at several places.

On the other side of the Pacific Ocean, the fold-mountains are worked for gold in Japan and in the Philippine Islands. On the mainland of Asia, gold is got from the rigid mass area in Korea, while in the south of Siberia the older fold-mountains are worked for gold in several parts ; Russia has gold-mines also in the Ural Mountains.

Mineral Regions.—It will have been noticed, in the foregoing references to the principal workings of coal, oil, iron and gold, that the names of some areas have recurred several times. A similar result would follow from a statement of the production of other minerals, and it may be concluded that there are certain regions specially important in respect of their mineral resources. The chief of these mineral regions, and their respective products, are as follows—grouped according to the general type of geological structure which they exhibit.

Rigid Masses.—Among the chief mineral regions are those of the rigid mass type. The Laurentian Shield has very great importance ; in addition to iron- and gold-mining areas is the Sudbury mining area which contains ore yielding the greater part of the nickel supply of the world, together with platinum, copper and iron, while not far distant is Cobalt where ore is mined in which cobalt, nickel and arsenic are associated with

silver. In the far north-west of the Canadian Shield, near the
Arctic Circle at Great Bear Lake, the world's richest deposit
of pitchblende is mined for the extraction of radium and
uranium. This latter mineral is of very great significance, for
it is a source of atomic energy, with incalculable potentialities
both for destruction and also for the peaceful production of
heat and mechanical power.

The fragments of " Gondwanaland " are, in general, rich in
mineral resources, although in some parts, and especially in
South America, their comparative inaccessibility and the difficult climatic conditions have retarded their development. In
the southern part of the African massif, besides coal and gold,
there are workings from which diamonds, platinum and copper
are obtained ; in central Africa are gold, diamonds, copper and
pitchblende ; west Africa has diamonds and manganese.
In the Deccan of India, gold, coal, iron, chromium, manganese and mica are produced. In Australia, while the western
plateau has given gold, the more easterly Broken Hill region
of ancient rocks has yielded silver, lead and zinc. In South
America, the corresponding area of the Guianas has already
produced much bauxite (the ore of aluminium), while in eastern
Brazil there are almost untouched deposits of iron, manganese
and bauxite, besides gold and precious stones. The Chinese
Table has iron, tin, tungsten and, on its margins, coal.

The Older Fold-Mountains.—The Hercynian fold-mountain
areas are, as already shown, in several cases producers of coal,
often accompanied by iron ore. In addition, in the European
areas, the ores of a number of other metals have been mined
for some centuries, but these have now become largely exhausted
except in the Ural region ; here, however, and also in the south
of Siberia, the U.S.S.R. possesses a considerable variety and a
great amount of mineral wealth awaiting full utilization,
including coal, oil, iron, gold, platinum, manganese and copper.

The Younger Fold-Mountains.—The circum-Pacific mountain
systems have great mineral resources. In the western Cordillera of North America, besides the oil, gold and coal already
enumerated, there are widespread deposits of a number of
metals, among which silver, lead, copper and zinc have been
produced in large amounts. In South America, the Andean
Cordillera have much the same range of productions, together
with platinum and tin. On the other side of the Pacific Ocean,

the fold-mountains are again metalliferous ; in addition to the oil and gold from the islands off the Asiatic mainland and in the East Indian Archipelago, much of the world's tin comes from the Malay Peninsula and adjoining islands, while Japan produces silver and copper. The mid-world belt of fold-mountains, as already stated, has very considerable oil supplies, and in the western Mediterranean region are iron ores in several parts and bauxite in southern France.

In enumerating the mineral resources of the world, the non-metals must not be omitted, for though they have not the same monetary value, as compared with their bulk, as the metals, they are of inestimable importance in many ways. Salt and potash, for example, are the basis of a great amount of chemical production, and are therefore of great value in many industrial processes as well as providing artificial manures for agriculture ; salt is, of course, essential in man's diet. Again, limestones are used for building, as also are clays and sands, while these latter materials are employed in making pottery, glass and other wares. Moreover, the non-metallic sources of mineral wealth are very widely distributed, even in regions such as the younger plains which are not so productive in metallic ores.

Addendum.—Since this chapter was set up in type there has been an intensive search for uranium, as a source of atomic power, in several States. Besides the deposits in Canada and the Belgian Congo mentioned above, others have been reported in the Murmansk Peninsula of Northern Russia, in South Africa, in the district of Australia overlapping the boundary between New South Wales and South Australia, and in the northern and southern portions of the Chinese Table ; all these areas are of the rigid-mass type. The possible occurrence of uranium in Antarctica has also been indicated.

CHAPTER IV

THE CLIMATIC ELEMENTS

The outstanding differences between the great regions of the world are essentially connected with their climates, of which the chief elements are the insolation, i.e. the radiation of light and heat from the sun ; the temperature and pressure of the air ; the winds ; the precipitation of rain or snow. How these elements are distributed over the earth will be first considered.

Insolation.—The climate of any place depends largely upon the light and heat which it receives from the sun. There are two factors determining this insolation : one is the length of the day, i.e. the time the sun is above the horizon and sends its rays to the particular place ; the other factor is the intensity of the radiation—greatest when the sun is overhead in the zenith and least when it is only just above the horizon.

These two factors of length of the day and altitude of the sun are shown in the familiar but necessary diagram in Fig. 12, for they depend upon the way in which the earth rotates upon its axis each day, and revolves around the sun in the course of the year. The diagram illustrates the conditions at four seasons. There are the two equinoxes, i.e. the times when the nights are of equal length with the days at all parts of the globe ; these equinoxes occur on March 21st and September 23rd. It should be noticed that at these dates rays from the sun fall directly upon the Equator. The other two seasons shown in the diagram are the solstices when rays from the sun fall directly, not on the Equator, but on one of the Tropics : on June 21st the sun is in the zenith at the Tropic of Cancer, $23\frac{1}{2}°$ north of the Equator, and on December 21st it is overhead at the Tropic of Capricorn, $23\frac{1}{2}°$ south of the Equator. At the solstices, day and night are not of equal length except at the Equator ; the hemisphere which has the sun overhead also has a longer period of insolation.

How places at different latitudes are affected by these conditions can be best understood by realizing how the sun appears to move across the sky in certain latitudes at each season.

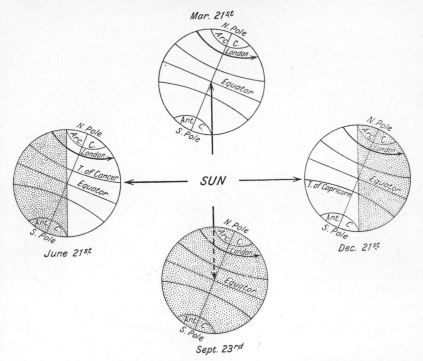

FIG. 12.—REVOLUTION OF THE EARTH AROUND THE SUN.

The Equator.—The diagram in Fig. 13 shows that on March 21st a man at the Equator would see the sun rise in the east, at 6 a.m. ; it climbs to the zenith by midday and sets in the west, at 6 p.m. From this date onwards, he would see the sun's path in the sky a little farther towards the north each day, till on June 21st its highest point at midday is $23\frac{1}{2}°$ from the zenith ; this situation is shown also in the diagram, giving the height of the sun in June and December, in Fig. 14. After June 21st the sun's course is seen daily a little farther towards the south until on September 23rd it is again overhead at midday, and on December 21st its highest point is $23\frac{1}{2}°$ on the south side of the zenith. After December 21st the path appears each day a little more to the north until on March 21st the sun again rises exactly in the east. Hence at the Equator the greatest intensity of insolation is received at the equinoxes in March and September when the sun is overhead at midday, and the intensity is rather less at the June and December

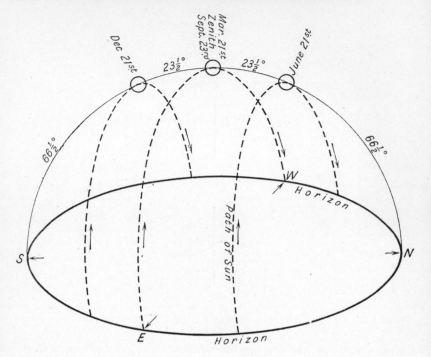

Fig. 13.—PATHS OF SUN AS SEEN AT EQUATOR.

solstices when the sun's highest altitude is $23\frac{1}{2}°$ from the zenith, i.e. $66\frac{1}{2}°$ above the north or south horizon.

The duration of daylight at the Equator, however, is always the same, viz. 12 hours, for the sun always rises at 6 a.m., and sets at 6 p.m. The result is that in equatorial latitudes, say between 5°N. and 5°S., there is not a very great change in the heat received at the various seasons of the year. Dwellers in equatorial regions do not know a contrast between summer and winter such as that which we experience in Britain.

The Tropics.—At the northern Tropic, as shown in the diagram in Fig. 15, at the summer solstice of June 21st the sun is directly overhead at midday, and also is above the horizon for about $13\frac{1}{2}$ hours ; hence people in this latitude have more insolation in their summer than is ever experienced at the Equator. At the equinoxes of March and September the sun shines for just 12 hours and at midday is $23\frac{1}{2}°$ from the zenith. At the winter solstice in December the day lasts only about

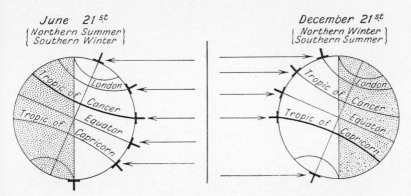

FIG. 14.—HEIGHT OF SUN IN JUNE AND DECEMBER.

Note.—The arrows represent rays from the midday sun reaching the various places, either from the zenith or at different angles from the overhead position.

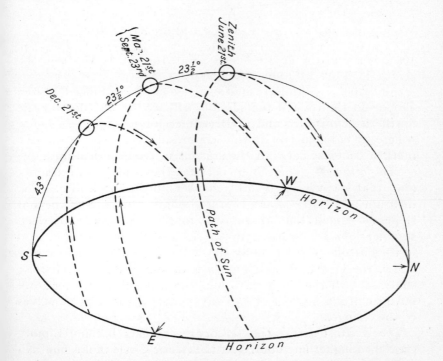

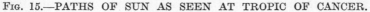

FIG. 15.—PATHS OF SUN AS SEEN AT TROPIC OF CANCER.

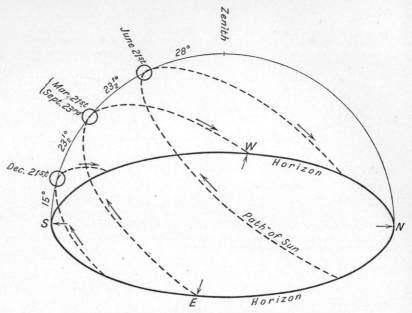

FIG. 16.—PATHS OF SUN AS SEEN AT LONDON.

10½ hours and the greatest altitude of the sun is 47° from the zenith, i.e. only 43° above the horizon.

Consequently, while insolation is very great indeed at the Tropics at the time of the summer solstice, i.e. in June for the northern hemisphere and in December for the southern hemisphere, it is much less at the winter solstice. The result is a marked contrast between the seasons in tropical latitudes.

Mid-latitudes.—The change between the insolation in summer and that in winter is still greater in mid-latitudes. The diagram in Fig. 16 shows that at London the path of the sun slopes so much that there is a marked difference between summer and winter both in the length of the day and also in the altitude of the midday sun. In our latitudes, as we well know, the long days and high sun of summer make a strong contrast with the short days and the low sun of winter ; we have to alter a number of our ways of living to adapt ourselves to the change.

The Arctic Circle.—The seasonal contrasts become rapidly greater in higher latitudes. At the Arctic Circle in lat. 66½° N., the path of the sun has such a slope that on midsummer day

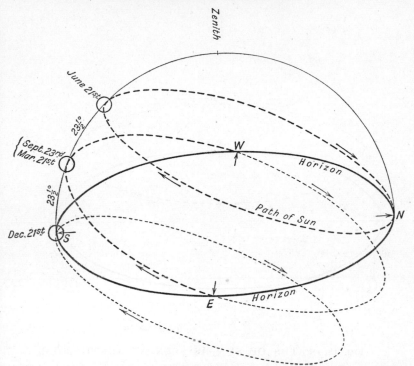

FIG. 17.—PATHS OF SUN AS SEEN AT ARCTIC CIRCLE.

the sun circles round the sky, rising at midday to 47° above the horizon and then descending so as just to touch the horizon at midnight; the "midnight sun" can therefore just be seen at this latitude on June 21st. At the equinoxes, here as everywhere else on the globe, the daylight lasts for 12 hours. At midwinter, on December 21st, the sun is out of sight below the horizon for practically the whole of the 24 hours, just rising as far as the horizon at "midday." (See Fig. 17.)

Hence there is considerable insolation near the time of the summer solstice, for although the sun does not give much heat while it is near the horizon, the days are very long. On the contrary, the winters have very little insolation ; the days are short, and even when the sun is visible it is low down in the sky and gives little heat. The people of the far north must crowd much of their year's work into the long days of summer, for in their winter there is so little light and heat from the sun that little activity is possible.

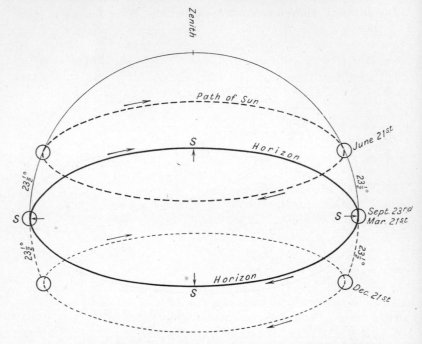

FIG. 18.—PATHS OF SUN AS SEEN AT NORTH POLE.

The Polar Regions.—Within the Arctic and Antarctic Circles there is a still longer period in summer during which the sun is visible. For example, while at the Arctic Circle the sun is continuously above the horizon for one day only, at latitude 70° it circles round for 65 days before dipping out of sight, and at latitude 80° it does not set for 134 days. Conversely, the sun remains invisible for similar periods during the winter.

At the North Pole itself the sun circles round the sky practically parallel with the horizon ; see the diagram in Fig. 18. It rises on March 21st and its continuous path becomes gradually higher day by day until on June 21st it circles at an altitude of 23½° ; then its course becomes lower until it sets on September 23rd. After that date it remains invisible as it circles round, first descending until on December 21st it is 23½° below the horizon, and then gradually approaching the horizon till it rises again at the March equinox. Conditions at the South Pole are like those at the North Pole, but the dates of the seasons are reversed.

Insolation is therefore continuous at the Poles for six months and then ceases entirely for the same period ; one may speak of a six-months day and a six-months night. As regards the intensity of the insolation it is important to remember that the only considerable amount of heat received from the sun comes for a short time near the summer solstice when the sun is highest in the sky ; during the rest of the six-months day the low sun gives little heat. Hence life near the Poles must be adapted to a summer which has a relatively long period of continuous light but is warm for less time, while in the winter there is a long period of constant darkness or twilight, and of intense cold.

It should be added that everywhere on the globe there is a period of twilight when the sun, though invisible, is less than 18° below the horizon. Twilight occurs each morning and evening when the sun rises and sets daily ; it occurs in polar regions for an extended period before the sun reappears after the long " night " of winter, and for the same period after the sun has disappeared after the long " day " of summer. Twilight is of special help to people in high latitudes during their dark winters ; the diagram on p. 421 shows how the " Polar Eskimos," in lat. 77° N., have varying periods of light, twilight and darkness throughout the year.

Temperatures.—When considering the air temperatures of different parts of the world it must first be noted that, broadly speaking, insolation results in a gain of heat during the day, but during the night there is a loss of heat from the earth by outward radiation. Further, a gain of heat causes the temperature of a land area to be raised more than that of a water area ; hence the air over the land becomes hotter during the day, and during the summer, than air over a corresponding mass of water. Conversely, air over the land tends to have a lower temperature than that over the water during the night, and during the winter. Therefore it is in the central parts of the northern continents that people commonly experience the greatest extremes of temperature change, from blazing heat during summer days to bitter cold during winter nights.

In accounting for the temperature of regions, weight must be given also to the effects of winds blowing from cooler to warmer areas, and *vice versa* ; the prevailing winds which thus tend to warm or to cool regions over which they blow are mapped on pp. 60 and 61.

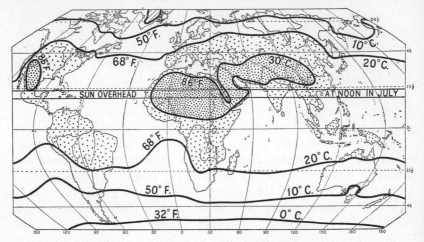

FIG. 19.—MEAN SEA-LEVEL TEMPERATURES IN JULY.

Note.—Land areas which are " hot " or " very hot " (when temperatures are adjusted to sea-level) are marked by dots ; those which are " cold " or " very cold " by lines.

It must be noted that the highest temperatures at a given place occur *after* the periods of greatest insolation both at midday and at midsummer. For this reason the map above shows the average temperatures of the air not for June but for July, which is in general the warmest month for the northern hemisphere and the coolest month for the southern hemisphere ; similarly, the map opposite shows the conditions in January as representing winter for the northern hemisphere and summer for the southern hemisphere. Also, the temperatures shown on the maps and referred to in the text are the averages for all the days and the nights of the respective months, as experienced over a number of years ; in actual fact, the days are generally warmer and the nights are cooler than is shown, while in particular years the conditions are above or below the normal.

The maps give the mean temperatures in Centigrade and Fahrenheit degrees, but it may be convenient to express the broad facts in a more concise form. Hence in the text the following labels will be employed :

Very hot = above 30° C. (above 86° F.); hot = between 20° and 30° C. (68°–86° F.); warm = between 10° and 20° C. (50°–68° F.); cool = between 0° and 10° C. (32°–50° F.) ; cold = between — 10° and 0° C. (14°–32° F.); very cold = below — 10° C. (below 14° F.).

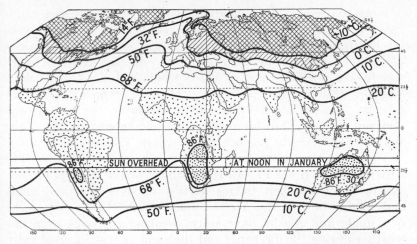

FIG. 20.—MEAN SEA-LEVEL TEMPERATURES IN JANUARY.

Note.—The explanation below the map for July applies also to this map.

It may be noted that some of these labels may not seem appropriate to those familiar only with temperature conditions in the British Isles, but they are necessary when the whole world is considered.

Temperatures in July.—When at the end of June the overhead sun has swung $23\frac{1}{2}°$ north of the Equator and the days there are fairly long, the insolation is so great that in the following month of July the regions of greatest heat in the world are in the neighbourhood of the Tropic of Cancer. From tropical North Africa to central China the great land-mass is shown on the map on p. 56 as having a July temperature of over 86° F. But this map, like that for January, gives "sea-level" temperatures, and at any considerable elevation the "actual" temperatures are markedly below those indicated; allowance must be made for altitude by subtracting 1° F. for every 300 feet above sea-level. Hence, while the lowlands are actually very hot, the highlands of Asia in sub-tropical (i.e. nearly tropical) latitudes are much cooler. Similarly, in North America the lands of sub-tropical latitudes are very hot only near sea-level. The apparent belts of heat are, in fact, entirely broken over the great highland regions.

The hot belt, where sea-level temperatures are between 68° and 86° F. in July, is very broad and is continuous even across the oceans. It includes all the equatorial regions, but is more extensive in the northern than in the southern hemisphere. Over the North American continent, it stretches so far north that there is considerable heat even in the prairies of western Canada in their summer. In the eastern hemisphere, the northern part of the hot belt includes the south of Europe, while in Asia it bulges northward even over part of Siberia. On the southern side of the Equator, the belt of heat does not extend so far, for July is the coolest month of the year ; the hot belt scarcely reaches the southern Tropic.

There are two warm belts where sea-level temperatures are between 50° and 68° F. In the summer of the northern hemisphere the warm belt bulges northward over the land areas and reaches beyond the Arctic Circle. In North America most of Canada and Alaska have warm weather (perhaps even hot weather during the daytime) and the same is true of practically all lowland Europe and Siberia. It should be noticed that we in Britain have a midsummer which, judged by world standards, is merely " warm." In the southern hemisphere, where July is the coolest month, all South Africa, most of Australia and a broad belt in South America are in the warm belt.

In July, the cool lands of the world, with temperatures between 32° (freezing-point) and 50° F., in the northern hemisphere are limited to the margins of the Arctic Sea. In the southern hemisphere, the southernmost part of America and parts of Australia and New Zealand have cool winters.

The cold regions, below 32° F., as given on a sea-level map for July are the interior of Greenland and the whole of the Antarctic continent. But because of its altitude the interior of Greenland is in fact *very* cold and is ice-covered, while on the vast ice-sheet above the high plateau of Antarctica the average winter temperatures are the lowest on earth—probably more than 60° below Fahrenheit zero.

Temperatures in January.—When the overhead sun and the longer days are near the southern Tropic, the higher temperatures are south of the Equator. The very hot areas, however, occur only in the interiors of South America, Africa and Australia.

The hot belt is continuous around the globe. In the southern hemisphere it extends south of the Tropic of Capricorn to include the sub-tropical regions of the southern continents ; the only exceptions are along the west coasts of South America and Africa where temperatures are lowered by cool masses of water coming as currents from southern latitudes or welling up to the surface from the depths of the ocean. In the northern hemisphere, the hot belt does not extend north of the Tropic of Cancer, except for relatively small areas over the warmer waters of the Atlantic and Pacific Oceans.

The January warm belt in the southern hemisphere is mainly over the oceans, for over the continents only the southernmost tips of Australia, the south and west coasts of Africa and a part of South America have summers with merely warm temperatures ; Tasmania and New Zealand have similar conditions. In the northern hemisphere the winters are warm over subtropical North America, North Africa and a tropical and sub-tropical belt in Asia.

The cool belt is scarcely represented in the lowlands of the southern hemisphere in January, but covers broad areas in North America, Europe and sub-tropical Asia. Britain, it will be seen, has a cool midwinter, regarded by world standards.

The cold regions in January, in addition to the Antarctic Plateau, form a continuous belt in the northern hemisphere, including a strip of North America in middle latitudes, much of eastern Europe, and a mid-latitude strip of Asia. Moreover, there are large regions which in January are very cold, with mean temperatures below 14° F. These cover all the northern area of North America and Asia, while the Arctic lands of these continents have winter temperatures far below zero F. The " cold pole " of the northern hemisphere is in north-eastern Siberia, where the mean January temperatures are about − 40° or − 50° F.

Annual Changes of Temperature.—A comparison of the January and July temperatures at a particular place gives its annual range ; e.g. in London the difference between the January mean of 39° F. and the July mean of 63° F. shows an annual range of 24° F. This is but a moderate amount and therefore indicates a fairly equable climate. The equatorial belt of the world is very equable, with an annual range of only about 5° F. ; tropical and sub-tropical regions, and most of the southern hemisphere, are also equable ; even the western and north-western coasts of the northern continents, warmed in winter by westerly winds from the oceans, may be considered equable, for their annual range seldom exceeds 30° F.

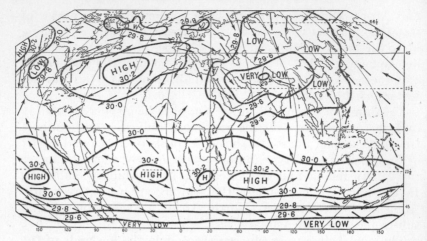

FIG. 21.—MEAN SEA-LEVEL PRESSURES AND PREVAILING WINDS
IN JULY.

On the contrary, regions of extreme climates, with an annual range of over 40° F., occur in the central, northern and north-eastern parts of North America and Eurasia, where the cold winters are little modified by oceanic influences. In north-eastern Asia the annual range exceeds 100° F.

A fairly complete idea of the normal changes during the year is given by graphs showing the " march of temperature " from month to month. For example, the very slight seasonal variations in equatorial latitudes, with mean monthly temperatures never deviating far from 80° F., are illustrated by the graph on p. 367 ; the moderate range of the temperate climates of the west coasts of middle latitudes is shown by the graph for Portugal on p. 384 ; the rapid march of temperature from a cold winter to a hot summer in North China, at about the same latitude on the eastern side of Eurasia, is illustrated on p. 395.

From the human aspect, the almost constant high temperatures of equatorial regions are unfavourable to human activities, more especially where, as will be shown in a following section, the heat is accompanied by rain and moisture in the air at all seasons. Also, a very wide annual range is a handicap if it subjects people in summer to great and perhaps enervating heat and in winter to such cold that agricultural work is impossible. The most favourable conditions are offered in regions

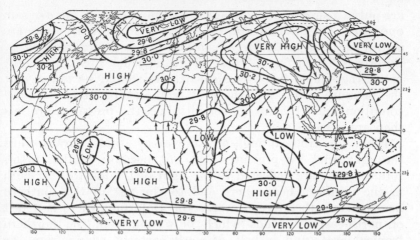

FIG. 22.—MEAN SEA-LEVEL PRESSURES AND PREVAILING WINDS
IN JANUARY.

where the climate is in general temperate, with a moderate range from one season to another.

Winds and Air Pressures.—It is beyond the scope of this book to give a complete account of the wind systems of the globe ; only the prevailing winds felt at the surface of the earth can be considered, and the air pressures closely connected with them. The pressure of the atmosphere at sea-level averages a little more than is shown by a barometer reading of 30 inches, but there are parts of the world where the air pressures are considerably above this average and others where they are much less. Winds blow from areas of relatively high pressure to those of relatively low pressure, and may be considered under two headings : (1) the belts of winds and pressures which are most clearly felt over the oceans and the western margins of the continents ; (2) the monsoon systems which interrupt the belts over the greater land masses, and greatly affect their eastern margins.

The Belts of Pressures and Winds.—The equatorial belt of high temperature broadly corresponds with an equatorial belt of low pressure known as the Doldrums, while there are areas of higher pressure on each side, near the Tropics, in what are known as the Horse Latitudes. These pressure belts are most clearly marked over the Atlantic and Pacific Oceans and the western margins of the continents, and the general conditions are put in a simplified form on the left-hand side of the diagram opposite.   On the maps on pp. 60 and 61, however, there are shown areas of particularly high and low pressure, marked by the words " high " and " low," some of which break or almost break the simple belt-arrangement.   It should be noted that the pressure maps, like those of temperature, show sea-level conditions, and that at higher altitudes the pressures are less than are marked.

From the tropical high-pressure areas winds blow toward the equatorial low-pressure belt, but because of the earth's rotation they are deflected to the right of the most direct path in the northern hemisphere and to the left in the southern hemisphere ;   therefore, towards the Doldrums there is a belt of north-easterly winds which blow out from the northern tropical area, and a belt of south-easterly winds from the southern tropical area.   These north-easterly and south-easterly winds are known as the trade winds, and are remarkably constant and steady.   Within the Doldrums the in-blowing air rises to higher altitudes, and at the surface there are felt only light and variable winds or complete calms.   On the maps for July and January the trade winds are most clearly marked over the Atlantic Ocean.

In the tropical regions of high pressure, there are calm conditions at the surface, for here the air sinks gently down from the higher layers of the atmosphere.   Part of this sinking air supplies the trade winds which blow out towards the equatorial low-pressure belt ;   another part supplies other winds which blow towards areas of low pressure on the opposite sides of the Tropics, most strongly developed in about latitudes 60° N. and S.   The latter winds tend to blow in a polar, as contrasted with an equatorial, direction, but they are so strongly deflected by the earth's rotation that in the northern hemisphere they generally blow from the south-west or even from the west, and in the southern hemisphere from the north-west or west ;   hence they are commonly known as the westerlies.

Because of the northward and southward swing of the over-head sun and of the associated areas of high temperature, there is a seasonal migration of the belts of equatorial low pressure and tropical high pressure and of the resultant wind systems. This northward and southward swing is not as wide as that of the overhead sun but it has a great effect on the regions in which

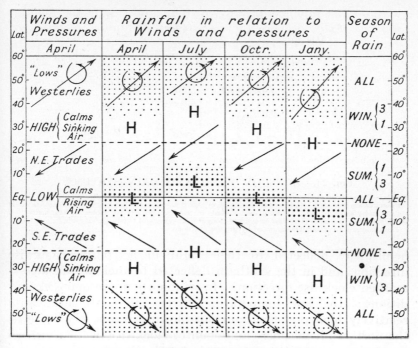

Fig. 23.—WIND AND RAIN BELTS.

it occurs ; its extent over the oceans can be seen on the maps for July and January, and it is diagrammatically shown above, where the normal positions of the belts are given for four months representing the four seasons.

The swing of the belts is not felt far beyond about latitude 50° north and south of the Equator ; beyond these latitudes a circum-polar (not polar) belt of low pressure is found throughout the year, except in Asia and North America in summer. Still farther to the north and south, beyond the areas shown in the maps on pp. 60 and 61, the polar regions themselves tend to be areas of high pressure ; this is specially marked in the Antarctic whence winds blow out, sometimes with great violence, towards the circum-polar low-pressure belt.

The Monsoon Systems.—Owing to the marked seasonal changes of temperature over the greater land-masses in mid-latitudes, there are corresponding changes of pressure and winds. The high temperatures over the continents in their summer cause relatively low pressures and in-blowing winds, in the northern

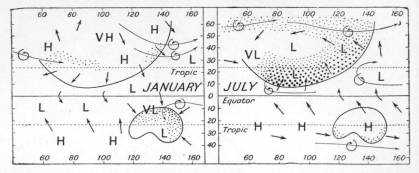

FIG. 24.—MONSOON WIND AND RAIN SYSTEMS.

Note.—The outlines of Monsoon Asia and Australia are marked diagrammatically.
Pressures are indicated by VH = very high ; H = high ; L = low ; VL = very low. Seasonal winds are shown by short arrows.   Tracks of mid-latitude or tropical cyclones are shown by long arrows, on which spirals indicate the clockwise or counter-clockwise directions of the in-blowing winds.
The amount of the rainfall is suggested by the size of the dots.

hemisphere deflected to their right in a counter-clockwise direction, and in the southern deflected to their left in a less-marked clockwise direction. In winter there are opposed conditions ; the low temperatures over the continents cause relatively high pressures and out-blowing winds, clockwise in the northern hemisphere and counter-clockwise in the southern hemisphere.   (See the maps, and also the diagram above.)

The monsoon system is most strongly developed in Asia, where there is an almost complete reversal of wind direction—outward in January and inward in July.   Peninsular Europe is mainly under the influence of the Atlantic system of winds, but Trunk Europe is more closely associated with the monsoon systems of Asia.   In North America there is a less marked change with the seasons than in Asia, and the maps show that over most of the northern part of the continent winds from a more or less westerly direction prevail throughout the year.

While the great land-masses of the northern hemisphere have monsoon systems which break up the belts of pressures and winds, over the southern continents these belts are much less broken.   Something of a monsoon system is observed in South Africa, but a clear reversal of winds occurs only in Australia.

Travelling Low-pressure Systems.—The maps show that the prevailing winds over the British Isles are the westerlies, but as people of these islands are well aware these winds are not the only ones.   Indeed, they are frequently interrupted by relatively small systems of changing winds and low air pressures,

termed mid-latitude " lows " or " depressions," which themselves travel in a general west-to-east course. As the systems
pass a particular place the in-blowing winds, often strong, are
felt to come from successive directions, e.g. they may veer from
south-east to south and south-west and thence to west and
north-west. In the diagram on p. 63 the winds of the travelling lows are shown by the curved arrows on the straight ones
of the westerlies.

Because of the changes of direction the winds bring changes
of temperature within moderate limits. Among other results
the lows thus have a stimulating influence upon people, due
both to the effect of variations of temperature, pressure and
humidity of the air upon internal processes and also to the
direct effect of wind upon the skin ; hence they help to make
the regions in which they are frequent very favourable as homes
of people able to maintain physical and mental vigour at all
seasons. The maps on pp. 66 and 67 show by long arrows the
most common tracks of the mid-latitude lows, and it may be seen
that they traverse those parts of Europe, North America and
Eastern Asia in which live peoples who have been active in
contributing to human progress.

In tropical regions there are smaller low-pressure systems,
with strong in-blowing winds. They originate over oceans,
and appear most commonly when and where the belt of greatest
heat has swung farthest south in the southern hemisphere, and
about six months later when and where the hot belt has swung
farthest north in the northern hemisphere ; they travel along
curving tracks, the most frequent of which are shown in the
maps on pp. 66 and 67. These tropical depressions, commonly
known as hurricanes near the West Indies, as typhoons off East
Asia and as cyclones in the Indian Ocean, are more intense
than those of mid-latitudes ; the winds are usually stronger
and sometimes are of very great violence, imperilling shipping
on the seas and even destroying buildings in coastal districts.

Precipitation.—The wind systems are the key to the way in
which regions receive, or lack, precipitation, for winds obtain
from the oceans water-vapour which they deposit as rain or
snow when they have been sufficiently cooled. The chief
cause of such cooling is by rising : e.g. in the Doldrums ; in
the travelling low-pressure systems of mid-latitudes and the
cyclones of tropical latitudes ; in all winds forced up over high

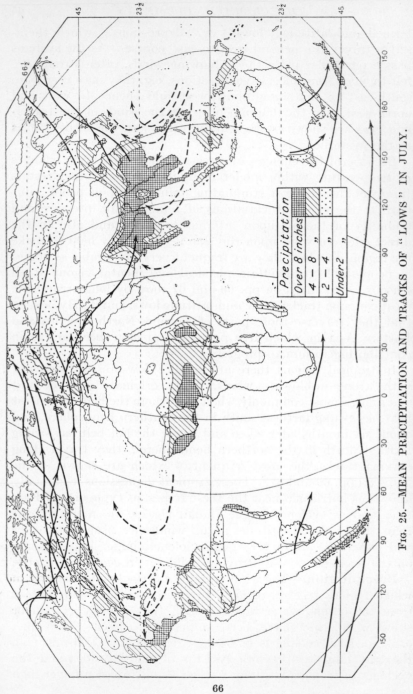

FIG. 25.—MEAN PRECIPITATION AND TRACKS OF "LOWS" IN JULY.

Note.—Continuous lines show frequent tracks of mid-latitude "lows" in northern summer and southern winter. Broken lines show frequent tracks of tropical cyclones during summer and autumn in the northern hemisphere,

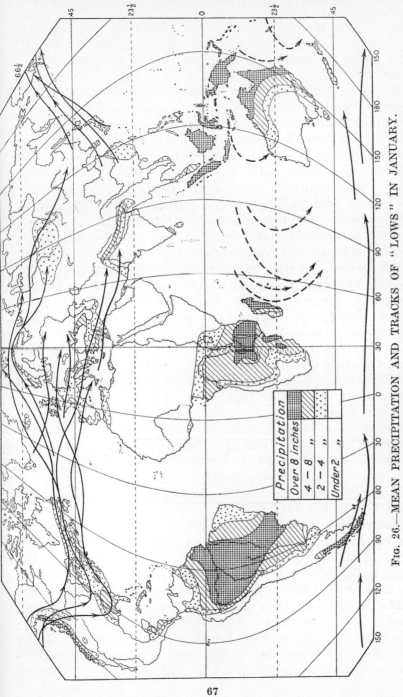

FIG. 26.—MEAN PRECIPITATION AND TRACKS OF "LOWS" IN JANUARY.

Note.—Continuous lines show frequent tracks of mid-latitude "lows" in northern winter and southern summer.
Broken lines show frequent tracks of tropical cyclones during summer and autumn in the southern hemisphere.

Precipitation
Over 8 inches
4 – 8 ,,
2 – 4 ,,
Under 2 ,,

67

lands. Thus the regions of heavy, moderate and scanty precipitation respectively can be related largely to the winds dealt
with under the headings of belts, with their travelling depressions, and of monsoon winds.

The Rain Belts and their Swing.—The equatorial belt of the
Doldrums has rainfall which usually occurs daily as torrential
downpours when the air rises after the noonday heat. This
rain belt is shown diagrammatically on p. 63, and it should be
noticed that the rainfall is heavy in the central part of the belt
and decreases towards the margins. As the belt of greatest
heat swings north and south of the Equator, so does that of
the rainfall ; this swing of the belt is illustrated on the diagram,
and is shown on the rainfall maps for July and January (pp. 66
and 67) particularly clearly in the case of inter-tropical Africa.
Regions within a few degrees of the Equator normally get rain
at all seasons, but have two maxima occurring soon after the
crossing of the overhead sun at the equinoxes. This type of
rainfall is illustrated in the graph for equatorial Africa on
p. 367, though the relatively dry season in July and August
is here exceptionally marked.

At about lat. 10° N. and S. the heavy rains come in the summer, viz. about July in the northern, and about January in the
southern, hemisphere, while the cooler season is one of drought ;
summer rainfall of this type is illustrated in the graph for
northern Nigeria given on p. 376. The right-hand column in
the diagram on p. 63 suggests how the period of precipitation
decreases from three seasons near the Equator to only one season
towards the Tropics, and the limits of the hot-weather rainfall
can be seen from the maps for July and January.

Tropical cyclones have within them rising air currents which
yield very heavy rain as they pass over a place. As these
cyclones generally occur in the northern hemisphere when the
hot belt has swung northward, and in the southern hemisphere
when it has swung southward, their downpours increase the
precipitation of the hot-weather type over the seas and coastal
lands of tropical regions ; they cause floods in low-lying areas.

The trade winds blow from cooler to warmer regions and
tend to become warmed ; as warmer air can hold more water-
vapour than cooler air they are therefore usually dry. There
are exceptions where the trades have received moisture from
the ocean and are then cooled by rising over mountains, as on

the eastern side of Madagascar. In the Horse Latitudes the air which descends and is therefore warmed does not yield rain ; hence this belt also is dry. For these reasons a broad area near the Tropics is characterized by drought throughout the year ; here are most of the deserts of the world.

The westerlies tend to be cooled where they blow in a poleward direction ; this cooling is particularly marked where they blow from the oceans over the western parts of the continents, and are forced up over high land and thus yield " relief rains." Moreover, in addition to this relief rain of the westerlies, heavy precipitation occurs in the rising air currents within the midlatitude travelling depressions. Hence the belt of the westerlies is one of frequent precipitation, and beyond lat. 40° the rainfall may come at any season. This is shown in the graph for Flanders given on p. 399. Nearer the dry belt, i.e. between lats. 40° and 30°, the rain normally comes only when the westerlies and their lows have swung equatorwards. At about lat. 40° this period lasts for much of the year, but towards the Tropics it may be limited to the winter (see the last column in Fig. 23) ; in any case there is a dry spell during the summer on the equatorial margin of the belt of the westerlies. These facts are illustrated by the graphs on pp. 380 and 384 : at Cairo, in lat. 30° N., there is only a very scanty rainfall which comes in the winter, while at Lisbon, in lat. 39° N. and open to Atlantic winds, the precipitation is considerable for three seasons and only the summer is dry.

In cooler regions, precipitation takes the form of snow, and statistics and maps are compiled on the basis of one foot of snow being equivalent to one inch of rain. The total amount of precipitation which can come from cool or cold air is not great ; hence the circum-polar areas have generally scanty precipitation and most of that comes in summer (see the graph for Sweden on p. 410). Yet the accumulation of unmelted snow in winter may give the impression of more precipitation than actually occurs.

Monsoon Rains.—As it is in the summer that the monsoon winds blow from the sea to the land, it is at that season that monsoon regions have most of their rainfall. This may be clearly seen by comparing the July and January maps for the " Monsoon Lands " of India, Indo-China, China and Japan, and also for the north of Australia. The precipitation is greatest

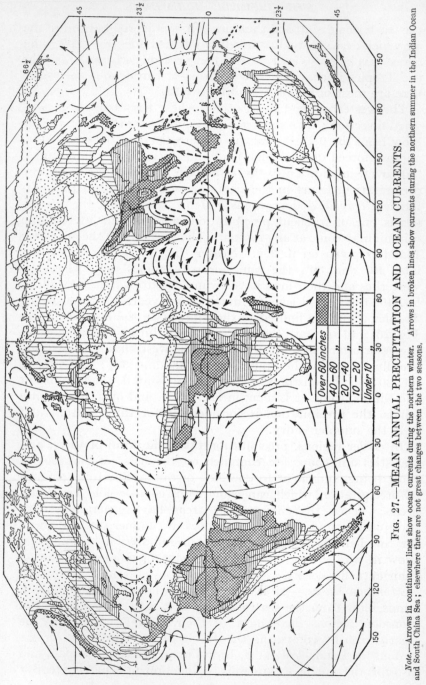

FIG. 27.—MEAN ANNUAL PRECIPITATION AND OCEAN CURRENTS.

Note.—Arrows in continuous lines show ocean currents during the northern winter. Arrows in broken lines show currents during the northern summer in the Indian Ocean and South China Sea ; elsewhere there are not great changes between the two seasons.

70

in the warmer parts of these areas (see the diagram on p. 64), and particularly where the sea-winds have to rise above high lands ; the Western Ghats of India provide a striking example, while one of the heaviest rainfalls of the world occurs at Cherra Punji on the southern slopes of the Khasi Hills of Assam.

Rainfall Regions.—The map on p. 70 shows the normal annual precipitation over the lands, and on it are marked the areas on which the rainfall is very heavy (over 60 inches in the year), heavy (40–60 inches), moderate (20–40 inches), scanty (10–20 inches) and very scanty (under 10 inches). But it is not only the total amount which is important, for the temperature of the air greatly affects the " efficiency " of the precipitation ; e.g. rain which comes when temperatures are high is evaporated much more rapidly than when they are low, and therefore is of less value to plants and to man. Also, one must take into account the way in which the precipitation is distributed through the year, and distinguish between regions which have rain mainly in summer, those which have it mainly in winter, and those in which it occurs at all seasons. Other factors also help to determine whether a region is " dry " or " wet," but in general one must balance the efficiency of the rainfall against the amount, either during the whole year or during a particular season.

It may, however, be noted that the arid regions are situated (1) in the tropical belt of the Horse Latitudes and the trade winds, except where these winds come directly from the ocean or where summer monsoons prevail ; (2) in the interior of Asia and North America ; (3) in the lee of high mountains.

The rainfall conditions shown on the maps and discussed above are based upon averages, but, as in the case of temperatures, variations from the normal must be reckoned with. It is found that where precipitation is slight, variations from the normal are relatively great. Hence in semi-arid regions the variability of the rainfall is an important factor, for at intervals there occur periods of drought or even a succession of years of drought which have serious consequences ; on the other hand, semi-arid regions may have times of relatively heavy precipitation, while even in deserts there are occasional storms which give transitory downpours of rain.

The contrasts between the well-watered and the arid regions show themselves in a variety of ways, because the former foster, and the latter restrict, life in many of its manifestations. From the human point of view, an interesting comparison may be made between the map showing the total annual precipitation (p. 70) and that of the population of the world (p. 295) ; there is a general suggestion that man's need of rainfall is " not too little, not too much," but there are exceptions to this rule.

Ocean Currents.—In later sections the influence of ocean currents upon land areas will have to be mentioned. Their main directions are shown on the map on p. 70. As regards the causes and effects of the ocean currents it must here suffice to point out (*a*) that the currents are largely directed by the prevailing winds, and (*b*) that their waters may warm or cool the air that blows over them, according to the warmer or cooler regions from which they come, and this air in its turn warms or cools the lands over which it passes.

CHAPTER V

CLIMATE REGIONS AND TYPES

THE interaction of the climatic elements in any particular area gives to that area a characteristic climate. Hence from what has been said about the distribution of the climatic elements over the globe, it will be understood that regions with similar positions have similar climates.

Moreover, when the climates are compared and grouped according to their similarities they fall into a number of types, such as the well-known " Mediterranean " type of climate. Some of these types may be arranged according to their situation in the great zones of the world, either along belts more or less parallel with the Equator, or depending also upon their positions in the continents. Other types are those of highlands of such altitude that they have markedly different conditions of temperature and precipitation from those of similar situation near sea-level, and therefore must be treated as having distinct types of climate. On this basis, the following scheme of climate types has been drawn up :

I. Zonal climates :
  1. Equatorial type (within about 10° N. and S.) ;
  2. Tropical types (extending on both sides of the Tropics) ;
  3. Sub-tropical and mid-latitude types (between about 30° and 60° on the west of the continents, and between about $23\frac{1}{2}°$ and 50° on the east of the continents) :
       (a) western marginal types ;
       (b) eastern marginal or monsoon types ;
       (c) interior continental types ;
  4. Sub-arctic type (about 50° to $66\frac{1}{2}°$) ;
  5. Arctic type (on both sides of the Arctic Circle).

II. Highland types in all latitudes.

The climates of each type will now be described and the regions in which they are experienced will be specified. A map showing the distribution of the regions is given on p. 74.

Equatorial Hot and Rainy Climates (Symbol on map : E.H.R.).—Climates of this type are found mostly within about

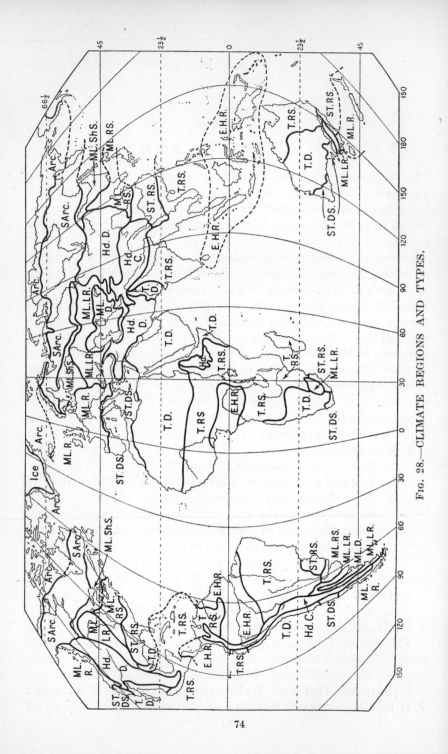

FIG. 28.—CLIMATE REGIONS AND TYPES.

10° of the Equator, where the considerable insolation at all seasons results in continuously hot weather, and the rising air gives heavy rain which may occur at almost every season—in many areas with two maxima during the year. These conditions may be realized by correlating the temperature and rainfall graphs for equatorial Africa (p. 367), though at this particular place there is one unusually dry season. It must be added that in this type of climate the difference between day and night temperatures, i.e. the daily range, is greater than the annual range ; another feature is the humidity of the air.

Not all the area, however, within about 10° of the Equator experiences this type of climate ; most notably, in South America and Africa the belt is broken by uplands and highlands on which the conditions are considerably modified. Hence there are four main regions of the equatorial type : the isthmus between North and South America ; much of the Amazon basin and the Guiana coast ; the western part of equatorial Africa ; the East Indian Archipelago together with the southern part of the Malay Peninsula and Ceylon. There are differences between the climates of all these regions, but their outstanding characteristics are similar.

The abundant heat and moisture which are typical of equatorial climates allow an abundant growth of vegetation, and there are some cultivated areas of great productivity and dense population. In most parts, however, the almost constant " damp heat " is harmful to health and hinders the activity of mankind, except for those racial groups such as the Negroes which have evolved bodily adaptations relieving its effects.

Tropical, Rainy-summer Climates (Symbol : T.RS.). —The common features of these climates are a season when the swing of the overhead sun brings at the same time great heat and much rain, alternating with a season of less insolation, lower temperatures and less rain.

An example of the tropical, rainy-summer climate is found in the Sudan region of North Africa. It is illustrated by the graphs for Northern Nigeria (p. 376) ; these show also how the great rains of July and August, with their accompanying cloud-cover to the sky, reduce the temperatures at that season. This west African region comes into the belt-arrangement of climates, and its counterpart is in Africa on the other side of the Equator ; two corresponding regions of the same belt-group occur on the northern and southern sides of the Equator in the Americas.

In the south of Asia and the north of Australia are other regions characterized by hot, rainy summers, but in these two cases the monsoon influences tend to strengthen the contrasts between the seasons. In eastern Africa the climatic conditions are more complicated, for there are winds of a monsoon type coming from the Indian Ocean and there is also the highland area stretching from Abyssinia to the southern Tropic ; the result is that here the tropical rainy-summer type of climate extends right across equatorial latitudes.

Moreover, in each of the southern continents where the trade winds blow from the sea to upland coasts they cause precipitation, contrary to their generally dry character ; hence where the trade wind belt swings southward in January it may extend the rainy-summer climate regions into more southerly latitudes. Finally, it must also be noted that several of these regions, in both northern and southern hemispheres, come within the range of the tropical cyclones which occasionally traverse coastal areas and bring sudden and sometimes devastating storms of wind and rain. Some tracks commonly followed by these tropical cyclones are shown on the diagram on p. 64.

In India we have an instance of how the climate of one region may differ from those of others of the same general type. Although India has tropical rainy-summer conditions, the exceedingly heavy monsoon rains bring about a distinctly marked modification of the simple two-season variety ; this is illustrated by the graph for Calcutta (p. 77), where there are three seasons known locally as follows : (1) the " hot weather " of March, April and May, which has rising temperatures while the overhead sun approaches this latitude and before the monsoon " bursts " ; (2) " the rains," which last from June to October and, because of the cloud-cover, are accompanied by a slight decrease of the heat even when the days are longer and the sun is nearly overhead ; (3) the " cold weather," which extends over November to the end of February and during which period there is little rain at Calcutta. It may be observed that the local phrase " cold weather " is an indication of what mean temperatures of 65° or 70° F. feel like to those used to the higher temperatures of the " hot weather " and the damp heat of " the rains."

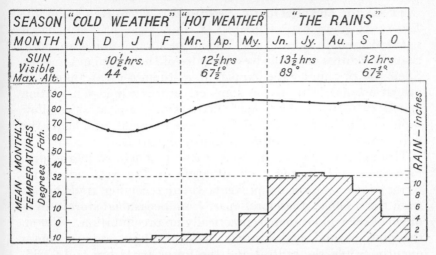

SEASON	"COLD WEATHER"				"HOT WEATHER"			"THE RAINS"			
MONTH	N	D	J	F	Mr.	Ap.	My.	Jn.	Jy.	Au.	S	O
SUN Visible Max. Alt.	$10\frac{1}{2}$ hrs. 44°				$12\frac{1}{2}$ hrs 67$\frac{1}{2}$°			$13\frac{1}{2}$ hrs 89°			12 hrs 67$\frac{1}{2}$°	

FIG. 29.—THE THREE SEASONS OF INDIA.

Note.—The conditions shown are those at Calcutta.
To aid comparison with other climates, this diagram is printed on the same scale as those of the Rhythm graphs in chapters 22–24. The lengths of daylight and maximum altitudes of the sun are given for the dates of the solstices and equinoxes.

West Africa gives a good illustration of the fact that there are seldom any definite limits to climate regions. A traveller going northward from southern Nigeria with its long period of summer rain would gradually find the wet season shorter and the country drier as he crossed into northern Nigeria (compare the graphs on pp. 372 and 376); indeed, the Sudan is sometimes divided into two climate regions, the southern termed wet, the northern dry. Yet the observer could not draw a definite boundary between the two areas, except perhaps when the climatic change might be accentuated by a change in the relief, and the same difficulty in determining the limits of a region would occur if he continued into the Sahara.

From the human aspect, a distinction must in several cases be made between the tropical, rainy-summer climate regions which have a relatively long period of fairly heavy precipitation and those which have a briefer and more scanty spell of rainfall; the former have possibilities of productive agriculture and many of their inhabitants are cultivators, while in the latter the poorer water-supply makes the people depend more largely upon rearing animals which may have to migrate from place to place to obtain sufficient pasture.

Tropical, Dry (Arid or Semi-arid) Climates (Symbol : T.D.).—Regions with climates of this type are in general situated on both sides of the Tropics of Cancer and Capricorn, near the centres or on the western sides of the great land-masses. Their position under the Tropics gives them a great amount of insolation and heat in the summer, but much less insolation and heat in the winter. With little rain, the clear skies allow rapid gain of heat by day and rapid loss by night, and hence the daily range of temperature is unusually great.

Throughout most of the year these regions are in the dry, high-pressure belt, and their situation on the west side or interior of the continents prevents them receiving trade winds from the oceans ; therefore, apart from occasional storms, over much of the regions there is practically no precipitation. Yet on the margins and higher areas there are light rains ; consequently, while the central and the lower parts are truly arid, there are frequently broad transitional or higher areas which are only semi-arid.

The greatest of the tropical dry regions is that which borders the Tropic in northern Africa and south-western Asia ; it includes the Saharan, Libyan, Arabian and Thar Deserts and their margins. In the southern hemisphere its counterparts are the South African region which comprises the coastal Namib Desert and the interior semi-arid Kalahari and Karroo, and the Australian Desert and its margins. In the south-west of North America is the " Great American Desert," and on the opposite side of the Cordillera is the semi-arid region around the lower valley of the Rio Grande. In South America the Atacama-Peruvian Desert extends from the Tropic to within a few degrees of the Equator, for along this coast the prevailing winds throughout the year blow from the south parallel with the great Andean barrier, or even down its slopes, and bring no rain.

While the arid regions in general do not offer homes to mankind, and very few people can make a living in the semi-arid parts, they nevertheless contain some populated areas ; reference was made in Chapter III to goldfields which have been discovered in desert regions, but far more important to human developments have been the oases and river valleys in which water is found. The greatest of these areas are the valleys of the Nile, the Euphrates and Tigris, and the Indus which bring down water and fertile soil from other regions ; these factors, together with the heat of the desert climate, make possible great production and a considerable variety of crops. Indeed, as will be shown later, it was in these desert oases that man made some of the most significant of his advances ; they have been, not only homes, but also nurseries and schools of civilized man.

Sub-tropical, Dry-summer Climates (Symbol : ST.DS.). —These are frequently called " Mediterranean " as they are well represented in the lands around the Mediterranean Sea in southern Europe, south-western Asia and northern Africa. They are situated on the western margins of the continents, mostly between the latitudes of about 30° and 40° N. and S. In this sub-tropical situation, they are subject in winter to the westerlies bringing warmth and the accompanying depressions bringing rain, while in summer they are under the influence of the tropical high-pressure belt with normally dry and hot weather. The graphs on p. 384 show typical conditions, though the length and severity of the summer drought are greater in the parts of the regions nearer the Tropics.

As South Africa extends a relatively short distance beyond 30° S., the Cape of Good Hope area of summer drought is but small. The shape of Australia brings two regions into this group, the one in Western Australia and the other in the east of South Australia and the adjoining part of Victoria. In New Zealand, the northern part is in " Mediterranean " latitudes, but its insular situation allows it to receive sufficient precipitation to make it very doubtful whether to include it in this group. In the New World, the Western Cordillera of both continents restrict the regions of this type to coastal areas— in North America to central California and in South America to central Chile.

From the point of view of human geography, the region around the Mediterranean Sea has been the scene of some of man's most brilliant and enduring achievements. The climate is particularly suitable for the growing of grain and of fruits, including the vine and olive ; corn, wine and oil were the material bases of the civilization of Crete (which developed independently of those of the great river valleys to the south and east) and of the later " glory that was Greece and the grandeur that was Rome." Only within the last hundred years or so has the cultivation of grain and fruit extended to the other regions of this type.

Sub-tropical, Rainy-summer Climates (Symbol: ST.RS.).
—Regions with climates of this type are situated in somewhat similar latitudes but on the opposite, eastern margins of the five great land-masses. The characteristics are shown in the most marked form in central China, southern Korea and southern Japan as a result of a strongly developed monsoon system. For this region the conditions are illustrated by graphs for central China on p. 388. In winter, Japan has a heavier rainfall than China, for the out-blowing winds cross the Sea of Japan before reaching the islands.

In North America this type of climate is experienced in the south-east of the United States, but the monsoon system is here less developed. Consequently the winters have not such persistently out-blowing winds, but are milder and have more rain than in central China ; in the summer the conditions of temperature and rainfall are closely similar to those in Asia. In both these regions in the northern hemisphere travelling depressions play a part in determining the weather ; for example, in winter, the moving lows of middle latitudes moderate the temperatures and bring precipitation, while in the summer tropical cyclones reach the coastal districts and may cause torrential downpours.

In each of the southern continents there is a region of this type in a corresponding situation, and in each the conditions resemble those of the south-eastern United States more closely than those of the Asiatic region, where alone strongly marked monsoonal contrasts occur.

Because there is an ample water-supply during the whole of a summer which is long as well as being hot at its maximum, man can obtain in these regions an abundant production of a number of valuable crops. Moreover, as the variations in the weather are also favourable to human well-being and activity, the regions are among the most densely populated in their respective continents.

Mid-latitude, Rainy-summer Climates (Symbol: ML.RS.).—This eastern marginal type is found where broad continental areas extend about half-way from Equator to Pole, i.e. in the eastern parts of Asia, North America and South America. The Asiatic region, comprising northern China, northern Korea and northern Japan, is subject to monsoon influences under which south or south-east winds bring considerable heat and rain in summer, while the prevailing north or north-west winds of winter are cold and dry. Characteristic graphs for north China are given on p. 395, showing a wide range of temperature, which gives it an extreme climate, and heavy rains in the latter part of the summer. Over the whole region cyclonic lows bring some rain at all seasons; nevertheless, the greatest falls are in summer.

In North America, the corresponding region covers much of the north-eastern part of the United States. The prevailing winds of summer are southerly, with considerable heat and rain; those of winter are from the interior of the continent, but travelling depressions are frequent and thereby the temperatures and the amount of the precipitation are both raised, especially near the coast. In South America, owing to the narrowing of the continent in mid-latitudes, there is no monsoon system with strongly marked changes between summer and winter, while travelling depressions tend to reduce the seasonal changes; in particular, the winters are not as cold and the summers are not as wet as those of regions of the same type in the northern hemisphere.

Because the heat is less in these mid-latitude regions (**ML.RS.** type) as compared with the adjoining sub-tropical ones (**ST.RS.** type) the range of crops and production is less; yet agriculture is important, and as the climate suits man's health and the regions also offer other means of livelihood these areas rank among the most important homes of mankind.

Mid-latitude, Rainy Climates (Symbol : ML.R.).—These are found where the westerlies with their lows blow at all seasons; hence they occur on the western margins of the land areas which extend sufficiently far from the Equator. The graphs for Flanders, given on p. 399, illustrate the resultant equability of the climate with a rainfall well distributed through the year.

In Europe the relief of the land allows the wind systems to penetrate far into the continent; hence, while upland districts bordering the Atlantic from Spain to Norway are more equable and have a greater rainfall, the plains of central Europe are less equable and have less rain. In North and South America, and in Australia, Tasmania and New Zealand the regions which receive the prevailing westerlies, with rain at all seasons, are restricted to much narrower limits than in Europe, and have more rain than the greater part of the European region.

The climatic conditions of this type were not very favour-able to agriculture, for the summers are not hot enough for the growth of some of the crops to which man had become accus-tomed in early times, and in some parts there may be too much rain for his requirements ; therefore, when farming spread from the Mediterranean area to central and western Europe the early agriculturists had to tackle new problems and to work hard in face of difficulties. Yet a cool temperate climate favours human energy, and the adoption of " mixed farming " (in which crops are raised partly for animals) became one of the factors which made possible a great population in this European region. Because the regions of the same type of climate in other con-tinents have a less extent, and in general possess less resources, they have seen much less development.

Mid-latitude, Light-rain Climates (Symbol : ML.LR.).— In Eurasia, north of the Black Sea and also forming a belt round the dry Caspian-Aral Depression, are the steppe-lands of Russia and Turkistan which have a considerable range of tem-perature due to their inland situation, and a light rainfall which comes partly from lows which occasionally penetrate from the Atlantic, and partly from storms caused by exceptional heating of the surface in the summer. In North America, the Great Plains of the United States and the Prairies of Canada are cut off from the Pacific by the Cordillera, and only the southern part is easily accessible to winds from the Atlantic. In the winter the winds are mainly out-blowing and only occasional travelling lows cause precipitation, but in the summer the monsoon-like in-blowing winds from the Atlantic bring more moisture; hence the rainfall is mainly in summer. The graphs on p. 404 show the conditions in the Canadian Prairies ; they are fairly typical of much of the North American and Eurasian regions, except that here in the northern part of the Canadian area the winters are " very cold " and the climate is more extreme than is generally the case.

In the southern hemisphere there are three regions of this mid-latitude, light-rain type. In the east of South America, in the lee of the southern Andes is an area almost surrounding the dry region ; here light and uncertain rains come in winter and in summer, due largely to travelling depressions.

In South Africa the High Veld region of the Transvaal and Orange Free State has more rain than the adjoining semi-arid

Kalahari, but it is largely shut off from the Indian Ocean by the Drakensberg Mountains. The summers are hot and wet; the winters are dry and they are cool or even warm.

Somewhat similar conditions occur in Australia in an area with a similar situation; i.e. where in New South Wales and Victoria the Basin of the Darling river adjoins the semi-arid interior of the continent, and is largely shut off from the Pacific Ocean by the Eastern Highlands. As in South Africa, the annual precipitation is light, but over part of the Australian region it comes mainly in winter from lows travelling from the west; also, as in South Africa, the summers are hot and the winters are warm.

Thus the climates of this type have considerable differences between them, and the most concise description generally applicable is that they have a light precipitation most of which occurs in one season; moreover, the rainfall is markedly variable from year to year and renders the regions liable to droughts. In the northern hemisphere the temperatures are generally extreme, but in the south they are equable.

The rather scanty precipitation of the mid-latitude light-rain regions makes them naturally suited to the growth of grasses; yet in the better-watered parts man has replaced this natural vegetation either by wheat or by other plants which grow under similar conditions. Hence some areas are useful for agriculture while others can afford only pasturage and have relatively few inhabitants.

Mid-latitude, Dry (Arid or Semi-arid) Climates (Symbols: ML.D.).—The map of total annual rainfall shows that in Asia, north-eastward from Arabia, the area with very little rain extends through the Iranian Plateau to Tibet and the Mongolian Highlands; these regions have, however, climatic conditions which vary so greatly according to their altitude that they will be considered later among the " highland climate " regions. North of the Iranian Plateau is another arid or semi-arid region—the low Caspian-Aral Depression which lies in the heart of the great Eurasian land-mass, cut off from the moisture-bearing winds of the summer monsoon by the highlands, and little affected by the moving lows which occasionally penetrate south-western Asia in winter. The seasonal contrast in the amount of insolation, without the moderating effect of either sea-winds or of cloudy skies, causes the annual range of temperature to be great ; so also is the change from day to night. It would be misleading to call this region either a " cold " or a " temperate " desert, as is sometimes done ; a short summary description is : *cold and dry in winter and hot and dry in summer.*

In South America, sheltered by the southern Andes from the prevailing westerlies, is the narrow arid or semi-arid region which includes part of Patagonia ; here the winters are but cool.

Apart from oasis cultivation and poor pasturage, the climatic conditions of these dry regions offer little to man and they are but scantily peopled.

Mid-latitude, Short-summer Climates (S y m b o l : ML.ShS.).—In the preceding sections the characteristic which distinguishes between the climates of mid-latitudes has been considered as the rainfall, either its total amount or the season in which most of it occurs, but near the cooler margins of these latitudes temperature becomes of more importance. In the northern hemisphere there are three areas of this type which adjoin the sub-arctic regions, viz. two situated on the eastern sides of North America and Asia respectively, and the third in eastern Europe with a narrow extension into Siberia. In each, the winters are cold and long, and the summers are merely warm and relatively short. Indeed, the effect of the shortness of the warm period is so marked upon the growth both of natural vegetation and of cultivated plants that the term " short summer " well distinguishes this type of climate from the others of mid-latitudes.

The curves in the diagram opposite show the annual march of temperature at four places in North America illustrating four types of climate. (1) The curve marked " Ci " shows how the temperature at Cincinnati, with a mid-latitude, rainy-summer climate, ranges from a cool winter to a hot summer. It shows, too, that the mean temperature normally reaches 42° F. early in March and remains above this level until the latter part of November ; as many plants grow only when the mean temperature is above 42° F. this period of about $8\frac{1}{2}$ months is referred to as the normal period of plant growth at Cincinnati. Similarly the period of " warmth," above 50° F., lasts from the beginning of April till November, i.e. about 7 months.

(2) The march of temperature in the mid-latitude rainy type of climate is illustrated by the curve marked " V," for Victoria, British Columbia. As the winter temperatures are by no

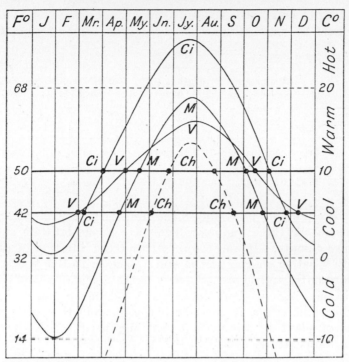

FIG. 30.—PERIODS OF WARMTH AND PLANT GROWTH.

means low, the growing season is long, viz. $9\frac{1}{4}$ months ; yet as the summers are not hot, the period of " warmth " is only $5\frac{1}{2}$ months.

(3) Conditions in the mid-latitude short-summer climate are shown by the curve marked " M," which relates to Marquette on the southern shore of Lake Superior. Here the winter is markedly cold and the period of plant growth is considerably shorter than at the preceding places, viz. only 6 months, while the " warmth " lasts but $4\frac{1}{2}$ months.

(4) To show how these conditions approach towards, but do not reach, those of the sub-arctic climate farther north, the curve for Churchill, on the shore of Hudson Bay, is added by a broken line ; in this place the growing period is reduced to $3\frac{1}{4}$ months, and that of " warmth " to 2 months.

The contrasts, in these respects, between the four types of climate are summarized in the following table.

MID-LATITUDE AND SUB-ARCTIC CLIMATE TYPES

Months of " Warmth " (above 50° F.) and of Plant Growth (above 42° F.)

Type	M-L. Rainy	M-L. Rainy Summer	M-L. Short Summer	Sub-arctic
Place	Victoria, B.C.	Cincinnati, Ohio	Marquette, Mich.	Churchill, Man.
Latitude	48° N.	39° N.	46° N.	59° N.
Above 50° F.	5½ mths.	7 mths.	4½ mths.	2 mths.
Above 42° F.	9¼ mths.	8½ mths.	6 mths.	3¼ mths.

A corresponding table shows the similarity between the conditions in the three regions which have a mid-latitude short-summer climate. It may be noted that the duration of plant growth is rather shorter at the other places with this type than at Marquette, and hence the general statement may be made that in these regions plants have less than half the year in which to grow ; moreover, it must be borne in mind that most processes of plant life, including ripening, need a considerably higher temperature.

MID-LATITUDE SHORT-SUMMER CLIMATE TYPE

Months of " Warmth " (above 50° F.) and of Plant Growth (above 42° F.)

Region	U.S.A.—Canada		E. Europe—W. Siberia		South-east Siberia	
Place	Marquette	Quebec	Moscow	Barnaul *	Middle Amur	Vladivostock
Above 50° F.	4½	4	4½	4	4	4¾
Above 42° F.	6	5¾	5¾	5¼	5	5¾

* Barnaul is just south of the eastern end of this region.

Although the rainfall in these regions is by no means heavy even in summer, and the annual amount may be described as scanty, yet because of the relatively low temperatures the efficiency of the precipitation is high, and there is seldom any lack in the water-supply. The graphs of temperature and rainfall on p. 410 show the conditions in central Sweden on the northern margin of the mid-latitude, short-summer region.

With this type of climate, cultivation is restricted to the

hardier plants and some parts of the area are near the limits where man can obtain a living by agriculture. Yet in other parts farming conditions are more favourable, and other forms of work have caused even great cities to grow up.

Sub-arctic Climates (Symbol : S.Arc.).—In the most northerly belt of the mid-latitudes and in the areas adjoining the Arctic regions are climates which may conveniently be called sub-arctic. In these relatively high latitudes the sun does not give much heat in summer, while in winter insolation is greatly exceeded by outward radiation ; hence the summer is merely warm and is distinctly short, and the winter is very cold and long. The precipitation is of moderate amount and falls mainly in the summer ; in the winter there are falls of snow which may remain as a cover upon the land for months. The efficiency of the precipitation is high, and despite the fact that the annual total is shown on the world map as "scanty " or " moderate," the country is by no means " dry."

In America, much of Canada and Newfoundland has a climate of this type, and in Eurasia the corresponding region occupies the north-east of Europe and most of Siberia.

The graphs for Mistassini in Canada (p. 415) are fairly typical for the southern parts of these regions ; it may be noted that the greatest annual ranges of temperature are experienced in some areas with this type of climate.

Agriculture is heavily handicapped by the severity of the sub-arctic climate ; the few people of these regions obtain their livelihood to a considerable extent by the cutting and transporting of timber from the forests, by hunting the fur-bearing animals which live in them, or by mining.

Arctic Climate (Symbol : Arc.).—For the most part, this type of climate is experienced on one side or the other of the Arctic Circle near the northern coasts of North America and Eurasia. In general, the summers are cool, for the mean temperatures in July are commonly below 50° F., and the winters are very cold and very long. Only a small precipitation is possible from air as cool or cold as it is in these regions, and much of it is in the form of snow. The efficiency of the rainfall is so high, however, that the appearance of the country may often give the impression of the region being a wet one. The graphs on p. 421 illustrate the conditions in a coastal lowland in north-western Greenland.

To make a home in Arctic climates, the very few inhabitants have had to adopt modes of life markedly different from those in most parts of the globe ; agriculture is practically impossible, reindeer are an important resource for some peoples, and in most coastal areas food and other necessities are obtained from the fish and animals which live in the sea.

Ice-cap Climates (Symbol :   Ice).—The conditions on the highland areas of the interior of Greenland and the continent of Antarctica are but little known.   Over both regions the mean " summer " temperatures are below 0° F., while those of the winter are far lower ; on the Antarctic Plateau they are perhaps 60° below zero F.   Under such conditions precipitation is in the form of snow which often comes in violent storms sweeping outwards from the interior towards the margins of these regions.   This type of climate has been named that of eternal frost.   Obviously, the ice-caps are not " homes of man."

Highland Climates (Symbols: Hd.D. and Hd.C.).—In the interior of North America and Asia are highland regions which, because they are shut off from sea-winds, have semi-arid or even arid conditions over much of their extent, and tend to extremes in temperature.   These regions include the Western Cordillera in Mexico, the United States and the south of Canada ;   Asia Minor and the Iranian Plateau in south-western Asia ;   the Highlands of Sinkiang and Mongolia in central Asia.   To indicate their predominantly dry character they are marked " Hd.D." on the map.   Yet the relief of these regions is so varied that there are considerable differences in their climates. Over large areas the structure is that of upland basins surrounded by mountain ranges ; consequently the temperatures vary according to elevation, while the precipitation is greater on the higher parts and the outer sides of the mountains and less in the interior basins than would be determined merely by their world-position.   Conditions on the Colorado Plateau of North America are shown on p. 426, and need two temperature curves and two rainfall graphs.

No general statement can be made about their relation to mankind, for the variety of natural conditions corresponds to a variety in modes of life ; in some parts people take advantage of neighbouring but contrasted environments to migrate from one district to another with the seasons, usually upward in the warmer periods and downward in the cooler weather.

Still more varied conditions occur in the two great regions which may be termed the culminating highlands of the earth's surface, viz. the Tibetan Plateau and its mountain margins in Asia, and the Andean Cordillera in South America. Because the most outstanding characteristic of these regions is their coldness, they are marked on the map " Hd.C." Yet temperatures may range from tropical on lower parts to the eternal frost of summit ranges ; precipitation conditions include on windward slopes heavy rainfall at lower elevations, and snow at higher ones, while aridity prevails within the high basins.

The population of these culminating highlands is generally small, and is restricted to the more favourable areas ; as on the lower highlands and uplands, seasonal migration is practised to make the most of the limited resources.

In addition to highlands which are predominantly either dry or cold, there are others of less extent and altitude ; they have no typical characteristic and yet stand out from the surrounding regions, e.g. in East Africa there are the Abyssinian Highlands and smaller ones farther south. No summary phrase can be applied to them except that they have a wide range of climatic conditions ; hence they possess wide possibilities for human use.

CHAPTER VI

STREAM, SURFACE AND SOIL CONDITIONS (1)

CLIMATIC conditions have a great effect upon the surface of the earth ; they have much to do with the character of the streams, the modelling of the surface forms and the development of the soils. The vegetation cover also influences these surface phenomena and is itself largely determined by climate.

The amount of water in streams and rivers is an important matter, and it must be realized how it is connected with the rainfall. Some of the rain-water is evaporated while some sinks into the soil and is there either utilized by the vegetation or slowly percolates into the streams ; the remainder forms the direct run-off into the rivers. This run-off is rapid where the slope of the surface is considerable, and in such cases an increase in the flow in the rivers may closely correspond with the seasonal distribution of the rainfall. In flatter country, however, the run-off is slower and the occurrence of high water is delayed ; moreover, a mass of vegetation like that of dense forests utilizes much water and thus moderates the swelling of the streams. Where the winter precipitation takes the form of snow, much of this may remain on the surface till spring ; with its melting a mass of water has a sudden run-off and the streams may be flooded. The diagram opposite shows how, in the case of a New England river, some of these factors combine to bring about a marked difference between the precipitation and the run-off in that region. The flow of water into the greatest rivers is also complicated by the fact that their tributaries may bring supplies from a region with a different type of rainfall.

Great contrasts between the soils of one region and those of another are brought about by differences of climate. Although soils are commonly formed from the underlying bedrock, it is mainly temperature conditions and surface moisture which in the long run determine their particular character. The bedrock supplies the material which is broken up by such agencies as

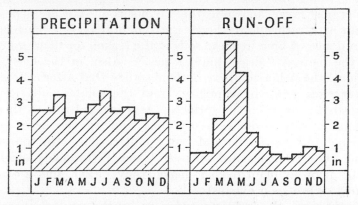

Fɪɢ. 31.—RELATION OF PRECIPITATION TO RUN-OFF
(NEW ENGLAND).

Note.—The left-hand diagram shows the average monthly amount of the precipitation over the basin of the Kennebec river ; the precipitation, reckoned in inches of rain, is fairly well distributed through the year, but in winter it is in the form of snow, much of which melts in spring.

The right-hand diagram shows the corresponding monthly amounts of water which run off into the lower course of the river. Note how in spring the melted snow has a rapid run-off, but in summer, and even in autumn, the evaporation of part of the rain-water and the use of another part by vegetation cause the run-off to be much less than the precipitation in those seasons.

change of temperature, winds, and water penetrating into cracks, into a mantle of rock fragments. These are slowly changed by further physical weathering and by chemical decomposition into a soil ; in this soil plants grow and, when they die, add organic residues. There are also bacteria in the soil which change the chemical composition of the substances upon which they live ; thus plant residues are decomposed, and at a certain stage in this process vegetable " humus " is formed. This humus is of great value in giving to the soil qualities favourable to the growth of plants and to the work of farmers. In these complicated ways, in the slow course of time the soil develops into a mature condition.

The action of water is of great importance. As it sinks through the soil it dissolves the soluble compounds, and where there is abundant rainfall these substances may be removed altogether and taken by the water into the streams. The lime, in particular, may be washed away and the resultant " leached " soils are characterized by the remaining insoluble compounds ; in the grouping of soils on the map on p. 94, these soils are labelled as " wetter (leached) types." On the contrary, in the drier regions the soluble constituents may be drained from the uppermost layer, known as the " A horizon," but are deposited again at a rather lower level, the " B horizon " ; the relative abundance of lime in these soils is the reason for their grouping on the map as " drier (limy) types." Also, in the most arid regions, the A horizon may become so dry that after a time the water rises again by capillarity and the soluble salts are re-deposited near or on the surface. As a general rule, if there is adequate water from rain or other sources, the drier, lime-bearing soils are fertile and repay cultivation. On the other hand, the wetter, leached soils are " sour " (i.e. acid) and tend to be poor in plant-foods ; hence they either give a scanty return or are soon exhausted.

To sum up, the bedrock, added to by the vegetation cover, is developed under one climate into a particular type of soil, while a very different type of soil is matured from similar parent rock under a different climate and with a different vegetation cover. Hence it is convenient to consider the stream, surface and soil conditions in the various parts of the world in connection with each climate type described in the preceding chapter.

Equatorial Regions (Climate symbol : E.H.R.).

Streams.—Generally speaking, rivers which obtain their water from almost constant rains of the equatorial type have a fairly regular régime : i.e. the alternation of high and low water during the year is not very great. This may be illustrated by the case of the head-stream of the White Nile. Where it drains the equatorial Lake Victoria it has a remarkably regular flow ; even lower down in lat. 5° N., when the river has received supplies from the summer rain region just north of the Equator, it has a fair amount of water at all months of the year. This is shown by the diagram opposite, comparing the régime of the White Nile with that of the Blue Nile and of the Nile in the middle part of its course.

The case of the Amazon is complicated, for while the main stream receives its most direct supply from the almost constant equatorial rains, it also gets much water both from the south where the rain comes chiefly in the summer (October to March) and also from the Andes where melted snows add to the supply. Moreover, the mass of water in the rivers takes weeks or months to work its way down the enormously long tributaries. All these factors affect the lower part of the main stream of the Amazon, and the floods which at high water cover huge expanses

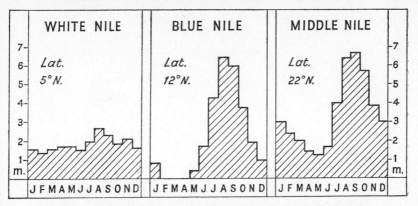

FIG. 32.—RÉGIMES OF NILE AND ITS HEAD-STREAMS.

Note.—The diagram shows for each month of the year the normal monthly height of the water, in metres, above the lowest level. A comparison of the graphs shows how the régime of the Nile is influenced by those of its main tributaries, the White Nile and Blue Nile.   The former has a comparatively regular flow, and during the cool season (December to May) brings down from the equatorial region the greater part of the water of the middle course of the river.   The Blue Nile has very little water during that season, but is swollen by the summer rains of the Abyssinian highland and supplies much of the flood-water of the middle and lower Nile on which Egypt depends.

are in fact greatest in the period between January and June. In the case of the Congo, the northern tributaries have their chief supply at the opposite time of the year from the southern ones, and the main river has floods in December and in May.

Surface and Soil Conditions.—In the flood plains, vast quantities of alluvium are constantly being added, and the rivers tend to raise themselves between high banks above the surrounding country.   In the other parts of the equatorial regions, the constant heat and moisture disintegrate the rock by weathering to a great depth, and upon the resultant mantle of rock fragments and soil grows a dense, though shallow-rooted, forest cover, which adds much organic matter to the soil. The continual downward drainage of water leaches the soil, i.e. washes out the soluble constituents.   Much of the insoluble material, exposed to chemical action under high temperatures, is reduced to certain compounds of iron and aluminium which give the soil a red colour.   Soils formed in this way are called laterites, and are characteristic of many equatorial regions. Their distribution is shown in a very generalized way on the map on p. 94, and it should be observed to what extent the lateritic soil type corresponds with that of the equatorial climate.

Under the equatorial conditions of constant heat and moisture, moreover, bacterial action goes on so effectively and decomposi-

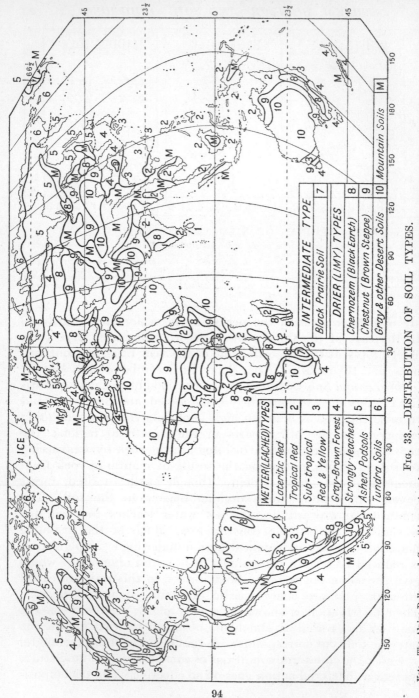

WETTER(LEACHED)TYPES	
Lateritic Red	1
Tropical Red	2
Sub-tropical Red & Yellow	3
Gray-Brown Forest	4
Strongly-leached Ashen Podsols	5
Tundra Soils	6

INTERMEDIATE TYPE	
Black Prairie Soil	7
DRIER (LIMY) TYPES	
Chernozem (Black Earth)	8
Chestnut (Brown Steppe)	9
Gray & other Desert Soils	10
Mountain Soils	M

FIG. 33.—DISTRIBUTION OF SOIL TYPES.

Note.—The Alpine-Balkan and Carpathian regions have mountain soils, but they are too small for the symbol to be inserted. The word "wetter" refers to the normal climatic conditions under which the soils are formed; in dry weather the soils themselves are dry.

tion of organic matter proceeds so rapidly and completely, that the stage of the production of humus quickly passes, and but little of this valuable constituent occurs in the soil. Laterites, therefore, lacking in humus and deprived by leaching of the soluble constituents of plant foods, are not naturally fertile. The equatorial forest, by leaf-fall and decay, returns to the soil sufficient organic matter for its own continuance, but if the forest is cleared, and in its place crops are planted and their products are removed, the lateritic soils of the equatorial regions soon become exhausted. Hence, agriculture is impeded and the nature of the soil creates another handicap to man's utilization of the equatorial regions.

There are exceptions to this general rule that equatorial soils are lateritic and therefore infertile. One is that of the flood-plains of recent alluvium washed down from the higher lands ; these river lowlands are fairly rich in plant foods but, on the other hand, they tend to be very wet and are liable to inundation. Another important exception is found in volcanic areas, notably in Java, where extraordinarily fertile soils have been formed from recently erupted volcanic ash and lava.

Tropical, Rainy-summer Regions (Climate symbol : T.RS.).

Streams.—In these regions there is a striking contrast between the amount of surface water in the two main seasons. In the rainy period the precipitation is so heavy that the soil is saturated and the rivers become flooded ; a sheet-wash of water over the surface is a frequent occurrence. In their upper courses the swollen streams rapidly cut their channels, and masses of alluvium are taken down to the broad beds of the main rivers. In the dry season what rain does occur has a low degree of efficiency ; hence the run-off is practically nothing, and many streams retain a mere trickle through the sands and gravels in their beds, while some dry up completely. The very irregular régime of the Blue Nile, which depends upon the summer rains on the Abyssinian highland, is strikingly shown on p. 93.

As a rule, only the greater rivers, or those which receive a supply of water from mountains or from the equatorial region, can persist as perennial streams and maintain their courses to the sea. On the other hand, in some parts of the regions of summer rain, and notably in the wettest parts of India, the precipitation is so heavy that the ground is saturated and it retains moisture even during the dry season, while the rivers maintain their courses ; in these areas the conditions approach those of the equatorial regions.

Soils.—As there is no sharp distinction between the regions with the equatorial type of climate and those which have most of their rain in summer, so the lateritic soils of the former pass without definite limits into the tropical red soils of the latter, marked 2 on the map on p. 94. (This lack of precise boundaries must be borne in mind in examining the distribution of all the soils shown in the map.) The tropical red soils, generally under less rainfall than near the Equator, are subject to less leaching, and the process of reducing them to laterites is less complete ; hence they retain more of the soluble plant foods. Also, these tropical, rainy-summer regions are characterized by an abundant growth of grasses whose annual decay yields more organic residue than the leaf-fall of forests, and the amount of humus in the soil is correspondingly greater than near the Equator. The tropical red soils, mostly loams, are therefore more fertile than the laterites.

Farther from the Equator, in Africa and in some other tropical areas, the alternation of a markedly dry with a wet period leads to the formation of a different type of soil. In origin and composition this resembles the " chernozem " or " black earth " of the Russian steppe lands, though in the hotter regions it is usually dark rather than black in colour. (In the map on p. 94 the tropical and mid-latitude chernozem soils are both included in group 8.) In the wet season, leaching removes soluble material from the surface to lower layers. In the dry season, on the contrary, the surface becomes parched, and water which has remained at some depth moves upward by capillarity bringing with it calcium compounds, especially lime ; as the water is evaporated these substances are deposited in a layer a little way below the surface. Moreover, the annual decay of the luxuriant growth of grasses gives a large supply of organic residues from which humus is developed in considerable quantity.

Thus the black earth exhibits definite horizons : the upper contains much humus and other organic material, and from this the dark colour is derived ; below is an horizon with an accumulation of lime. The humus and the plant foods from the organic residues in the A horizon together with the lime in the B horizon render the chernozem soils in general very favourable to cultivation. It may be noted that, in general, the darker the colour of the A horizon of a soil the greater is its productivity. The " Black Cotton Soil " of the Deccan of India, in parts developed from lava, is famous for its fertility and its power of retaining moisture. In other tropical, rainy-summer regions, however, the value of the black earth may be reduced by the tendency to become wet and sticky with heavy precipitation, and dry and hard in the rainless and still hot season.

Towards the more arid regions, the soil gradually changes to a lighter brown, chestnut colour, since the dark humus decreases in amount where the plant life from which it is derived is less abundant ; moreover, with less water sinking through the surface, there is less leaching and the upper horizon retains more lime. The " chestnut " soils are in themselves moderately fertile, but the climatic conditions do not favour their utilization. In some of the cooler maritime areas of these rainy-summer regions, sub-tropical red soils develop ; they will be described in a later paragraph.

Dry Regions (Climate symbols : T.D. and ML.D.).

Streams.—Where the period of rainfall becomes shorter as the Tropics are approached, the surface and soil waters become less until they almost cease to exist in the arid regions. In such areas occasional downpours may fill the water-courses for a very brief period, but these " torrential " streams quickly disappear ; they are known as wadis in the Arabic-speaking countries in and near the Saharan region.

The only perennial rivers are those which are abundantly supplied from other regions, such as the Nile which is flooded in late summer and autumn after the heavy summer rainfall on the Abyssinian highland. The Euphrates and Tigris have a quite different régime, for they derive their water from the highlands of south-western Asia where the main precipitation comes in winter ; hence the melting of the snow in spring causes these rivers to flood in April, while after the heat and evaporation of summer the autumn brings low water to Mesopotamia. Besides the Indus and a few other long rivers which traverse the larger arid regions and reach the sea, smaller ones cross the narrow Peruvian desert from the Andes. Some of the streams which enter tropical arid regions drain into inland basins and form small lakes or swamps.

The mid-latitude arid region of the Caspian-Aral Depression is one of entirely inland drainage, receiving rivers both from the mountains of central Asia, e.g. the Syr-Daria and Amu-Daria, and from the cool rainy regions of the north, especially the Volga, which is the chief source of supply to the Caspian. These seas, like all lakes with no outlet to the ocean, become more saline because dissolved salts from the inflowing rivers are accumulated while water is gradually evaporated ; in this respect the most notable is perhaps the Dead Sea at the end of the course of the river Jordan.

Apart from surface streams coming from distant areas, the chief water-supply in arid regions is from underground sources where water, which had its origin either in occasional rains or in neighbouring regions, has been protected from evaporation. From these sources, oases may obtain supplies by natural springs or by wells.

Surface and Soil Conditions.—Weathering in arid regions is due chiefly to the great and rapid changes of temperature, acting both directly upon the rock surfaces and also indirectly by affecting the water which at rare intervals penetrates crevices and on freezing expands and splits the rock. Weathered rock fragments are rapidly removed, mainly by the wind and gravity, and are progressively reduced in size till they reach the condition of sand.

In some parts of the true deserts the wind sweeps the rock fragments, large and small, from the desert floor, leaving a stony pavement, while elsewhere the gravels accumulate to form the surface and in other parts sand is collected and blown into dunes. Occasionally sheet-floods on the margins of the uplands may spread out mud which quickly becomes dry and cracked ; in other parts hollows are occupied by temporary lakes, the evaporation of whose waters leaves great stretches of extraordinarily level surface. Yet the desert landscape often has a most striking appearance. Without a protective vegetation cover, the slopes are quickly denuded and rock fragments may form screes around the base, while upstanding rock-masses, undercut by blasts of sand driven horizontally by the wind, rise steeply—sometimes like cliffs and even pinnacles.

With the lack of vegetation the soils lack humus, and as the occasional rains cause little leaching the upper horizon retains lime and other soluble constituents of the original rock ; the commonest colour of soils formed under these conditions is gray. Where water exists below the surface, it tends to rise by capillarity bringing with it dissolved matter, and after evaporation it may leave upon the surface a hard crust of calcium carbonate or of gypsum or an efflorescence of salt ; also the water of occasional pools or lakes may be replaced by sheets of glittering crystals.

True soils probably cover but a small proportion of the arid regions, for their development is commonly prevented by the removal of the weathered rock material. As a rule desert soils contain adequate materials for plant foods, and with irrigation they may prove extremely fertile ; in hollows, however, their high saline content may make them difficult to utilize even when water is available for cultivation.

Mid-latitude, Light-rain Regions (Climate symbol : ML.LR.).

Streams.—In the northern hemisphere, large areas of the regions of this type have winters with temperatures below freezing-point, while the summers are distinctly hot. In the winters, therefore, water which is on or in the soil becomes frozen ; in all but the drier parts, a thin snow cover remains until spring when it melts and aids the rain of that season to give a useful water-supply to the soil and the streams. In the summer, the heat causes a low efficiency of what rainfall occurs and hence, in spite of the summer precipitation shown by the meteorological statistics for some places, that season is normally one of drought. In the better-watered areas, the autumn brings a second period of rain before the soil and surface waters are frozen in winter. Hence there is an absence or a shortage of available water both in winter and in summer, in contrast to an intervening maximum supply in spring ; these conditions are reflected in the régime of the rivers, which are liable to be frozen in winter, to be flooded in spring, and to dwindle or in some cases even to disappear in summer.

In the southern hemisphere, the corresponding regions do not have a period of frost in winter, and the rains which occur in that season have not such a low efficiency as in the summer. Thus streams and soils have their main water-supply in the cooler part of the year, while drought and a lack of surface water usually characterize the summer ; the smaller streams have an intermittent flow, and only the larger rivers which are supplied from other regions are perennial.

Surface Conditions and Soils.—The light-rain regions are generally grasslands. On some marginal areas a slow accumulation of fine dust is blown from the neighbouring deserts and settles between the stems of the grasses ; this deposit is generally known as loess, for in origin and nature it is akin to that of the loess of north-west China where in the dry highlands it forms a thick mantle. The loess is valuable as affording material for the development of fertile soils.

Over most of the mid-latitude, light-rain regions the soils are of the lime-accumulating types. In the drier areas with a poor vegetation cover, the light-brown, chestnut soils suffer little leaching and there is but a moderate amount of humus. In the better-watered areas with a more luxuriant growth of grass are found the dark chernozems described above. Here there is a very considerable amount of humus, due on the one hand to the abundance of organic residues added yearly, and on the other hand to its slow decomposition ; the decomposition is slow because of the inactivity of the micro-organisms in the soil during both the winter cold and also the summer drought. In consequence of the high humus content, the chernozems are exceptionally fertile and have a crumbly structure which makes cultivation easy—at least in the autumn and spring seasons to which work on the soil is limited by the climatic conditions. The rich " black earth " area of south Russia, and the most productive parts of the North American prairies, are examples. A serious disadvantage of the drier areas is the liability to soil erosion, which will be described in a later chapter.

Sub-tropical, Rainy-summer Regions (Symbol : ST.RS.).

Streams.—Although these regions have a water-supply which is most abundant in summer, there is not such a marked fluctuation as in the tropical rainy-summer regions, partly because more rain occurs in the winter and partly because the precipitation has a greater efficiency in the cooler latitudes.

The Asiatic Monsoon Lands are crossed by great rivers which come from the central highlands of the continent, and there obtain water from melting snow in spring and summer in addition to the rain in the regions themselves, and the result is a season of high water which in the case of the Chinese rivers may last from spring till early winter, with only a short period

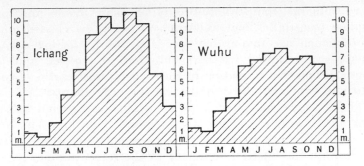

Fig. 34.—RÉGIMES OF THE YANGTZE KIANG.

Note.—Above the gorge at Ichang the rapid rise of the Yangtze is due to the combined effect of the summer monsoon rains in the upper basin and the melting snows of the Tibetan Highlands. At Wuhu on the lower Yangtze the monsoon rains are the chief cause of the rise ; the waters spread slowly over the central lowlands of China, the great lakes tend to regulate the flow, and consequently the high water lasts into December and the river has a more regular régime.

of low water.   This is well shown in the régime of the Yangtze Kiang (see above).   Occasionally floods occur and the great plains of China are inundated ;   in the long run this results in the beneficial spreading of fertile silt over the lowlands, though it also causes the immediate destruction of growing crops and even of houses, animals and people.   In North America the lower Mississippi is occasionally subject to spring and summer inundations ;   in this region, however, the floods are limited to the well-defined flood-plain of the river.

Soil Conditions.—With much heat, and with moisture during the greater part of the year, chemical weathering proceeds rapidly enough to break up the rock to a considerable depth and thus to provide abundant material for the formation of soils.   Also, when formed, the soils are not, as in the drier regions, liable to erosion but are protected by a natural vegetation cover of forest, though in some of the less well-watered areas there is only grassland.   Where man has cut down the forests, as in China and the United States, rain which was previously held for a time in the soil or used by the trees has a rapid run-off ;   on hillsides this has often resulted in the formation of innumerable gullies and of serious soil erosion.

The sub-tropical red soils which characterize large parts of these regions differ from the red soils of tropical and equatorial latitudes because they have been developed under conditions of less continuous heat during the year and, in general, less moisture ;   hence leaching is less complete and there remain more mineral compounds providing plant food and more organic material. The resultant soils must be classed among those which are favourable for cultivation. Yellow-coloured soils are also found in these sub-tropical regions, and they appear to mark a transition to the brown forest earths of cooler latitudes which will be described in the next chapter.

The " prairie soils " are another group transitional in situation and character. They are of great importance in North America, where they occupy a wide area in the " Middle West," just within the western boundary of the rainy-summer regions. They are of an intermediate type, for they are not lime-accumulating, while on the other hand they resemble the chernozems in their dark colour and their ample content of humus and other organic material. They are fertile and, in combination with the favourable climate, give to the Middle West much of its agricultural importance. In South America, similar prairie soils are found around the La Plata estuary ; this region, too, has a rainy-summer climate and is of great agricultural value. Prairie soils occur also on the High Veld of South Africa ; here, however, in the lee of the Drakensberg the climate is rather drier than in the prairie soil areas of the western hemisphere and belongs to the light-rain type.

CHAPTER VII

STREAM, SURFACE AND SOIL CONDITIONS (2)

Mid-latitude, Rainy-summer Regions (Symbol : ML.RS.).
Streams.—The chief differences in the surface conditions of the mid-latitude, rainy-summer regions of eastern Asia and the Americas, as compared with those of their sub-tropical neighbours, are due to the colder winters. In the northern hemisphere, the mean temperatures are below freezing-point for a period which may last, according to the situation, from a week or two to a few months. During that period the water in the soil and on the surface is frozen ; there is a snow cover to the land and the streams are ice-bound. In the spring the melting snow rapidly swells the rivers, which generally have their highest level, sometimes amounting to flood, during the heavy rains of the summer.

In North China tragic illustrations of such inundation are given by the Hwang Ho, " China's Sorrow," which as a consequence of its floods has repeatedly changed its lower course, revolutionizing the physical and human geography of the coastal region. In the east of the United States, the Mississippi river has a spring and summer period of high water (see the diagram on p. 104).

Soils.—Where the regions of the mid-latitude, rainy-summer type show considerable contrasts with the sub-tropical ones because of their relatively long and cold winters, there is a partial development of the process of " podsolization " ; that is to say, the soils approach, though they do not reach, the condition of those known in Russia as " podsols." These podsols are typical of the sub-arctic climate regions with very long and cold winters and with a short summer when the rainfall has a moderately high efficiency and water is fairly abundant. Also, the sub-arctic climate regions have a natural vegetation of coniferous forest beneath which accumulates a cover formed of the pine and fir " needles." These are only partially reduced

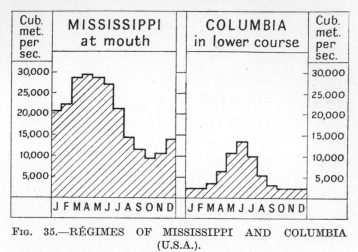

FIG. 35.—RÉGIMES OF MISSISSIPPI AND COLUMBIA (U.S.A.).

Note.—In this diagram the flow of the rivers is measured by the amount of water passing a given point each second.

The greater part of the supply of the lower Mississippi comes from the eastern part of its basin, and the high water in spring and early summer is due to the rains in the Appalachian region ; an important factor in producing the minimum in late summer and autumn is the use of water by vegetation in the summer. The Columbia is largely supplied by the precipitation on the Western Cordillera, which is greatest in winter and is then in the form of snow ; hence the spring melting brings about an early summer maximum in the lower course of the river.

to humus, for the decomposing organisms cannot carry on their work during the long winters, and hence there is often a superficial layer of little-decayed forest residues of a brownish hue.

Moreover, in the soil itself the acids which are formed in the organic material accumulate to a much greater degree than in warmer latitudes ; hence in summer the abundant water is acidulated and leaches from the upper horizon the iron and aluminium which elsewhere give it a red colour, leaving it with a light, ashen hue to which it owes its Russian name " podsol." Lime, humus, and material in the form of fine clay are also washed down from the upper horizon which is therefore poor from the point of view of supplying plant food and has a loose, sandy structure unfavourable for cultivation. Further, in the lower horizon there sometimes forms an impermeable layer or " pan " of an iron compound, or a sheet of clay may accumulate, and in these circumstances the downward movement of water is impeded ; a swampy condition of the surface results and peat is formed which adds to the acidity of the upper horizon.

Such are the characteristics of the podsols matured under the sub-arctic climate, but these are not completely developed in the mid-latitude, rainy-summer regions now considered. First, the warmer conditions allow a longer period for the bacteria to develop the valuable humus, and its greater amount in the upper horizon gives the soil a darker colour, frequently brown or grayish-brown. In the second place, the forests are either of the deciduous broad-leaved type, or " mixed," i.e. with both deciduous broad-leaved trees and coniferous needle-leaved trees ; hence the leaves add more useful constituents to the material from which the soil is developed. Also an impermeable pan is less frequently formed and the surface is better drained. The " brown or gray-brown forest earths " of the relatively warm regions of mid-latitudes thus have less acid, more available plant food and a better physical condition for tillage than the podsols ; they are of greater value for farming, although thorough manuring is necessary to keep them in good condition.

In the drier parts of the mid-latitude, rainy-summer climate regions, the soils are less leached. Consequently, in some areas, notably in the interior of the North American region and around the La Plata in South America, the intermediate prairie type prevails, while in Manchuria there are soils of the black earth and even the brown steppe types.

Thus in this group of climate regions, soil conditions vary from place to place ; moreover, widespread deposits of loess and of glacial material have occurred so recently that the soils have not been maturely developed and they still retain special characteristics which will be described in a later section.

Sub-tropical, Dry-summer Regions (Symbol : ST.DS.).

Streams.—The lack of rain in summer is intensified by its low efficiency in this hot season, while the greater precipitation of the cooler part of the year has a higher efficiency. Hence the streams are frequently torrential ; in winter they may cut wide beds and bring down masses of gravels which in summer are exposed and almost or quite waterless. As in other mid-latitude regions, the removal of the natural forest cover leads to the removal of the soil, and in this way the hillsides of the Mediterranean Lands of the Old World have suffered considerable erosion during many centuries.

Soils.—The soils found in these regions vary in character. Gray-brown forest earths of one kind or another are common in the better-watered areas, while in the drier parts there are soils akin to the chestnut-brown types.   In the lands around the Mediterranean Sea a red soil, the " terra rossa," is widespread and may perhaps be classed with other sub-tropical red soils.

Mid-latitude, Rainy Regions (Climate symbol : ML.R.).

These regions have an abundant run-off, and the rivers are generally well supplied with water throughout the year ; the maximum flow frequently occurs in winter when the rainfall has its greatest efficiency.   Where, however, there are highlands on which the winter precipitation is stored in the form of snow, the melting in spring and summer may cause floods in those seasons.   Like many other great rivers, the Rhine has a " mixed " régime, as shown in the diagram opposite.   In the more continental part of the European region of this climate type the winter is cold enough for the precipitation to form a snow cover for a short period, with the accompanying cessation of run-off and the freezing of rivers, followed by their rapid rise of level in the spring.

The highest parts of these regions have the mountain soils which will be dealt with later ; over most of the remaining areas there are the brown or gray-brown forest earths described above, and podsols are found near the wet oceanic margins where leaching has been heavy.

Sub-arctic and Mid-latitude, Short-summer Regions (Climate symbols : SArc. and ML.ShS.).

Streams.—The fact that precipitation is in the form of snow for a considerable part of the year is very important in northern latitudes.   Over the sub-arctic regions the winter cover of snow normally lasts for half the year or more, and rivers are frozen for about the same length of time ; the spring melting results in floods over very wide areas, especially where the rivers drain northward and their lower courses are still frozen when the water pours down into their lower basins.   The mid-latitude, short-summer regions have a shorter period of snow cover and frozen rivers, varying according to situation from about three to six months ; moreover, as the streams do not drain to Arctic seas they carry off the spring waters with less obstruction.

In the warmer part of the year the precipitation in both sub-arctic and short-summer regions is at its maximum and has a moderate degree of efficiency.   Consequently, except for the period when the ground is frozen and snow-covered in winter, these regions have no lack of water.

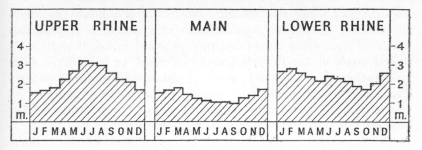

FIG. 36.—RÉGIMES OF THE RHINE AND ITS TRIBUTARIES.

Note.—The upper Rhine has an "Alpine" régime with a summer maximum due to melting snow and ice. The Main is an example of the large tributaries of the middle Rhine ; these are supplied by rains at all seasons, but evaporation and the needs of vegetation reduce the flow in summer and autumn. In the lower Rhine the summer maximum of the upper basin is balanced by the summer minimum of the middle basin, and the resultant "mixed" régime is fairly regular though with a short autumn minimum. Compare the regularity of the flow of the lower Rhine with the irregularity of other rivers as shown in the preceding diagrams, and note its relative advantage for navigation.

Soils.—In the sub-arctic and mid-latitude, short-summer climate regions, the soils vary according to differences of climate and natural vegetation. The sub-arctic regions have, almost everywhere, a cover of coniferous forest, and here the podsols described above have been generally developed. The thorough leaching to which they have been subjected and the swampy nature of parts of the surface make the podsols difficult and comparatively unremunerative for cultivation, in addition to the unfavourable climatic conditions. The mid-latitude short-summer regions also have strongly leached podsols in those parts where the winters are most severe and the forests are of the needle-leaved type.

But over extensive areas which have a less severe climate and where the forests are of the mixed type, notably in Europe and western Siberia, the more fertile gray-brown earths have been developed. Further, in some drier and warmer parts, e.g. in the prairie lands of Canada, where grasses form an important element in the natural vegetation cover, the soils are of the chernozem type, and agriculture has fairly favourable conditions.

Arctic Regions (Climate symbol : Arc.).

Streams.—In these regions temperatures play a large part in determining the conditions of the water-supply. Although air temperatures may be above freezing-point for quite a considerable time, the surface is frozen for most of the year, and the subsoil never thaws ; it is therefore impervious. There are floods when the winter snow melts, and in parts the ground is waterlogged when not frozen. Add to these facts the high efficiency of the rainfall, and it becomes clear that, in spite of the statistics indicating an annual precipitation as small as that of desert areas in the Tropics, the Arctic must be considered as a wet, rather than as a dry, region from several points of view. The larger rivers come from more southerly areas and, as in the adjoining sub-arctic climate regions, they bring wide-spreading floods at the opening of the summer.

Soil Conditions.—The low-growing vegetation of the tundra supplies organic material as a soil constituent, but this is very slowly decomposed because of the very short season of bacterial activity. The surface normally contains undecomposed plant residues as well as humus, and peat is quite commonly formed ; acidity is a frequent characteristic of the tundra soils. Where the drainage is better the soils may not be inherently infertile, but climatic conditions prevent their utilization.

Highland Regions.—The term " ice cap " indicates the condition of the Arctic and Antarctic highland areas ; the snow is compressed to ice which works slowly downwards and outwards until it melts or breaks off as icebergs into the adjoining seas.

On the culminating heights of lower latitudes, snowfields above the snow-line are perennial and from them glaciers work downwards into the valleys. In these highland regions the summer.is the season when the streams are fed from the melting snow and ice, and the precipitation also comes mainly in the summer over large parts of the highland areas of the globe.

At great elevations frost and ice are important agents in shaping the scenery. The corries or cirques formed by them at the heads of valleys cut back the water-partings to sharp, irregular ridges and may ultimately reduce these to pyramidal peaks or horns ; the heights have angular shapes and jagged summits due to the action of frost. The valleys widened by glaciers have a U-shaped cross-section in place of the V-shape resulting from the action of running water, and their courses are interrupted by bars and lake basins.

Rock surfaces at high altitudes are attacked by frost, and changes of temperature are responsible for the physical weathering which provides material for soil ; yet because of the frequency of steep slopes and the great erosion by glaciers and streams this material is relatively rapidly removed. Only in the valleys can the material accumulate, and the mountain soils are in general thin and are not maturely developed. At high altitudes, the soils are akin to those of the tundra, while podsols of different degrees of leaching occur at lower levels.

In the broad basins of the semi-arid and arid highlands there is a greater accumulation of rock fragments, and mature soils develop to a greater extent. As the climatic and vegetation conditions broadly resemble those of the dry regions, the soils also show broad resemblances, and the brown steppe soils and gray desert soils described in previous paragraphs are common. The possibilities of utilization are therefore similar to those of lower dry areas, though allowances must be made for the relative inaccessibility of the highland regions.

Regions of Past Glaciation.—Although surface conditions are largely influenced by the present-day climates, in certain parts of the world the effects of past climatic conditions still have great importance. This is specially true of the conditions of the " ice age "—actually the last of several such cold periods in the earth's history. This ice age lasted for perhaps half a million years at the opening of the Quaternary Era (refer to the table on p. 17), and during this time it changed the surface conditions over a large portion of Europe and North America and over smaller areas of other continents. In the northern hemisphere sheets of ice extended from the Arctic regions and were pushed generally southwards as shown by the arrows in the map on p. 110.

Yet within that half-million years or so, variations of climate occurred : at the coldest periods the ice advanced farthest, but in relatively warm intervals—the inter-glacial periods—the sheet melted along its margin more rapidly than it was renewed from the north, and thus its edge " retreated." Similarly, in the coldest periods the ice extended from the higher parts of mountain regions, e.g. the Alps, down the valleys and even over neighbouring regions, but retreated when warmer conditions returned. At the end of the ice age the final retreat of the ice-sheet from the lowlands was accomplished in stages, between which the edge remained almost stationary for a considerable time. As the last of these stages was only a few thousand years ago, the present-day processes of weathering, erosion, deposition and soil development have not had time to do more than modify the main results of the ice age.

Highland Areas.—The sharp ridges and pyramidal peaks

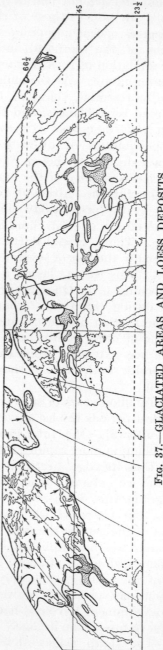

FIG. 37.—GLACIATED AREAS AND LOESS DEPOSITS.

Note.—The lines enclose (*a*) the great ice sheets of North America and Europe, and (*b*) smaller glaciated highlands beyond the main areas. The direction of ice flow in the great ice sheets is indicated by arrows. Loess deposits are shown by dots.

referred to in the preceding section as the work of ice are still seen in the less elevated parts from which it has now retreated ; the valleys have U-shaped sections and they have in their courses rock bars and basins, while " hanging " tributary valleys join the main ones at higher levels. In the basins are lakes and the bars are commonly marked by rapids, while the exits of the hanging valleys cause waterfalls ; the present streams have frequently cut but narrow gorges in the glacial deposits of the valleys.

Lowland Areas.—(1) In the *central* areas from which the ice sheets pushed outwards, e.g. in Scandinavia and in the north-east of the glaciated part of North America, the ice had a considerable scouring effect and in consequence there are districts where the hard rock lies bare of weathered fragments and soil. There are also wide expanses of boulder-clay formed from material scraped away elsewhere and deposited as ground-moraine beneath the ice ; in some parts there are groups of drumlins— masses of boulder-clay which form more or less oval-shaped hummocks or hills.

Such accumulations interrupted the pre-glacial drainage, and so little time has passed since the ice retreated from these central areas that the post-glacial streams have not yet established a mature system ; hence, lakes and swamps are frequent and the streams have rapids and falls. Similarly, the pre-glacial soils have disappeared and new ones have not yet developed ; some boulder-clays are composed of material which is fairly easy and profitable to work, but others are difficult and poor. Taking into account also the areas of bare rock, lake and swamp, it may be seen that the central glaciated regions are on the whole unfavourable for farming. On the other hand, both here and in the glaciated highlands, the falls and rapids give water-power, which is of special value where steadiness of supply is ensured by the drainage from lakes.

(2) The *marginal* glaciated areas have different characteristics. Along the edges of ice sheets which remained nearly stationary for a considerable time, terminal moraines were deposited, in which all kinds of glacial débris were heaped up into the form of generally low, but long, lines of hills.

Also, in front of the terminal moraines are found sandy outwash areas, i.e. sheet-like masses of sands deposited by the water from the melted ice. Moreover, this water formed great rivers which cut wide valleys ; the rivers of the present time, dependent only on the rainfall of the locality, appear in these glacial valleys as relatively small streams, or they may have been diverted into other courses and have left the broad valleys with almost dry beds of sand and gravel. Good examples of these valleys are seen in the South Baltic Lowlands, where the abandoned stretches have made it easy for canals to be constructed to join the present rivers and form a system of inland waterways ; at the exit of the system to the North Sea the great port of Hamburg has grown up.

In some parts, lakes were formed in hollows in front of the melting ice, and with the alterations in the position of the retreating edge, the water surfaces found new outlets and the overflowing streams took different courses and had varying effects upon the landscapes. The present form of the Great Lakes of North America is due to such complications, and the Mohawk valley which cuts through the Appalachian Upland was deepened by one of their glacial outflows ; this valley and the canal constructed through it were the reasons for the commercial predominance of New York in North America— another example of the influence of the ice age on modern developments. Farther west, another great marginal lake, known to geologists as " Lake Agassiz," occupied much of what is now Southern Manitoba, and in its bed were deposited the fertile soil materials of the level plains of that region ; the present lakes Winnipeg and Winnipegosis have remained in the lowest parts of the old lake bottom.

Because the ice retreated from the marginal areas many thousands of years before it disappeared from the central areas, there has been a longer time for the work of weathering and streams ; the surface has been somewhat smoothed, many of the falls in the rivers have worn down, and lakes and marshes have been drained. Also, in the marginal areas lies material brought from the central areas, and on this material soils have been matured to a certain extent and some of them are of unusual fertility. On the whole, the marginal areas offer greater opportunities for farming than the central regions of glaciation.

One more effect of the ice age may be here mentioned, as it had an influence upon the early development of mankind which will be discussed in a later chapter. Great masses of water were literally " frozen " on the land and thus withdrawn from the circulation which would otherwise return them to the ocean. Hence with less water in the ocean its surface was lowered and coastal areas were free of sea water to a greater extent than at present ; the continents extended farther and the coastlines were about 600 feet lower than at present, i.e. they were situated at about the present 100-fathom line below sea-level.

Loess Areas.—It has already been explained that loess is being formed by wind action in the regions bordering the deserts. This process has gone on so vigorously and for so long in north-west China, within the semi-arid region bordering the Gobi Desert, that 100,000 square miles of country have been covered to depths reaching several hundreds of feet (see the map on p. 110).   The finely divided, yellowish material is easily worked and of great fertility, and it can hold moisture during dry periods ; it has therefore attracted settlement wherever it is found.   In north China loess has also been washed down from the interior semi-arid region by the Hwang Ho, and forms a valuable constituent in the flood-plains of that river.   In Turkistan belts of loess are now utilized by irrigation and are densely populated areas.

In Europe belts of loess, wide in the east but narrower and more broken in the west, lie just beyond the limit of glaciation. It is probable that they were formed by winds blowing out fine material from the sandy outwash areas in the ice age, in part at least during the inter-glacial periods when the climate was both warmer and also drier and resembled that of the steppe-lands of the present time.   The black earth of south Russia has been formed partly upon the loess, and in central and western Europe other areas of fertile soil have been developed upon it. In North America a loess deposit occurs over a considerable area both within and beyond the margin of the ice sheet in the Mississippi Basin ; it has a similar origin to that of Europe, and has added to the productivity of the U.S.A. " Middle West."

CHAPTER VIII

NATURAL VEGETATION AND ANIMAL LIFE (1)

THE natural vegetation of the earth's surface is composed of a number of groups of plants which live together in close association and give a distinctive appearance to each of the regions in which they are dominant. This vegetation cover of the earth's surface forms an important link between the physical conditions of relief, climate and soil on the one hand, and on the other the human inhabitants of the globe. Moreover, there is such a close connection between natural vegetation and wild animals that the two forms of life will be considered together.

The largest of the vegetation communities are known as plant formations ; each has a more or less definite area in which it lives, and its members possess certain special characters— adaptations—enabling them to live in that region. In general, climate is the factor most closely affecting the broad characteristics of vegetation, and therefore the distribution of the plant formations corresponds to a considerable degree with that of the climate regions indicated above ; local soil conditions and minor differences of relief show themselves by variations within the plant formations. The great formations are commonly arranged in three main classes : various types of forest, of grassland and of hot or cold desert. There are also some intermediate types, e.g. the semi-deserts, and the associations composed of trees scattered among grasses and other herbaceous (non-woody) plants.

In explaining the occurrence of some of the important plants in the great formations, and the characteristic animals of some regions, account must be taken of the effect of barriers of seas and highlands in preventing their spread into particular areas. In this connection, it may here be noted that Australia, Tasmania, New Zealand and some of the Pacific Islands form an exceptional region as regards their plant and animal life, for these lands have been separated from the other continental areas for so long a time that migration into this region was early checked and evolution within it has proceeded along special lines. Thus the animal life, apart from recent introductions, has very few of the higher mammals found elsewhere, while in Australia the " pouched " marsupials, which have become almost extinct in the rest of the world, have here survived ; indeed, they have developed remarkably varying forms as adaptations to the different habitats in the continent. Similarly among the plants, eucalypts are peculiar to Australia and the neighbouring islands, where they are widely distributed and include many species of trees as well as shrubs ; only recently eucalyptus trees have been taken to other continents.

" Natural " vegetation is here regarded as that which has been but little changed by man, as is still the case over considerable areas ; in some instances, however, it is uncertain to what extent the vegetation of a region was affected by the people who inhabited it before the arrival of Europeans.

Some plant formations have a definite limit, but in other cases there are gradual transitions, and also there are intermediate types ; moreover, exceptional areas of vegetation are found within the more common formations. Hence there are differences of opinion in determining the formations and in drawing boundaries to their regions. The map on p. 116 is an attempt to show only the general character and distribution of the natural vegetation.

1. Dense, Evergreen Forests.—*Plant Life.*—These formations are sometimes termed *Equatorial Rain Forests* or the *Hot, Wet Forests*. They occur (*a*) in the equatorial regions of constant rain and (*b*) in those parts of the adjoining rainy-summer regions which have a very heavy rainfall and therefore constantly moist subsoils. The distribution of these forests, as shown by the regions marked " 1 " in the map on p. 116, almost corresponds with that of the regions of constant rain in Africa and the East Indies. In Asia, however, these forests cover also the Western Ghats and the wettest parts of the lands bordering the Bay of Bengal and the South China Sea, while the north and east coasts of Madagascar and smaller areas of north-east Australia have a similar type of vegetation. In the Americas these forests, here called *Selvas*, cover the equatorial regions of constant rain, and appear farther north

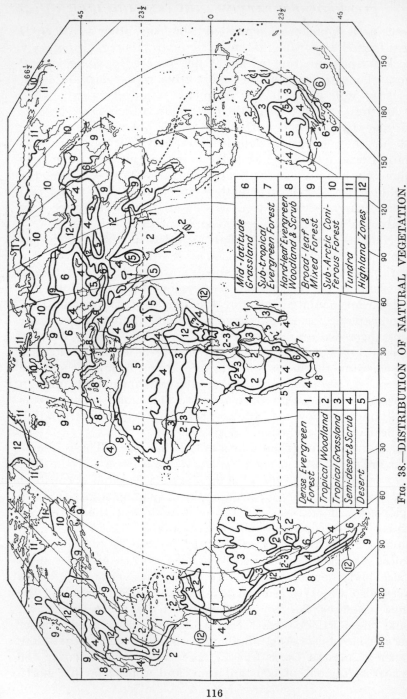

1	Dense Evergreen Forest		6	Mid-latitude Grassland
2	Tropical Woodland		7	Sub-tropical Evergreen Forest
3	Tropical Grassland		8	Hard-leaf Evergreen Woodland & Scrub
4	Semi-desert & Scrub		9	Broad-leaf & Mixed Forest
5	Desert		10	Sub-Arctic Coniferous Forest
			11	Tundra
			12	Highland Zones

FIG. 38.—DISTRIBUTION OF NATURAL VEGETATION.

Note.—In areas marked 2–3, either there are patches of woodland and of grassland or the vegetation is composed of both trees and grass without either predominating.

116

NATURAL VEGETATION AND ANIMAL LIFE (1)   117

over part of Central America and the West Indies, and farther
south on the coast of Brazil.

Three climatic factors are important : (1) the almost continuous high temperatures of the air and soil, enabling the
vegetative processes to continue throughout the year ; (2) the
abundant and constant supply of water allowing nutriment to
be absorbed in liquid form by the roots ; (3) the great amount
of insolation—sun energy—for the manufacture of organic
compounds by the plants and the raising of the sap from the
roots to the tops of the trees. Together these factors make
possible a luxuriant growth of plant life—a dense mass of
vegetation of strikingly different yet closely associated kinds.
There are trees whose crowns form a continuous canopy to the
forest at a height of over a hundred feet, while many other
species grow to less heights. Some yield valuable timber, e.g.
the mahogany, a native of Central America ; there are also
palms of many kinds and varied uses. The branches of some
of the trees grow downwards to form new roots, thus making a
living lattice-work ; lianas, too, help to render the forests almost
impenetrable, for they may be of the length and stoutness of
ships' cables and intertwine themselves with the trees. At
lower levels in the forests are a tangled undergrowth of plants
of diverse forms, and a carpet of decaying vegetation often
covered by an accumulation of fallen leaves.

The forests are composed of hundreds of kinds of trees ; the
individuals of any particular species are widely scattered, and
hence the difficulty of obtaining particular products, e.g. of
special kinds of timber or fruit. The processes of plant life
in general may go on at all times of the year, and although particular varieties have their own annual rhythms of flowering,
fruiting and shedding of leaves, there is no seasonal change for
the forest as a whole ; it is evergreen.

Within each of the great forest formations, there are local
plant associations of special character in habitats of peculiar
type. For example, areas liable to flood, as in the low parts
of the Amazon Basin, have a marshy floor which allows no
undergrowth like that common to the drier areas. Again, by
the coasts are frequently mangrove swamps with a tangle of
branches growing both upward and also downward into the
salt or brackish water ; these may prevent access from sea to land.

While the general characteristics of all the dense, evergreen forests are similar, the particular plants which compose them have a more limited range. Thus rubber is a characteristic product of these forests, but of the trees producing it the specially valuable *Hevea brasiliensis* grew only in South America until it was planted in Ceylon and Malaya.

Rapidity of growth in these forest regions is an advantage as regards the natural, as also the cultivated, plants which man desires, but it is quite as much a disadvantage as regards the unwanted vegetation ; e.g. when it necessitates the repeated weeding of native patches of cultivation and of the larger plantations, as well as constant clearing of paths and roads.

Animal Life.—In the dense, evergreen forests the animal life, including mammals, reptiles, birds and insects, is not developed to anything like the same degree as the plant life. This is partly because for each kind of animal living directly upon vegetation the food consists mainly of either the flowers, fruits, seeds or leaves of certain plants, and this food is scattered and cannot support any considerable number of individuals of that particular form of animal life in one locality.

The animals are not generally visible, for apart from the fact that the light is normally poor in the forest, some are hidden in the dense vegetation near the ground, many live in the higher levels, and others move about at night. Because of the lack of food near the ground, most of the mammals are arboreal and are therefore small in size ; besides the apes and monkeys there are the bats and squirrels which are found in greater variety. Snakes too, inhabit the trees, living upon the smaller mammals, birds and insects. Other animals, such as the leopards and tigers of the Old World and the jaguars and ant-eaters of the New World, climb the trees although they do not have their home in them. In the upper levels of the forest-growth there is a great variety of bird life, often distinguished by brilliance of plumage, as among the parrots. At the edges of the forests, and especially by the streams, the large number of animals is in strong contrast to the general rule in these regions ; in such habitats most of the larger mammals live, and in the rivers themselves crocodiles are numerous.

The dense, evergreen forests, however, are not the only habitats of most of the animals which are found in them ; thus, the tigers can live throughout south and east Asia and even in the steppes of Persia and the cold forests of Siberia.

Among the forms of animal life in the hot, wet forests, insects are exceptional in their variety and great abundance. They provide the direct food of birds, bats, ant-eaters, etc., and therefore indirectly contribute to the food-supply of many of the reptiles and mammals ; in this respect the multitudes of ants are of considerable significance. Moreover, insects have a great importance to mankind as carriers of diseases ; this is true not only in the equatorial forest areas but also in other inter-tropical regions and to a less extent in the warmer parts of the extra-tropical belts. Mosquitoes and ticks have a special importance in this respect ; certain mosquitoes transmit malaria to man and others carry yellow fever, while ticks of several species transmit a number of diseases to man and to animals. Insect carriers of disease, and therefore the diseases themselves, can now be combated by scientific methods. For example, areas of moderate size have been rendered safe from malaria by spreading a film of oil over the stagnant water in which mosquitoes must breed ; also, these insects, and many others, can be killed by insecticides, such as " D.D.T.," developed and used with great effect during the war of 1939–45.

2. Tropical Woodlands.—*Plant Life.*—These formations, marked " 2 " on the map of natural vegetation, represent a lighter growth of trees, varying from forests scarcely distinguishable from the dense, evergreen forests to scrub formed of thorny growths, or to areas in which trees grow among grasses— the wooded savannas. They occupy much of the tropical, rainy-summer climate regions, with the exceptions, on the one hand, of the wettest parts with dense forest growth, and on the other hand the drier parts which are typical grassy savanna lands. Some areas cannot be definitely termed woodlands as distinct from savannas and are therefore marked " 2–3 " on the map.

The rainy-summer regions have a period in which the trees must be adapted to conditions of drought. One form of adaptation is that of checking transpiration of water through the leaves by shedding the leaves during the dry period ; such trees are thus deciduous. Another means is for the leaves to take a form in which transpiration is never rapid ; e.g. they may have a thick skin, perhaps with a coating of resin, wax or varnish, or they may be rolled up to needle-like shape, or hard and pointed, i.e. thorny, or mere spines. Where the rainfall is markedly limited the trees must have some such adaptation strongly marked, or they must be much smaller in size, or they must be few in number and have a scattered growth.

In south-east Asia the natural vegetation, here marked " 2," includes in the wetter parts the deciduous monsoon forests. In these summer-green forests, there is not the great range of plants found in the equatorial regions, and there are " teak forests," " sal forests," etc., in which a timber industry has grown up. Palms of various kinds grow in these monsoon areas, and the shady banyan tree with its vast rooting branches. Other districts are jungles, and dense bamboo thickets are of frequent occurrence. The drier parts have a more open appearance or even verge upon scrub-land.

In the north of Australia the areas of tropical woodland are marked by a somewhat similar gradation from dense evergreen forest towards scrub or grassland ; eucalyptus and acacia trees and shrubs are common. In Africa the tropical woodlands are most clearly represented in the coastal belt of East Africa near the Equator, and also south of the Congo forest in a wide area (marked simply " 2 " on the map) over which a " dry " thorny tree-growth is characteristic.

In Central America and the northern coast-lands of South America, the tropical woodlands have a considerable amount of rain during their wet season and in general resemble the better-watered parts of the tropical monsoon lands. Farther south, however, in the Guiana Highlands region the growth is of the drier type, while on the Highlands of north-eastern Brazil the scrub or thorn forest known as the " Caatinga " presents a striking change from the green luxuriance of the rainy period to the deadness of bare, whitish wood during the dry season.

Animal Life.—In general, the forms of animal life found in the tropical woodlands extend also into the dense forests and the open grasslands. For example, in the Old World, the great herbivorous animals, such as elephants, buffaloes and rhinoceroses, are thus widely distributed, while of the carnivorous animals which have a similar range lions may be mentioned. The smaller mammals, birds and insects are likewise seldom restricted to habitats within this group of woodlands and scrub.

In south-east Asia man has cleared large areas of the tropical woodlands and also of the denser forests of the equatorial type, and has turned them into plantations or crop-lands, at the same time considerably reducing the numbers of the wild animals ; in the other continents these changes have been more limited. In general, where such transformations have occurred, the productivity and therefore the human population of the areas show marked contrasts with those where the natural flora and fauna still remain.

3. Tropical Grasslands or Savannas.—*Plant Life.*—

Grasslands occur over most of the tropical regions which have a fairly long dry period in their cooler season. Grasses and other herbaceous plants grow luxuriantly with the combination of heat and water in the summer, and die down in the drought. They may reach very considerable height, even ten feet or more, and may grow in compact tufts separated by bare ground. Bulbs and tubers are common adaptations of the herbaceous plants to store fluid and nutriment for use when the growing season begins. Trees are rare, and commonly grow widely scattered among the grasses with far-spreading roots to collect sufficient moisture. Closer growths of trees can live only in hollows where they can reach down to the water-table beneath the surface ; thus strips of " gallery (i.e. tunnel-like) forest " may extend along the rivers far into the grasslands. Where small clumps of trees stand up from the grass cover, the appearance of the landscape has led to the savannas being called " park-lands."

Savannas have no great extension in Asia, for most of the tropical monsoon lands are well watered. In Australia they occupy a wide belt of country between the rainy north and north-east coast-lands and the arid interior ; here they include areas of " bush " where the grasses are interspersed with low, and somewhat dense, growths of eucalypts or acacia scrub.

In Africa, the tropical grasslands fall into two main groups : better-watered areas (2–3) adjoining the dense equatorial forests, and drier areas (3) bordering the Sahara north of the Equator. They also extend southward from the Abyssinian Highlands through East Africa. The wetter savannas are characterized by long grass so dense that it is difficult to walk through it, with a large number of low trees reaching little above the grass cover of the land. The drier savannas have shorter grass from which stand up scattered trees, or quite low grasses with small thorny trees or bushes ; in these last areas the period of growth is very short and for most of the year the trees are leafless and the grasses dry.

The South American savannas include the following areas : (a) In the basin of the Orinoco, the *llanos* have tall grasses, with few trees except by the rivers where palms are characteristic ; (b) south-east of the Amazon Lowlands, in Brazil, the great *campos* have in general tall grasses with low trees or shrubs ; (c) west of the river Paraguay, in the Chaco region (marked " 2–3 " on the map), in addition to the more usual forms of savanna, are areas of thorn bush and cactus thickets.

Animal Life.—In many regions the grasses and other herbaceous plants, together with the foliage of trees, support large numbers of herbivorous animals, though in the dry periods and in the poorer districts the herds may have to migrate to places where there is more water and better pasture. Many of the animals are physiologically adapted to living with small supplies of water, e.g. some antelopes can survive for months without drinking ; yet in severe droughts whole herds may die.

In Australia, kangaroos and the related wallabies were the characteristic animals of the grasslands. In Africa the very extensive savannas are by nature the homes of great numbers of antelopes of many very different species, including the large elands and the small and graceful gazelles. In South America there are fewer savanna animals, deer being the chief.

Especially in Africa, the grass-feeders are hunted by carnivorous animals, e.g. lions, which are frequently followed by hyenas to share the prey. Those herbivorous animals which have developed great swiftness and can escape their enemies on the open plains, have been best able to survive and have become characteristic of the savannas ; in some cases the horns of the males are a protective adaptation.

During many centuries, and especially in more recent times, man has made considerable changes in the natural vegetation and the animal life of the tropical grasslands of Africa, partly by cultivation and the introduction of domestic animals and partly by hunting. The changes have been less extensive in Australia and South America, where cattle-ranching is now the chief use made of the land.

A very serious danger both to man and animals in the savannas of Africa is the tsetse fly, which carries the deadly " sleeping sickness " from man to man, and the " nagana " disease among the wild game and the domesticated cattle. The tsetse fly lives in the best areas, such as the well-watered river valleys and the park-lands, causing the death of great herds of animals and driving the people away to poorer lands. By insecticides and other means it is possible to rid at least relatively small districts of the pest, but the fly has advanced into other territories and thus hindered or prevented the utilization of parts of the African grasslands. After over a quarter of a century of medical research, a drug has recently been devised by means of which a large proportion of the sufferers from sleeping sickness can be cured if treatment can be given soon after infection.

4 and 5. Scrub-lands, Semi-deserts and Deserts.—*Plant Life.*—On their drier sides, the savanna lands commonly pass by various transitions to wide scrub-lands or semi-deserts and finally to the less extensive wastes of the true deserts.

There are many kinds of semi-desert vegetation. There are stiff grasses which grow in tight tufts widely spaced in the naked soil. There are shrubs adapted to severe drought by extremely long root development together with low growth and small surfaces above ground, or by the substitution for leaves of spines, small scales or hairs, or by storage of fluid in succulent, fleshy stems protected by impervious coats—these adaptations are illustrated by the numerous forms of cacti. In the deserts where rain occurs only in very rare showers, tubers may be hidden beneath the soil till they send up shoots for a little while after rain ; again, small seeds may lie dormant for years, then, with moisture, they go through their life-cycle in a few weeks or even days, finally leaving other seeds to continue their species. Oases are quite exceptional spots in arid regions, and their plants do not show the characteristics of desert vegetation.

In the Old World, a very broad belt of deserts, semi-deserts and scrub-lands separates the habitable lands of the Mediterranean Region and Europe from those of the Sudan and of southern and eastern Asia. In this belt, however, and even in the Sahara itself, there are large expanses with drought-resistant, sparsely growing forms of vegetation ; e.g. in central Asia there is the region in which the main growth is the wormwood shrub. Areas of true desert are diagrammatically separated from the semi-deserts on the map on p. 116, but it is impossible to show their often patchy distribution on a small-scale map.   Somewhat similarly, in the semi-arid upland and highland regions which are shown as semi-desert or desert, there are belts of mountains which have a forest cover.

In Australia, much of the interior which may be considered as having an arid or semi-arid climate is not true desert ; some parts are characterized by various types of scrub, while elsewhere are areas of " salt bush " or of " spinifex," a tufted grass so hard and sharp that it injures the legs of horses and camels. In Africa, south of the Equator, there is the relatively narrow strip of true desert known as the Namib along the western coast, and behind this are the Kalahari and Great Karroo scrub-lands or poor grasslands.   In South America, as in South Africa, true desert is mainly limited to a western coastal strip, the Atacama desert ; in the lee of the Westerlies in Argentina, including Patagonia, is poor grassland and scrub with small salt plains and areas of sand and shingle.   In North America, true desert is again on the western side of the continent, together with smaller areas in the upland and highland basins of the Western Cordillera, where most of the interior is occupied by semi-desert.   Characteristic forms of scrub vegetation in these arid and semi-arid regions of North America are sage brush (worm-wood), cactus, yucca and agave.

Animal Life.—In these regions of little vegetation, the animal life is necessarily very scanty ; it must also be adapted to survive with very little water, and where the sun is seldom obscured by clouds protection against heat may have to be found.   Hence, in the semi-deserts much of the life seeks shelter beneath stones or underground ; multitudes of insects and many lizards and snakes adopt this habit.   Moreover, burrowing animals can get food and water from the underground parts of the plants.   The giraffe is adapted by its long neck to browsing on the leaves of the acacias and other trees of the South African scrub.   Many of the grazing animals migrate, following the rains and the resulting verdure.

The camel is of special interest and importance as being able to drink the salt or brackish water and to eat the thorny leaves and shrubs of the semi-deserts, and also to subsist for a time, even in the true deserts, without water and living on the store of fat in the hump.   The two-humped camel of central Asia is protected from the great winter cold of that region by a thick coat shed in the spring ; the Arabian one-humped camel, known as the dromedary, has become extensively used for transport in northern Africa and southern Asia, and has been introduced into Australia and North America.

From the desert or semi-desert regions, insects and mammals may raid the neighbouring cultivated lands ; for example, in Africa, Asia and South America, swarms of locusts breed in inconceivable numbers in the dry regions and migrate for hundreds of miles destroying all the vegetation of the better-watered country through which they pass. Progress in combating locust plagues has been shown recently by new methods, including spraying poison bait upon them from aeroplanes and the use of new insecticides such as gammexane.

6. Mid-latitude Grasslands.—*Plant Life.*—These formations are frequently called " temperate grasslands," but it seems best to restrict the term " temperate " to areas which have a fairly mild winter, whereas a characteristic of large areas of these grasslands is that they have a cold or very cold winter. The natural vegetation of the mid-latitude grasslands, like that of tropical savannas, consists largely of grasses and other herbaceous plants adapted to a seasonal lack of water, but in mid-latitudes these plants have to live under lower temperatures and with less insolation, and in consequence have a less luxuriant development ; moreover, over large areas the growth of the plants is checked not only during the drought of summer but also by the cold of winter.

Grasslands of this type, where they have not been brought under cultivation, occupy the mid-latitude light-rain regions and spread also into parts of adjacent climate regions. In these latter cases, notably in North and South America, it is possible that the extension of grasses into better-watered areas was brought about long ago by man burning an earlier forest cover or by other influences of man or animals. For this reason, and others, there are marked differences within this group of mid-latitude grasslands.

In Europe and Asia these grasslands, or at least their less-watered and poorer areas, are known as steppes. The growth of the grasses and herbaceous plants is prevented in winter by the cold, and takes place mainly in spring and early summer ; by midsummer the heat so reduces the efficiency of the rainfall that it cannot support plant life and the grasses wither and die ; in autumn there is a second but less marked growth of some of the vegetation before it disappears with the coming of winter. In the better-watered areas tall grasses are dominant, but where there is less rain poorer growths of grass and drought-resistant shrubs take their place. On the northern margins of the grasslands of Eurasia, where the climate approaches the short-summer type, trees appear especially along many river valleys ; here the formation is known as the wooded or forest steppe, and constitutes a transition to the adjoining true forests. Most of the natural grasslands of Eurasia are now farmlands.

In North America somewhat similar sub-divisions appear. In the central part of the grassland region there were rather long grasses which formed a rich cover to this " prairie " region until it came under cultivation. In the north and east are transitional areas of mixed trees and grasses—the " wooded prairies." West of about 100° W., the Great Plains have a lower rainfall and consequently a much shorter growth of grass, becoming patchy in the drier parts.

In South America is the Pampa region which broadly corresponds to the warmer and wetter part of the North American prairies ; here the first Europeans found a grassland now in part displaced by cultivation. In Patagonia a strip of poor grassland adjoins the Andean Highland.

In South Africa the High Veld has a natural vegetation cover of long grasses broadly resembling that of the prairies of North America. In Australia the tropical grasslands in Queensland change gradually southward into those of mid-latitudes found in New South Wales and Victoria. Both in South Africa and in Australia cultivation has encroached upon the better-watered areas.

Animal Life.—The mid-latitude grasslands, like those of the Tropics, were once the home of great numbers of migratory grazing animals, but the suitability of the regions for farming has led to their almost entire disappearance, and sometimes to their replacement by herds of domesticated cattle, sheep or horses. Among the once numerous forms of animal life may be mentioned the zebra of the South African grasslands and the bison (" buffalo ") of the North American prairies, while in Australia were kangaroos and other marsupials. In the Eurasian steppes and the Great Plains of North America rodents and other burrowing animals obtained in the ground protection from the winter cold as well as a supply of food and water from the underground parts of the plants.   Great birds, of grazing habit and depending upon swiftness of running instead of flying, evolved in several regions of this type : the ostrich notably in South Africa, the rhea in the Pampa and the emu in the south-east of Australia.

CHAPTER IX

NATURAL VEGETATION AND ANIMAL LIFE (2)

7. Sub-tropical, Evergreen Forests.—With small exceptions, these formations are found in the fairly warm and wet areas of the sub-tropical rainy-summer regions. These areas have no marked shortage of water at any season though they have not the abundance of the equatorial regions ; their summers are hot, and their winters may be cool but not cold ; hence there is no need for marked adaptations to a seasonal lack of heat or moisture, and the natural vegetation consists of forests intermediate in luxuriance of growth between those of tropical regions and those of higher latitudes.

Most of the trees are evergreen, but where there may occur periods of relative scarcity of water the leaves are often leathery, as for instance those of the eucalyptus and magnolias, or they are rolled up to needle form as in the case of pines and other coniferous trees ; some of the plants, however, are deciduous. Near the Tropics there are numerous varieties of palms, and beneath the larger trees there are lower growths, e.g. ferns and shrubs, and also climbing plants, while in some parts grasses grow beneath the trees ; bamboos are common in some areas.

In south-eastern China most of the original sub-tropical forest has been destroyed, but magnolias, camellias and camphor trees still bear witness to the natural vegetation, while there are also woods of pines and firs, and considerable growth of bamboos and palms. In eastern Australia there are still extensive forests of this type in which varieties of eucalyptus form an important element and ferns are abundant. In South Africa, along the coast from near the Tropic through Natal, there are woods and thickets in which grow palms and wild banana trees. In the east of South America the sub-tropical forest is situated mainly behind the coastal belt and has a less luxuriant growth ; the Parana pine is a valuable source of timber and another product is yerba maté, a relative of holly, from which Paraguay tea is obtained. In the region of this type in the south-east of the United States the soils are unusually sandy and dry, and pines are dominant.

The warmth and moisture of the sub-tropical forests make them possible habitats for many forms of animal life, and their various kinds of vegetation have enabled the fauna of neighbouring habitats to extend into these regions. Hence the animal life is varied and has no marked individuality.

8. Hard-leaf, Evergreen Woodlands and Scrub.—The term " Mediterranean " is commonly applied to these formations, for they are adapted to the " Mediterranean " conditions of warm, wet winters and hot, dry summers. Broadly speaking, the growth of vegetation in these regions is continued during the warm winter, and the critical condition for plant activity is the supply of moisture ; with the heat of summer the efficiency of the rainfall is so low that this season is a period of drought during which growth of trees and woody shrubs is checked and grasses and herbaceous plants die down. Spring, with its rising temperatures and adequate rainfall, is the season in which plant activity is most marked and the natural vegetation has its brightest appearance with the fresh green of the foliage and the varied hues of the flowers.

The perennial plants, viz. trees and shrubs, are protected against excessive transpiration by low growth and by such devices as long roots (e.g. the vine), thick bark (e.g. the cork oak), leaves which are either leathery and small though broad-shaped (e.g. the evergreen oak, olive and holly) or needle-shaped (e.g. pines). With these adaptations most of the plants retain their leaves throughout the year.

Extensive forests of evergreen trees of this kind have in many areas disappeared, though woodlands may remain. The most common formation is that of scrub formed of bushes such as juniper, broom and heaths ; thickets of such plants go by various local names, e.g. maquis in southern Europe and chaparral in California. Lower and poorer growths of woody plants together with brightly flowering and aromatic herbs occupy many areas but they do not form a continuous vegetation cover, and between them appear patches of bare ground ; the garrigues of southern France are of this character. Grasses are not common, nor do they constitute meadow-like pastures ;

the tough-fibred esparto or alfa grass of southern Europe and northern Africa is of value for making paper.

The largest region of this type of evergreen, hard-leaf woodland and scrub is that around the greater part of the Mediterranean and Black Seas in southern Europe, northern Africa and south-western Asia ; centuries of pastoral work and cultivation, however, have caused great modification or even complete transformation over large areas. In North America a corresponding region is the western side of central California. Less extensive changes have been brought about in the other continents. In South America, central Chile represents the " Mediterranean " type in vegetation as in climate, as the south-western part of the Cape Province does in South Africa. In Australia the corresponding regions are in the south of Western Australia and in South Australia near the Great Australian Bight ; in this continent the forests are formed of several species of eucalyptus trees, some of high growth and great value as timber, while smaller species form mallee scrub.

The animal life of the regions of evergreen, hard-leaf woodland and scrub has no outstanding peculiarities, for the reasons given in the preceding section about the regions of evergreen, sub-tropical forests.

9. Broad-leaf and " Mixed " Forests.—This phrase is a concise label for the forests of mid-latitudes which in some parts are composed mainly of deciduous, broad-leaf trees, while in other parts evergreen, coniferous trees form a considerable part of the natural vegetation. Herbaceous plants also can live under the same conditions as the deciduous trees ; grassy glades are found in the forests, and meadows occur in well-watered areas. The regions occupied by such formations fall into two groups. The first comprises the rainy western parts of land areas in Europe, the Americas and Australasia, which have westerly winds throughout the year, together with an eastward extension of the European area into the neighbouring region with the mid-latitude, short-summer type of climate. The second group consists of the eastern parts of North America and Asia centring on about latitude 40° N. ; these include the regions of the mid-latitude, rainy-summer climate type (except where the forests appear to have been displaced by prairie), and extend on the south into the interior, drier parts of regions of the sub-tropical, rainy-summer type, and also extend north into the mid-latitude areas with a short summer.

From the point of view of plant geography, the common characteristics of all these regions are that their summers are warm enough and also wet enough to enable the growth of trees to proceed with considerable vigour during that season, yet the winters are such as to prevent *continuous* growth; although there may be rains in winter, there are periods when temperatures are too low to allow plants to obtain fluid from the soil, and hence there are longer or shorter periods of " physiological drought." Consequently the trees in these regions are protected against this danger in one of two ways. There are the deciduous trees which have broad and thin-skinned leaves ; these leaves are able to function with great efficiency during summer and they fall when the drought of winter is imminent. There are also the coniferous trees which are evergreen but have needle-leaves and therefore transpire very slowly during the time they cannot obtain water. Apart from this common characteristic of physiological winter drought, the forests exist under conditions which vary considerably from region to region, as the following statement of their main forms will show.

Although the natural vegetation of Europe has been greatly affected by human agency, the cool, temperate part of the continent still shows frequent traces of its earlier forest cover. In many parts there are areas in which deciduous, broad-leaf trees are dominant, e.g. beeches, oaks, ash, elms, etc. ; in wetter ground, willows and alders ; on dry, sandy soils, a thinner growth of pines. Eastward in the adjoining short-summer region and extending into Siberia, oaks and other deciduous trees are found among an increasingly large proportion of conifers.

In North America, the climate region corresponding to north-western Europe is almost limited to the coastal highlands facing the Pacific Ocean. Here, conifers are dominant, and abundant precipitation and equable temperatures allow them to grow to great size ; valuable timber is obtained from giant sequoia, spruce and fir trees. The counterpart to this region in South America is southern Chile, with pines and both deciduous and evergreen species of beech. In about the same latitudes, the extreme south-east of Australia, with Tasmania and New Zealand, has more varied types of natural vegetation.

On the eastern side of North America, the south of the mixed forest region is characterized by oaks, pines or hickory trees ; farther north the yellow birch and the sugar maple are most common, and in south-eastern Canada the woods are mainly of conifers. In eastern Asia the natural vegetation shows a somewhat similar transition from deciduous forests in China to those of south-eastern Siberia where conifers are dominant.

To a greater or less extent, all the regions of this mixed type of forest are, or have been, timber-producing areas, the deciduous trees giving " hard wood " and the coniferous yielding " soft wood," but where the climatic conditions encourage cultivation the natural vegetation has now largely disappeared.

Animal Life.—Although the deciduous and mixed forests have their period of growth in the summer, they can supply food for animal life at all seasons ; when in winter the leaves and young shoots are no longer available, nuts or berries may be obtained from the deciduous trees and seeds from the conifers. Moreover, the forest gives more shelter in inclement weather than the open grasslands or scrub-lands. Hence there was originally a considerable amount of animal life in these regions. Among the herbivorous animals the deer, bear and wild boar may be mentioned ; among the carnivorous were wolves, badgers and foxes ; by the streams lived otters and beavers. Marked adaptations to arboreal life are shown among the mammals by squirrels, dormice and bats. The cold of winter is guarded against by the possession of a furry coat by many of the animals, by the underground dwellings of some, e.g. badgers, foxes and beavers, and also by hibernation, e.g. bears and bats.

10. Sub-arctic Coniferous Forests.—*Plant Life.*—These formations, known in Canada as the Northern Forests and in Siberia as taiga, occupy very extensive areas in North America and Eurasia ; their distribution is, broadly speaking, the same as that of the sub-arctic climate to which they are adapted. As the vegetative period here is even more restricted than in the mid-latitude short-summer regions of the mixed forests, it is an advantage for the trees of the sub-arctic forests to be able to grow whenever in spring or early summer the temperatures allow them to obtain nutriment through the roots ; this is secured by the trees being evergreen and the leaves being ready to function whenever conditions permit. Moreover, the leathery surface and the tightly rolled form of the leaves make them able to withstand the falls of snow and the strong winds of winter, and in contrast to deciduous broad-leaved trees, conifers can thrive on strongly leached podsols of colder areas.

The most common trees of the sub-arctic forests are varieties of pines and firs ; there are also spruces in wet areas, the larch, unusual in being deciduous although cone-bearing and needle-leaved, and birch and willow which are here exceptional because they are deciduous broad-leaved trees.

With little heat and poor soils, growth is restricted and the trees are slender and of only moderate height : the formation gives but a thin vegetation cover.   In some areas two or more varieties live together ; elsewhere one variety is dominant and the forest assumes a monotonous, often even forbidding and gloomy, appearance.

The sub-arctic, coniferous forests gradually change their character at all their margins, on the warmer sides to the mixed forests and steppes as already explained, and on the north to the tundra ; here the trees become fewer or limited to river valleys, or their normal growths are replaced by dwarf varieties.

Where the timber is of commercial value and can easily be transported the forests are cut, but very large areas of the sub-arctic forests remain in a practically virgin state.

Animal Life.—The food and protection in winter afforded by these forests allow the existence of two groups of animals : those which always have their homes in these regions and those which are winter migrants, e.g. the caribou and arctic hare from the tundra.   Characteristic of the sub-arctic forests are the elk of Eurasia and the red deer of Asia, also known in North America as the moose.   The protection of a fur coat is shown more commonly in the animals of the coniferous than in those of the mixed forests ; those which are hunted or trapped for their furs include the mink, marten, lynx, sable, otter and ermine. Another common protective adaptation is the seasonal change of colour to white to harmonize with the winter snow.   Bird life is abundant in summer, but in winter many kinds migrate southwards, often to very distant regions.   Insect life, too, is abundant in these forests ; in summer it is specially noticeable and may even be pestilential.

11. Tundra.—*Plant Life.*—Tundra vegetation extends behind the northern coasts of North America and Eurasia and parts of the coasts of Greenland and other islands of the Arctic seas.   It is adapted to the Arctic climate with its very short and cool summer, very long and cold winter, " physiological drought " for much of the year, and frequent winds of great violence. Unfavourable, too, are the tundra soils, frozen in winter, and in summer sticky and frequently wet and acid, while the sub-soil is always frozen. The vegetative period is too short and cool— —the mean temperature of the warmest month being below 50° F.—for the growth of trees, save in exceptional cases ; the common forms of vegetation are low plants which require little heat and nutriment and offer little surface to the wind, and even these often have a dispersed growth, leaving between them patches of stony ground, wet soil or pools of water.

As in the hot desert regions, so in these cold semi-deserts, a very short life-cycle is a necessity, and in some parts the transitory wealth of blossom has earned the name of the " flowering tundra." Small evergreen bushes, such as the crowberry and bilberry, grow in fair abundance ; in wet and peaty areas there are sedges, cotton grass and mosses, while in drier parts lichens may form a continuous mat upon the ground.

Animal Life.—The cold and the snow cover to the land in winter make a large part of the animal life of the tundra migratory, as, for example, the Canadian reindeer, known as caribou, and some of the Eurasian reindeer ; other reindeer, however, live throughout the year in the mainland tundra or isolated upon the Arctic islands. The broad spreading hoofs of these animals not only allow them to travel easily over the snow but also enable them to dig down beneath it to obtain their only winter food, the lichen known as " reindeer moss " ; in summer the reindeer eat herbs and leaves. The musk-ox of North America and Greenland, protected by a long fleece which hangs over its woolly undercoat, is also a permanent inhabitant of the tundra. Lichens, mosses, berries, seeds, and shoots of dwarf shrubs give food, especially in summer, to herbivorous animals, including rodents ; upon these live wolves and foxes.

The animal life of the coasts and the adjoining seas is of special importance. Even in Arctic and Antarctic regions there is near the surface of the water a great development of microscopic plants, and upon these subsist minute, simple forms of animal life ; together these constitute the *plankton*, the drifting food material upon which fish depend. Upon the fish depend mammals which either live in the sea, e.g. the whale,

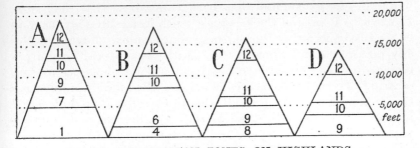

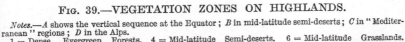

FIG. 39.—VEGETATION ZONES ON HIGHLANDS.

Notes.—*A* shows the vertical sequence at the Equator ; *B* in mid-latitude semi-deserts; *C* in "Mediterranean" regions ; *D* in the Alps.

1 = Dense, Evergreen Forests. 4 = Mid-latitude Semi-deserts. 6 = Mid-latitude Grasslands.
7 = Forests of sub-tropical type. 8 = Hard-leaved Woodlands. 9 = Deciduous and Mixed Forests.
10 = Coniferous Forests. 11 = "Alpine" Vegetation. 12 = Cold Deserts.

or live on the land or ice but hunt in the water, e.g. the seal and walrus ; the polar bear preys both upon such animals and upon fish. The skin and furs which protect these animals from the cold, and the accumulation of fat beneath the skin which serves also as a store of food, are animal adaptations upon which man largely depends for his own life in Arctic regions.

In summer birds are very numerous, especially those feeding upon fish and living near the coasts ; most of the birds, like most of the mammals, migrate southwards in winter. In the Antarctic, fish form the food for birds, among which the penguin is the most striking example.

Insect life abounds during the brief Arctic summer, and the numerous pools and swamps give a breeding-place to almost inconceivable swarms of mosquitoes ; the winter frost does not injure their eggs, and the ice prevents the existence of small freshwater fish which in other regions feed upon the larvæ. Other flies are also summer pests to animals and men.

12. **Highland Zones.**—*Plant Life.*—The natural vegetation of highland areas changes appreciably according to elevation within vertical distances of a few thousand feet. An increase of altitude is normally accompanied by a decrease of temperature and, for a considerable distance from sea-level, an increase of precipitation ; hence there are differences in the plant life which occur in zones of altitude and succeed one another till life is no longer possible. The particular vertical sequence varies according to the world-position of the highlands.

The sequence of vegetation from the base of an equatorial

mountain to its summit has been compared with that from
Equator to Pole, and there is some truth in the analogy, as may
be seen by comparing this series of zones, shown diagrammatically on p. 135 and marked "A," with the natural vegetation
regions from the Equator to the Arctic along the eastern margin
of Asia. To facilitate such comparisons, the numbers indicating
the zones on p. 135 (except the uppermost "cold desert"
mountain zone) are the same as those of their nearest counterparts in the map of the natural vegetation regions.

Yet there are several differences between the two sequences.
For instance, in equatorial regions the temperatures of highlands are lower than those at sea-level but do not vary markedly
from one season to another as they do, e.g., in the sub-tropical
regions of eastern Asia ; moreover, the precipitation remains
fairly steady throughout the year and the humidity of the
atmosphere is always high in the lower zones of the equatorial
mountains. Hence in the forests of the "sub-tropical" zone
of the vertical sequence there is a greater luxuriance of growth
than in the corresponding sub-tropical latitudes ; ferns, lianas
and much undergrowth are generally very characteristic.

At higher altitudes, decreasing temperatures limit the period
during which water can be absorbed by the roots ; the forests
therefore are deciduous and, still higher, coniferous, until at
last the tree line is reached. Above this there is a zone, snow-
covered for much of the year, of "alpine" vegetation somewhat
like that of the tundra. Perennial plants are represented
largely by dwarf trees and shrubs, and in the short growing
season a fairly dense cover of herbaceous plants and grasses
offers valuable summer pasture. Cushion-like growths of
alpine plants are also common. In South America and Asia
there are considerable areas at high altitudes, e.g. the Andean,
Pamir and Tibetan plateaus ; these may be described as cold
scrub-lands, in which there is a scanty vegetation including
tufted, hard grasses and cushion-like growths of alpine character.
At still greater altitudes, culminating heights may rise above
the limits of plant life to the "cold deserts" ; the greatest of
these are the ice caps of Greenland and Antarctica.

In the case of highlands in mid-latitudes, the vertical decrease
of temperature and the increase of precipitation at all except
the highest latitudes bring about changes which may be
broadly deduced from the principles already exemplified. In the

part of the diagram marked " B " it is shown that a mountain area rising from a semi-desert region receives on the lower slopes sufficient rain to support a grassland ; above that, the precipitation, having a relatively high efficiency at the lower temperatures, is sufficient for drought-resistant coniferous forest ; still higher are the alpine and cold desert zones.

Similarly, in the " Mediterranean " climate regions the mountain areas (diagram C) at a moderate elevation have a greater rainfall, and this has a higher efficiency than at sea-level ; hence deciduous, followed by coniferous, forests clothe the slopes. Diagram D illustrates the sequence found in the Alps of Europe, where the lower areas have mixed forests, and these give place to conifers and then to alpine vegetation.

In the highland zones, as in the lowland regions, there are gradual changes in the vegetation, and the sharp dividing lines in the diagrams on p. 135 must be interpreted like those indicating boundaries on the maps. Moreover, there are often considerable differences between the vegetation on opposed sides of a mountain area at the same elevation ; for example, where the highland faces sea-winds, the greater rainfall may give forest as opposed to grassland on the lee side.

Animal Life.—To a certain extent, the animal life of the respective vegetation zones of highlands shows adaptations like those of the corresponding lowland regions. But the highland zones are normally distant from the corresponding lowland areas, and moreover are individually of very limited extent. Hence, the animals of highlands are not usually restricted to particular zones, but in many instances migrate up and down to obtain conditions in which they can exist at each season. A common characteristic is the possession of strong and spreading hoofs to facilitate climbing—the chamois, ibex, and wild mountain sheep and goats afford examples. At considerable elevations there are few carnivores as compared with the herbivorous animals ; to some extent their place is taken by vultures and other flesh-eating birds. Warm-coated bears, of several species, which feed both upon vegetation and upon the smaller forms of animal life, are well adapted to highland conditions. In the alpine zone there is a striking development of insect life during the flowering of the vegetation.

On the extensive plateaus of the Andes and Central Asia are animals not found elsewhere. In Tibet the long-haired, hardy and agile yak can feed on the hard grasses, the mosses and lichen of that region, and is used as a beast of burden. On the Andean plateaus there are members of the camel-tribe adapted to life in a cold climate; the vicuña yields a soft and delicate wool, and the llama, which in appearance is half-camel, half-sheep, is used either for transport or for wool and meat.

Human life in mountain regions has to be largely dependent, except where minerals can be worked, upon hunting wild animals or rearing domesticated ones. Two consequences are noteworthy : man, like the other animals, is generally migratory, and the total population is small.

PART II
HUMAN DEVELOPMENTS

CHAPTER X
RACES AND MIGRATIONS (1)

THE early stages of the history of mankind, and the ways in which various groups of men became adapted to different environments, have to be deduced from fragmentary evidence ; the following account can therefore claim only to be an attempt to set out the main facts as they appear in the light of our present knowledge.

The evolution of man from the man-like apes had its origins late in the Tertiary Era, perhaps a million years ago, in a warm grass-and-trees area in the great land-mass of the Old World, and probably in the region which includes central Asia and North Africa. Fragments of skulls claimed to be of very early human development have been found in south eastern England, at Piltdown and Swanscombe, but their nature and date have been questioned. More certain forms in the series from ape to man date from early inter-glacial periods of the ice age, about half a million years ago ; these are not the ancestors of modern man, and are represented by some bones found near the margins of Eurasia. Marking a definite development from ape to man are " Pekin man " and " Java man," so-called from the respective situations of their fossil remains, and it is possible that they were forced to these places near the limits of the great continent by the emergence of still more highly developed branches in favourable areas in the interior. By such slow evolutionary processes came true man, *Genus homo* (refer back to the table on p. 17) ; one species of this genus was " Neanderthal man," whose skeletons were discovered in central Europe, but this particular line has become extinct.

Primary Racial Types.—Man of the present time, *Homo sapiens*, is a still higher species of *Genus homo* ; he appears to have evolved during a later part of the ice age, and to have

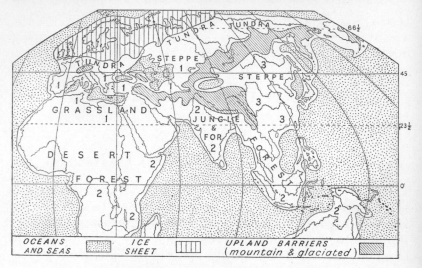

FIG. 40.—PROBABLE ENVIRONMENTS OF EARLY MAN.

spread over considerable areas of Eurasia and Africa before the final severe period of cold caused the ice to extend over much of Europe and to turn the Asiatic highlands into barriers not able to be crossed by man (see the map above). At the same time the distribution of land and sea was somewhat different from that of the present, for the Mediterranean Sea was not such a complete barrier between the lands to the north and south, while a large inland sea stretched over the sites of the Caspian and Aral Seas ; also, Asia extended eastward beyond the present coast to include the Japanese islands, while in the south-east the continent continued over much of the East Indian Archipelago, while New Guinea joined Australia.

Moreover, the physical conditions of the period gave to the habitable lands a different character from that which they have today.   South of the European ice sheet was a belt of tundra which gave place in central Asia to steppe, while in the west, around the present site of the Mediterranean Sea, was a warm and well-watered grassland.   This grassland, together with the cooler steppe of central Asia, occupied an extensive area reaching into the present position of the northern Sahara in Africa.   On the map the whole of this region is marked " 1," and may be briefly referred to as the " western grassland." The desert belt lay farther south, approximately in the latitude of the Sudan, and together with the mountains of western Asia it separated the western grassland from the " southern forests and jungles " in equatorial Africa and the south of Asia (marked " 2 ").

In Asia, the glaciated central highlands cut off the western grassland from another habitable area in the eastern part of the continent ; this had a climate in which the winter monsoon was more marked than today, and in consequence the winters were long, very cold, dry and sunny, while the summers were shorter and less rainy than at present. Consequently, eastern Asia was a poorly watered grass- and scrub-land ; it may be referred to as the "eastern steppe" (marked "3" on the map).

The " southern forests and jungles," largely cut off from the others by the African desert and the long line of highlands in central and southern Asia, were situated around the Indian Ocean. Here in the south abundant heat and rain allowed a natural vegetation of forest and jungle which in the south-east extended almost unbroken to Australia (again refer to the map).

Thus, at a time which may have been about 35,000 years ago (more than 1,000 generations), mankind was living in three strongly contrasted climatic regions ; consequently, three separate groups evolved for a very long time under distinctive climatic controls. The warm, western grasslands were probably similar to the early home of *Homo sapiens,* and the early lines of physical development could continue in this area.

In the southern area of hot and wet jungles and forests, however, changes in the human body occurred ; in particular, in the skin there was the development of loose pores and numerous, large sweat glands which allowed the system to adapt itself to greater heat and moisture. Such modifications had a survival value, i.e. those individuals in whom they occurred tended to survive longer than the others and they had children with the same characters ; as this process continued for many generations their descendants became more and more numerous until the characters became normal to this southern group of mankind. Moreover, in the skin of the people in these latitudes there occurred a greater development of a pigment resulting in the colour becoming a deeper brown and in extreme cases almost black ; as the pigment was a protection against excessive solar radiation, this change proved a significant adaptation to the climatic conditions. Further

modifications had a survival value in the hot, wet regions ; e.g.
a broad nose with wide nostrils which facilitated the cooling
process was a useful adaptation to men who had evolved earlier
under cooler conditions, and a large mouth with wide, everted
lips had a similar value. The hair of these people was oval in
section and, having curved roots—possibly because of the loose
texture of the skin—was distinctively curly, woolly or kinky.

Thus in the southern area a special type of man developed
in which the characters just described are inherent and have
been transmitted from generation to generation to the present
time. This great division of mankind (sometimes called the
Black race) will be referred to in this book either as the woolly-
haired or Negro-like primary race.

The very different conditions of the eastern steppe gave a
different trend to the evolution of the men who lived in and
around the central area of the Mongolian plateau and in the
more eastern Asiatic lands which then had a similarly extreme
and dry climate. For much of the year man needed to conserve
bodily heat, and it was advantageous when the superficial
layer of his skin became thick and dry with the blood-vessels
deeper below the surface ; because of this and the moderate
amount of pigmentation the skin assumed a yellowish or
yellowish-brown colour. In dry regions it was of value when
the sweat glands were diminished, and with the hair pores
constricted the hair acquired a round section and grew straight
and lank. Facial peculiarities also appeared, but these are
less clearly related to the environment. On the inner side of
the eyes, the lid became down-folded so as to give them an
almond-like shape, and possibly this narrowing may have had
a value as a protection against strong sunlight, or even against
strong winds which carried loess from the interior. A common
character, too, was a broad skull and a rather flat face in which
the cheek-bones tended to stand out. These physical characters became representative of an eastern branch of mankind—
the straight-haired or Mongolian-like primary race, sometimes
called the Yellow race.

In the western grassland, with moderately high temperatures
and a moderate amount of moisture, and with frequently cloudy
skies reducing insolation, man did not become specially adapted
either to the loss or to the retention of heat. The skin was
moderately open in texture and of a light-brown colour ; the

hair was neither straight and lank, nor woolly, but it was wavy or at the most curly. Later, however, descendants of the people of the ice age were able to move into northern Europe, where there was a relative lack of insolation, and consequently any considerable amount of pigmentation which screened the sunlight was a positive disadvantage. Among these northern people, therefore, the colouration became less ; a " white " skin, fair hair and blue eyes became characteristic. For this reason, the whole of this north-western division of mankind has been called the White race, in spite of the obviously darker colour of many of the peoples which compose it ; a better term is the wavy-haired or European-like primary race.

In such ways as those now described, three great divisions of man evolved in broadly contrasting habitats, but all of these three primary races must have included types showing minor differences. Moreover, there were very possibly other primary races, for traces of somewhat older types remain in a few of the more remote parts of the world. Finally, right up to the present time racial stocks have mingled at numerous points of contact, and the concurrent mingling of their physical characteristics has made the appearance of the resultant peoples much less uniform than was formerly the case. Indeed, nowadays, pure " races " nowhere exist ; hence in many connections it may be better to employ the phrase " racial groups."

It must also be clearly recognized that " race " is a physical matter, showing itself in certain bodily characteristics which are transmitted by nature from one generation to another ; hence the term " race " should not be used in connection with those groupings of mankind, such as nations, religious communities and language-groups, which depend upon the feelings, ideas or habits of people and can be changed by the conscious wishes of individuals or by actions of themselves or others.

Early Migrations.—Migrations have been a great factor in the evolution of modern man ; some have been caused by natural conditions, such as a change of climate, or the inability of a region to support the natural increase of population, while others, especially in recent times, have been due to political conditions making people seek homes in distant lands.

Even during the ice age there may have been some migration from one of the three great habitable areas to another, either near the north-west of India where men of the western grasslands might penetrate between the African desert and the Himalayan mountains into the southern area, or in Indo-China where the eastern and southern areas come together. Yet it was at a later stage, and very slowly, that migrations became an important factor in the development of the present groups of mankind.

Probably the movements which have had the greatest influence have been due to climatic variations, especially important in the Heartland where the recurrence of relatively dry periods caused wave after wave of migration, the later comers tending to force the earlier settlers still farther towards the margins of the great land-mass of the Old World. Hence, considerable numbers of people who show most of the characters of one primary race live in regions which were once part of the habitat of another ; e.g. members of the wavy-haired race from southwestern or central Asia form the main part of the population of India. As a result, characters which can be adapted to the needs of a new environment within a relatively short period, i.e. within perhaps a hundred generations, have become changed ; other characters, however, which are not so easily susceptible to modification remain and show the original stock from which the population was derived. Thus in India people from western Asia have become adapted to the greater amount of insolation in the south by an increase of pigmentation which has given them dark-brown or even very dark-brown skins, though other characters of the primary race which previously lived in this region, such as the woolly hair, have not been developed in the later comers.

As the ice age slowly passed away the ice retreated from the lowlands of Europe and the snows disappeared from the uplands. Then considerable areas of northern Europe and Asia became open to settlement by the wavy-haired peoples ; moreover, the mountain barriers of Asia no longer presented the same difficulty to movement between the respective habitats of the primary races. Yet from the human point of view there was not everywhere a steady improvement in the physical conditions, e.g. in Africa the desert advanced northward over the grasslands while the Mediterranean Sea extended its limits, and later over much of Europe followed several minor changes of climate which have lasted into recent times and have caused the natural vegetation to alter considerably.

The combined effects both of these changes and also of the

accompanying migrations of peoples have been to check human evolution along the earlier and simpler lines and to produce complications among the primary races, and the development of numerous intermediate types. Moreover, within each of these composite groups the individuals commonly show contrasts one from another, some bearing witness to one side of their ancestry and some to another element in the common stock ; even members of the same family differ considerably from one another. Purity of race is a rare phenomenon ; individuals and racial groups are normally the product of complicated descent.

Present-day Racial Types.—The complication due to repeated migrations means that there can be no simple relation between the physical characters of the groups of modern man and the environments in which they now live ; a very marked misfit, explained later, are the American Indians in the Amazon valley who are even less able than Europeans to withstand the constantly high temperatures. The complicated descent has also removed any possibility of clear-cut distinction between the races, and attempts to distinguish and classify them differ.

In this work of distinguishing and classifying the present-day types, mention has been made of obvious physical characters the structure of the hair, the colouration of the skin, hair and eyes, and facial peculiarities such as the width of the nose, the form of the lips and the shape of the eyes. There is another physical character which is transmitted from parent to child and is therefore a test of descent and race ; this is the skull-form, as expressed by the proportion of the width from side to side compared with the length from front to back. When the ratio of width to length is considerable, viz. more than 80 to 100, the head is said to be broad ; when the ratio is much less, viz. under 75 to 100, the head is termed long. Yet the mere statement that a skull is broad or long is insufficient to describe its actual shape ; e.g. a long head may be due to a development of either the back or the front of the skull, and peoples who are as widely different as some of the woolly-haired Negroes and the wavy-haired North Europeans may be equally long-headed. Head-form is perhaps of more value in distinguishing between the sub-divisions than between the main groups of mankind.

The average stature of peoples is a marked character— witness the contrast between the African pygmies of the equatorial forest who have an average height of less than 4 feet

8 inches and the Sudanese Negroes of the savannas who commonly exceed 5 feet 10 inches. A certain stature, however, like a certain head-form, may be due to several distinct bodily differences. Moreover, apart from the fact that the height of individuals may be affected by such factors as malnutrition and disease, the normal stature of a group may be altered relatively rapidly by its environment ; hence stature is regarded as a subsidiary, rather than a primary, criterion of race.

Racial classification is therefore based upon the particular *combinations* of hereditary physical characters which people possess. The main divisions of mankind may be usefully determined by the hair-structure ; the racial groups within these divisions may be distinguished by pigmentation and head-form, further aid being obtained from facial peculiarities, stature and other characters. The method is partially illustrated by the appended table of the chief racial groups among the wavy-haired peoples ; the first column shows in a generalized way the progressively darker colour of the so-called " White " and " Brown " peoples from northern Europe to tropical regions, while in the second column the extent to which the skull-form is long or broad is indicated by the position in which the name of each group is printed.

WAVY-HAIRED RACIAL GROUPS

	SKIN-COLOUR	LONG ←—SKULL-FORM—→ BROAD
"WHITE"	Reddish or Blond	NORDIC — EAST EUROPEAN [?]
	Medium	AINU — ALPINE—IRANIAN TURANIAN [TURKI]
	Tawney or Brunet	MEDITERRANEAN
	Mixed type	BERBER
"BROWN"	Very light or light brown	ORIENTAL INDO-AFGHAN — POLYNESIAN
	Medium	HAMITIC NESIOT
	Dark	DRAVIDIAN
	Very dark	PRE-DRAVIDIAN
	Chocolate or "Black"	[AUSTRALIAN]

The Wavy-haired Division.—The passing of the ice age and the post-glacial climatic changes stimulated a complicated series of migrations of large and small bodies of men ; here we can indicate only the general direction of some relatively late drifts of racial groups, in order to explain their present location and to throw light on their physical characters.

Mediterranean Group.—The name given to this group indicates its early area of settlement in the lands around the Mediterranean Sea. The people were characterized by a rather dark or tawny white skin, associated with very dark hair and generally very dark eyes ; the stature is rather short and the body slender ; the skull is long. This group appeared in Europe about 8,000 or 10,000 years ago, and spread westward, often among earlier peoples. Later, other groups encroached upon its eastern homes and either drove out or so absorbed its members that its characters appear only as a minor element in the new populations. The modern representatives of the Mediterranean racial group are now found mainly in the southern extremities of the Balkan and Italian peninsulas, and on both the European and the African sides of the western Mediterranean Sea, while a further drift is shown by the frequency of its characters among the people of the Atlantic sides of France and the British Isles.

Alpine-Iranian Group.—The second wave of peoples to enter Europe, about 6,000 years ago or more, was distinguished by being broad-skulled and of shorter and more thick-set build, and their descendants have a rather lighter skin, and often lighter hair and eyes, than the Mediterranean group. They migrated along the plateaus of south-west Asia into the Balkans and central Europe, occupying the valleys of the Carpathian and Alpine mountains and the neighbouring lowlands. They are known as the *Alpine* group, as their descendants now form the greater part of the population of that region as well as of much of central France and southern Germany. One branch spread out from the neighbourhood of the Carpathians into the plains of eastern Europe, where it forms an important element in the population of Russia, especially in the central area. The members of this branch are sometimes referred to as the Slavs, because they speak one of the Slavonic languages ; but when dealing with the race or descent of people it is important to keep as clear as possible of terms and ideas connected with languages, religions, cultures or political States, for these can

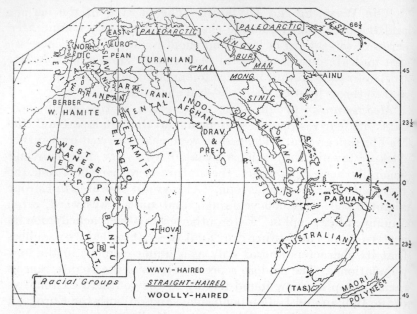

FIG. 41.—RACIAL GROUPS IN EASTERN HEMISPHERE.

Note.—P. = Pygmies. *B.* = Bushmen. Square brackets show racial groups of unusually mixed, or uncertain, origin.

be changed at will or by the compulsion of others, and are not inherent in the racial stock.

Behind the Alpine peoples came others pressing westward along the uplands from south-western Asia ; in Europe there is the *Dinaric or Illyrian* group which forms a large part of the population of the Balkan region, while in Asia there is the *Armenian or Anatolian* group. These are in most respects similar to the Alpines but are taller ; occasionally they are of markedly tall stature. Still farther east on the same line of uplands are peoples of the *Iranian or Pamiri* group ; they also are broad-headed, but as compared with the Alpine peoples are of finer physique and often have lighter skin and eyes.

These four racial groups are sometimes linked together under the term Euro-Asiatic, but they are here labelled Alpine-Iranian to indicate more precisely the extent of the regions in which their representatives are the most common types.

Nordic Group.—The third of the specifically European racial groups migrated into Europe after the Mediterranean and Alpine peoples (possibly about 5,000 years ago) from the

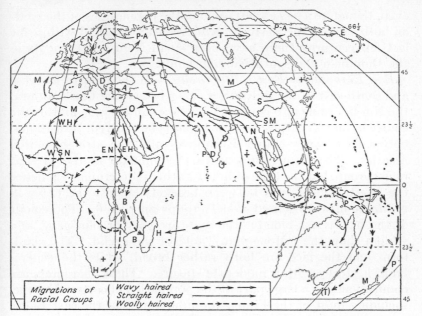

FIG. 42.—RACIAL MIGRATIONS IN EASTERN HEMISPHERE.

Note. Arrows show probable routes in a simplified form.
Crosses denote places of refuge in which early racial types have been preserved. Initials correspond with names on map of racial groups.

Asiatic steppe-lands to what is now south Russia, and they thence moved north-westward ultimately occupying the southern parts of the Scandinavian Lands.   In these northern latitudes the amount of their earlier pigmentation became reduced, as has already been explained, and they acquired the characters because of which they are regarded as a distinct racial group known as Nordic. The table given above shows that the Nordics can be distinguished from the neighbouring, and actually overlapping, Alpines by their long skull-form.   During the thousand years which preceded the Christian era, Nordic migrants worked their way southwards from Scandinavia and occupied the lands adjoining the southern shores of the Baltic Sea and the south-eastern shores of the North Sea.   Still later, after the beginning of the Christian era, other Nordic adventurers settled in the east of Britain.   In all these localities they still form the most common, but not the only, element in the population.   Still later, other conquests resulted in a Nordic admixture among the Alpine peoples of central Europe and even, though to a less extent, among the populations of the lands on both sides of the western Mediterranean Sea, and within the last few centuries there have been small Nordic settlements in the Danubian and south Russian lands.

East European or East Baltic Group.—In the area to the east and south-east of the Baltic Sea, long before the Christian era, the Nordics came into contact with Siberian peoples, and in the course of many centuries a new racial type evolved, transitional between the wavy-haired Europeans and the straight-haired Asiatics. The former appear to predominate in the present racial group, but the type of hair is rather indeterminate ; hence the question mark put between brackets against the name in the table of wavy-haired racial groups on p. 146. The colour of the hair is ash-blond ; the eyes are gray or blue-gray, and seldom show the " Mongolian " fold of the eyelid. The skull-form and the face are both rather broad, while the general build is stocky with a moderate stature. These characters are common among a large part of the population of eastern Europe, including most of the Finns, the inhabitants of the east Baltic countries, the people of part of Poland and many of those of European Russia except in the south. The group has been given different names by anthropologists, and the term East European is here adopted because it best indicates its present distribution.

Turanian or Turki Group.—North of the Iranian plateau are the semi-deserts and steppes of Western Turkistan, known to the ancient Persians as Turan. Apart from more or less recent immigrants, the people of this region are of the Turanian or Turki group. They are akin to the Armenian racial group whom they resemble in most respects, but as the steppes of Turkistan have allowed Mongolian tribes again and again to raid westward, some of the Mongolian characters are found in a number of the Turki population. For this reason, and also because their language is one of an Asiatic family, the Turki peoples have sometimes been placed among the straight-haired instead of among the wavy-haired races.

Indo-Afghans, Dravidians and Pre-Dravidians.—The repeated south-eastward drifts of wavy-haired peoples into India have resulted in an extraordinary mixture of racial types. The last invaders form the bulk of the population in the north and west of India as well as in Afghanistan ; they belong, therefore, to the *Indo-Afghan* group, and their physical features are well shown among the people of Kashmir ; a photograph of a typical Kashmiri is reproduced opposite p. 164. These characters distinguish them from the peoples whom they displaced and thrust farther to the south-east, viz. the much less clearly defined group which is found over a considerable part of southern India and goes by the name *Dravidian*—not a quite satisfactory term, because it is used also to denote a group of languages. Most of the Dravidians are similar in several respects to those of the Mediterranean race ; they differ chiefly in complexion, for this group is characterized by dark, sometimes even brownish-black, skins, apparently due to mixing with darker predecessors, and to a very long residence, extending over several thousands of years, in tropical latitudes. Among the Dravidian-speaking peoples of India are also indications of an influx of Alpine racial origin.

The *Pre-Dravidians*, as the name implies, had been in this region at a still earlier date, and in general have been forced into the less favoured parts of the central Deccan, i.e. into rough hill-country, forests and dense jungles ; some migrated into Ceylon where they are known as the Vedda. Among the various tribes which are grouped together under the name of Pre-Dravidian there are considerable differences, but in general they have very dark skins, short stature and rather broad noses ; of the peoples of India they are the least like the European groups in appearance, and it is quite possible that they owe some of their characters to still earlier inhabitants. Among these very early peoples may have been members of the woolly-haired primary race, and indeed some of the present tribes have closely curling hair and markedly thick lips. There may also have been representatives of the race from which are derived the aborigines of Australia who will be discussed later.

Nesiot and Polynesian Groups.—The Dravidians and Pre-Dravidians migrated into a cul-de-sac in the Deccan of India and Ceylon, but later other wavy-haired peoples passed from northern India into Indo-China, the Malay region and the East Indian Archipelago ; their relatively light skin-colour is probably to be explained by their comparatively short residence in the Tropics. Because some of them live on the East Indian islands, these people have been called Nēsiot, from a Greek word for islanders ; yet they form only a small minority of the population of the East Indian Archipelago, as this region has

been a crossing place in migrations of all three primary races.[1]
After the Nesiots, there followed still another south-eastward
drift of wavy-haired peoples. These Polynesians worked their
way relatively quickly through the equatorial region, and in
consequence have retained a light-brown colouration, and they
have retained also the facial characters which indicate their
kinship with the European peoples. After they had arrived at
the south-eastern extremity of Asia, they became adventurous
seafarers and eventually settled in the islands of Polynesia ;
thence one group, the Maori, migrated to New Zealand as late
as 1350 A.D. There has been some admixture of these Polynesians with Asiatic migrants, and in consequence the island
groups differ somewhat from one another ; nevertheless as a
whole they show clearly their racial relationship to the great
belt of wavy-haired peoples which stretches more than half-way
round the globe, from Iceland to the South Pacific Ocean.

Oriental, Hamitic and Berber Groups.—In the scrub-lands and
semi-deserts of Arabia and even of the Sahara are the homes of
a racial group typified by the Arabs ; these people are wavy-
haired, have a light-brown skin but jet-black hair, long skulls,
and a sharp profile with a prominent and characteristically
narrow nose. The name *Oriental* has been applied to this
group to indicate its location in the Orient (if the Middle East,
and not the Far East, is understood by this term). Another
name which has been used for these people is Semitic, but this
is open to the objection that the word Semitic relates to the
languages which may or may not be spoken by members of the
group. Also, the term Semitic is commonly associated with
the Jews and is therefore liable to misunderstanding; e.g. the word
anti-Semitic implies hostility to the Jews but not to the Arabs.

The Jews were originally of this Eastern Mediterranean stock,
but during their dispersion they have become mixed with other
peoples. At the present time there is no distinctive " Jewish
race " ; the Jews are a religious and cultural, but not a racial,
group. Yet because they tend to intermarry they tend to

---

[1] Because of the area of past migration and of present influence upon peoples,
the name " Indonesian " was formerly given by ethnologists to this Nesiot
group, but ambiguity arose when the same term " Indonesian " was used by the
nationalist leaders in the Netherlands East Indies to denote all the native peoples
whom they wished to liberate from Dutch rule. It may be added that the name
" Indonesia " was also used by the nationalist leaders as a collective name for
the islands for which they claimed independence ; this term has, moreover,
now been popularly applied to the Archipelago as a whole.

retain the so-called Jewish nose, with curved outline and depressed tip, apparently derived from one of the peoples of the Armenian group.

Northern Africa, including the Sahara on the west and Abyssinia and Somaliland on the east, is inhabited mainly by people derived from three racial groups, viz. Oriental, Hamitic and Berber. The Oriental element is around the lower and middle Nile and in the habitable areas of the eastern Sahara. The Hamitic peoples form the main stock of the population of northern Africa and may be divided into two groups. The *Eastern Hamites* include the Egyptians of the lower and middle Nile valley, the Beja and Galla peoples of Abyssinia, and the Somali ; the *Western Hamites* include the Tuareg of the central uplands of the Sahara region and the Fula (also known as Fulani or Fulbe) of the savannas of the western Sudan. The physical characters of the Hamites show them to be related more nearly to the Mediterranean than to any other racial group, though their colour is brown instead of a darkish white ; among the southern Hamites the skin is even a dark brown. The hair is generally curly and the nose tends to be broad.

The *Berbers* of the Atlas Lands [1] show a mixture of types. While there are found among them the physical characters common among the Mediterranean and allied groups, there are also taller and fairer elements ; the existence of yellow hair and blue eyes suggests an early blond, if not Nordic, immigration.

The Ainu.—An isolated group of wavy-haired people among the straight-haired inhabitants of eastern Asia are the Ainu who live in the north of Japan. In several respects they are akin to the European peoples and probably represent an early drift of a wavy-haired group now cut off from other descendants of the same primary race by a northward movement of the Mongolian division of mankind.

The Native Australians.—The aborigines of Australia, often referred to as "Blackfellows," are darker than any other of the wavy-haired peoples. Indeed, it is questioned whether they should be grouped with the Pre-Dravidians of India or whether they should be regarded, not as descended from the wavy-haired primary race, but as a remnant of a different primary

---

[1] The Berbers are the sedentary agriculturists, as distinct from the pastoral Arabs, of this region ; the townsmen are mainly of Berber descent though most of them have adopted the Arab speech and culture.

race—one which has been thrust out of the more central areas of the habitable world and has survived only in this far-off continent, completely isolated since the rising of the sea-level. The hair is generally curly, though occasionally almost woolly and occasionally almost straight. The facial characters are certainly not those common among the wavy-haired peoples, for they include a flat, retreating forehead with prominent brow ridges, and very wide noses. The uncertain relationship of the Native Australians is indicated by the name being put within brackets in the table on p. 146, and in the map on p. 148.

The Woolly-haired Division.—The present-day descendants of the woolly-haired primary race are found on both the western and the eastern sides of the Indian Ocean, but on the northern side, i.e. in the Indian area, they have been displaced by repeated invasions of other races.

The Negroes.—The true Negroes have spread from Eastern Africa westward along the open savannas of the Sudan, reaching southward to the Guinea coast and to the northern part of the Congo Basin. They have the characteristic woolly hair ; their skin is very dark brown or even black ; they are tall and powerfully built ; their skull-form is long ; they have thick lips and broad noses.

The Western Sudanese Negroes of the savannas have been invaded by Hamitic peoples from the north and west, and groups of mixed descent and physical character are the result ; thus, the predominantly Negro-like Hausa of Nigeria show Hamitic influence partly due to the Fula who became their overlords.

In general, the Western Sudanese Negroes of the grasslands show clear differences from the related tribes of the more southerly forests along the Guinea Coast and in the Congo Basin who appear to have mingled with earlier inhabitants, of shorter stature and broader skull-form. These " Palæo-Negro " people of the forests were, moreover, of a lighter skin-colour than the dwellers in the savannas, possibly because the dense vegetation has screened the people from the most intense insolation.

The Eastern Sudanese Negroes, who live in the neighbourhood of the Upper Nile, are sometimes known as Nilotic Negroes or *Nilotes*. They have been so influenced by Hamitic elements that they have been described as merely " Negroid," i.e. Negrolike ; yet they show typical Negro characters quite clearly.

Among them are tribes who are remarkably slimly built and, because of the length of their legs, the tallest in the world.

The Bantu.—From Africa north of the Equator, the great southward road of racial migration has been the relatively open country of the Eastern Highlands, and along this route wave after wave of the Negro race has advanced into all the more habitable parts of the continent. These widespread tribes have mingled with Hamites and with others, such as the Arabs who adventured along the East African coast. Consequently, as regards their physical characters the peoples vary, but they are collectively known as Bantu, because they speak languages of the Bantu family. They generally have the typical woolly hair, but their skin-colour includes brown of several shades as well as almost black, their lips are frequently less thick and their noses less wide than those of the true Negroes. Among the best known of the Bantu are the Baganda, Kikuyu, Masai, Swahili, Matabele, Zulu, Bechuana, Basuto and Swazi peoples. The virile Bantu tribes have exterminated or absorbed most of the earlier inhabitants of Central and South Africa, thrusting the survivors into the least attractive areas.

The people of Madagascar are only in part of Negroid origin, for there have been immigrants from almost all the borderlands of the Indian Ocean. Although the island is relatively near Africa, the strong currents of the Mozambique Channel for long hindered its occupation by the non-seafaring Bantu ; on the other hand, it has been several times reached by the adventurous seafarers of the East Indian Archipelago. These peoples were of Malayan-Polynesian origin, and are of lighter colour ; among them are the Hova, now the dominant group in Madagascar. Arabs also appeared as slave-traders, and recently settlers from India and China have come to the southern part.

Bushmen, Hottentots and Negrillos.—The semi-desert of southwest Africa has formed a refuge for the Bushmen (marked " B " on the map of racial groups on p. 148), who formerly were more widely spread over the south of Africa. Their classification, from the point of view of their derivation, is an unsolved riddle to anthropologists. Their woolly hair is of the Negro type and it is so twisted that it forms close-knotted tufts showing bare skin between them ; on the other hand, their colour is a brownish yellow or yellow-brown like that common among the straight-haired races ; they also show other " Mongolian " characters, including narrow and slanting eyes, recalling those of the peoples of eastern Asia. Their stature is considerably less than that of most other races. Although the physique of the Bushmen has been described as poor, yet they are capable of remarkable endurance, shown, for instance, in running down game till it is exhausted, or in going a long time on very little food ; such a physical characteristic is a necessity for their survival—given their way of life and their environment. The Hottentots, who have a wider distribution in south-west Africa than the Bushmen, are of mixed Bushman and Hamitic or Bantu origin, for while they have hair-form, skin-colour, and some bodily and facial characters like those of the Bushmen, other features and their greater stature seem to be derived from Negroid ancestry. In addition, Bushmen and Hottentots have some bodily characters which are not found among any other present-day racial group, and some which recall those shown on the cave drawings of prehistoric people of Europe.

Another place of refuge from Negro or Negroid invaders is the dense forest on both sides of the Equator. Scattered within its deepest recesses have been found the " pygmies " (marked "P" on the map) who are termed Negrillos. Their facial characters are in general like those of the Negro-like primary race, but their colour is lighter—possibly because the forest has protected them from much intense insolation ; they resemble the Bushmen in having unusually closely intertwining hair. Their stature is considerably less even than that of the Bushmen, and some of the tribes are among the smallest peoples of the world. The Negrillos appear to represent a relatively primitive race, and their pygmy-form is probably a response to long-continued existence in their present environment. In this connection it may be noted that among several species of animals those inhabiting equatorial forests have become smaller than those living in other habitats.

Negritos, Papuans and Melanesians.—On the eastern side of the Indian Ocean there are fewer racial groups of the woolly-haired type. As the pygmy Negrillos have survived in the depths of the African equatorial forests, so other groups of pygmies, known as Negritos, still remain in isolated districts of the forests of south-eastern Asia and the adjoining islands ; e.g. in the Indian Ocean there are the Andaman Islanders and in the Malay Peninsula there are the Semang people. Others of very short stature are found farther east in the Philippine Islands and in New Guinea, where they may perhaps be a modification of the normal population.

In the much-traversed bridge-region of the Malay Archipelago, most traces of the woolly-haired primary race have been wiped out by later comers, especially by those from eastern Asia.   In New Guinea and Melanesia, woolly-haired peoples again predominate.   The people of Melanesia, i.e. the Black Islands, are not actually black but rather chocolate-brown in colour ; their hair is usually woolly and, especially among the Papuans of New Guinea, it is longer than that of African Negroes.   Their stature is generally medium or rather short.   As might be expected from their geographical situation, they have had considerable admixture with groups belonging to the other primary races.   Akin to the Melanesians were the natives of Tasmania, but these people came to an end in the latter part of the nineteenth century.

CHAPTER XI

RACES AND MIGRATIONS (2)

The Straight-haired Division.—The descendants of the straight-haired primary race have occupied practically the whole of eastern and northern Asia ; they have also passed farther eastward by the old land-bridge across Bering Strait and have spread through North and South America (see map on p. 140).

The Tungus Group.—The characters of the straight-haired division of mankind are most clearly shown among the main racial group of north-eastern Asia ; here are observed the typical coarse, straight black hair, the brownish-yellow skin, the narrow, almond-shaped eyes, the rather short and stocky build, the broad, flat face and very broad skull. Because these characters are those of the people of Mongolia, this particular group is sometimes referred to as Mongol or Mongolian, but as these terms are used in other connections it has been given the name Tungus, from the branch which lives in Siberia north of Mongolia. Other Siberian peoples, though not by any means all, belong to the same group, e.g. the Buriat, and also some of those who live on the western side of the Gobi desert region, e.g. the Kalmuk of eastern Turkistan. The Manchus, who made themselves masters of China, were also of this racial group, but at the present time the greater part of the population of Manchuria is the result of migration from China, and therefore belongs to a different category.

The Sinic Group.—Although Sinic means Chinese, it seems better to employ it in this connection, as the latter term may give rise to misunderstanding. The Sinic racial group does not by any means coincide either with the people who belong to the Chinese State or to those who use the Chinese language ; it is represented mainly by the dwellers in the Hwang-Ho basin and in the central and lower parts of the Yangtze basin, with an eastward extension into Korea.

The Sinic people are not such typical " Mongolians " as those of the Tungus group, for their build is rather slighter and taller ; the face has not such a flat appearance ; the skin is paler and is of an almost yellow-olive colour ; even the " Mongolian fold " of the eyelid is less marked.   It may be noted that in spite of the limited extension, as it appears on a map, of the Sinic group, it includes more people than any other in the world.   In repeated drifts, often impelled by famine, people of the Sinic group have moved southward in China, but long ago members of the South Mongoloid racial groups, described in the following paragraph, had advanced northward as far as the Hwang-Ho basin ; thus two types are now mingled in China.

The South Mongoloid Groups.—The racial characters which are most marked among the Tungus group, and less among the Sinic people, are further weakened among the widespread groups classed as Southern Mongoloid.   In southern China and northern Indo-China, the climatic conditions during the period of racial differentiation were so unlike those of the steppes that the " Mongolian " development was not carried to so great a length.   Even among the southern Chinese the skin is perceptibly darker and has a less yellow tinge than in the north, and there are other indications of the differences which are progressively more noticeable towards the south—in Indo-China, in the Malay Peninsula and in the East Indian Archipelago ; e.g. the build becomes slighter and the features and form are more graceful, the hair becomes brown-black rather than black, and smooth rather than straight and coarse, while the true " Mongolian fold " is present only among those whose ancestry includes northern elements.

A westward drift took some of the Southern Mongoloid groups into the cul-de-sac of the Tibetan Plateau, and others made their way across the mountains into the north-east of India.   The main movement, however, was to the south-east ; here this stock became the dominant one among the Malays and the other peoples of the Archipelago, and later advanced north along the island belt off eastern Asia and even reached Japan.

The Japanese are of mixed origin, for there was the aboriginal Ainu element, still extant in the north, and the better-favoured part of the islands has been settled to some extent by Sinic migrants from the adjoining mainland and to a greater extent by shorter and darker Southern Mongoloid peoples.

The Palæo-Arctic Group.—Much of the northern zone of Asia is so remote from the central area of human evolution, and so poor, with its vegetation cover of tundra and scanty coniferous forest, that it became one of the places of refuge for successive peoples. Early groups of the European-like primary race had advanced into the north of Eurasia as the cold of the ice age decreased, and these formed the basis of the population of this region ; upon this stock were superimposed various drifts of the Mongolian-like peoples who worked their way northward in Asia, apparently before acquiring the most marked of the Mongolian characters. As a result, the racial characters of the present population are rather indeterminate—transitional between those of the two primary races which have contributed to their ancestry. The stature of the people is short, and this has been attributed to their unfavourable environment, but as a rule they are well built and hardy.

These Palæo-Arctic peoples still live in the far north-east of Asia and, while they have mainly been displaced from the central part of the northern belt of the continent, they remain also in the north-west and extend into the north of European Russia and, as Lapps, even into Scandinavia. It was the Palæo-Arctic group that gave an Asiatic ancestral stock to the Finns, and the group is sometimes known as Ugrian or Ugro-Finn because of the languages spoken by some of its members.

Racial Groups of America.—At the time of the retreat of the ice, when man was pushing his way into the newly accessible lands, the Bering land-bridge allowed a series of movements from Asia to North America. It is quite possible that there had been still earlier migrations to America, but these post-glacial drifts resulted in the north-west of the American continent being inhabited by peoples resembling those of the northern belt of Asia, and they continued their way eastward wherever the environment was the same as that to which they had adapted themselves. A general name for these tundra folk of America and Greenland is Eskimo ; although they vary to some extent they are mostly rather short and their eyes are narrow, though the Mongolian fold is not usually present.

Other groups of somewhat similar origin, probably including no large number of persons, pursued more southerly routes, and while the earlier of these, generally showing more of the European-like characters, were pushed farthest towards the south and east, the later ones of more clearly Mongoloid stock spread over the greater part of the two continents.

Most of the native peoples of the Americas, to denote whom

the term " Amerinds " has been coined, are more or less straight-haired and, like the straight-haired races of Asia, are inclined to be broad-skulled. Yet they do not normally show the characteristic Mongolian eye-fold, and the prevailing skin-colour is brown of various tones—sometimes yellowish, and sometimes the " red " or " copper " tint far too widely attributed to the " Red Indians." Their facial appearance in some parts resembles that of the Mongoloid groups, but elsewhere it is quite different and is characterized by a sharp profile ; their stature and build also vary considerably.

Moreover, it appears that the various Amerind peoples have not lived long enough in their particular and strongly contrasted environments for the evolution of local adaptations, e.g. their colouration does not show any clear gradation from pale to dark according to latitude ; even in the regions of greatest insolation there are not " black " tribes like those of the Old World. This is but one example of a relative lack of physical adaptation among the peoples of the western hemisphere, and in some areas this is a definite handicap ; thus, in the Amazon Lowland the natives are to a considerable extent descended from stocks evolved in cool, dry steppe-lands and they still suffer considerably from being physiologically unable to stand the great heat and moisture—an obvious factor in hindering both the past and the future utilization of that region.

Recent Migrations.—During the last 300 years there have occurred movements of population of the first importance, for in the fifteenth and sixteenth centuries began the " geographical revolution," i.e. the great discoveries of the New World and of ocean ways to all parts of the globe, together with continued improvements in travel and transport ; these developments made it possible for Europeans to occupy vast areas in other continents, and also to drive out or even exterminate peoples of other races in distant regions. Further, the coming of the machine age, with improved methods in all forms of production, allowed great increases of population first in Europe and then in other continents. Other causes, such as the trade in slaves from Africa to the Americas, and the stimulation of the Far East to economic and political developments, contributed to complicated racial changes which went on at a rate unprecedented in the history of mankind.

Europe.—For various reasons, within this continent there

have been repeated shiftings of population, and therefore further complexity among the racial elements ; one consequence is that the inhabitants of the various political States now show even less signs of belonging to any particular racial group.

In the nineteenth century and the first part of the twentieth century, overseas migrations took place on the largest scale ; but after the First World War and the world-wide depression which began in 1929 there was very considerable restriction of immigration by the countries overseas which had previously allowed or welcomed it, viz. the United States, several States of South America, and the British Dominions. European advances over distant regions of the world greatly slackened, though the devastations and persecutions of the Second World War stimulated their renewal on a smaller scale.

The Americas.—The migration of Europeans to the two Americas was mainly to the mid-latitude regions, and it has brought about an extensive mingling of races.

It is estimated that in pre-Columbian times there were over a million Indians in what are now the United States and Canada ; conflicts between them and the white settlers, the effects of disease and drink brought by the latter, the expulsion of the Indians from their lands, the break-up of their simple economic and social systems—these factors reduced them to much less than half a million by the end of the nineteenth century, but since then their numbers appear to remain about stationary. Of these, however, a considerable proportion are half-breeds, and also there is a certain amount of Indian blood among the population regarded as of European descent.

At about the beginning of the nineteenth century, there was a great development of the trade in African slaves to provide labour for the plantations of sub-tropical products, mainly cotton, and there has been intermingling between the " Whites " and the " Blacks." At the present time, those regarded as " Negroes " form about 10 per cent. of the total population of the United States.

On the Pacific side of North America there has been an immigration of members of the " Yellow race," Japanese and Chinese, but this has been restricted as much as possible because of a fear of their too-great success in economic competition, and because of the objection to a foreign element which cannot be assimilated to the European population and to their type of culture. Thus, north of the Tropic of Cancer the great majority of the population is derived from European stock.

Although the West Indies are within the Tropics, their maritime situation so ameliorates their climate that the descendants of the Spanish and other European conquerors and immigrants have managed to survive, though after a heavy toll of health and life. The Indian tribes were practically wiped out by one means or another, and Negro slave labour was imported. Consequently, on some of the islands, e.g. Cuba and Puerto Rico, the majority of the population is now of European descent and the minority is of Negro or mixed origin, while on other islands, e.g. Jamaica and Hispaniola, the converse is the case.

Over the larger part of Mexico, Central America and South America, Europeans still form a minority. Between the Tropics no large proportion of the New World appears suitable for permanent settlement by people of the White racial groups ; apart from the highlands, where settlement is limited by need for irrigation, the main areas of South America which offer to Europeans healthy conditions of life are in southern Brazil, Uruguay, Argentina and part of Chile. Only in these areas is the population now largely composed of immigrants—Spanish, Portuguese, Italian or German—or their descendants.

Most of the equatorial and tropical regions of the western hemisphere have presented such great obstacles, climatic and other, to European occupation that they are inhabited either by a scanty population of American Indians or by one of mixed origin in which the proportion of Indian ancestry is considerable ; there is not in " Latin America," i.e. in the countries in which the official language is Spanish or Portuguese, the same prejudice against intermingling of race that is found in " English-speaking America." Moreover, Negro slaves were brought into some inter-tropical parts of the mainland ; as they are well adapted to the physical conditions, their descendants are increasing in number and their interbreeding with Indian and European people has introduced further complications. The extraordinarily varied racial composition of the populations of the central parts of the New World has contributed to the difficulties in social, economic and political development which will be described later.

Africa.—In recent times, there has been a small-scale migration of people from southern Europe across the Mediterranean

Sea into northern Africa.   Important movements of population
affected the whole of Africa south of the Sahara, after the sea-
way was opened about the beginning of the sixteenth century.
The slave trade probably resulted in a total loss of about twenty
millions of people from the inter-tropical regions.   It was
accompanied and followed by movements in the reverse direction : Europeans landed at various points along the coasts, but
the main settlements were made by the Dutch and British in
the extreme south of the continent.   Here climatic conditions
were found suitable but the area of productive land was small,
and the Europeans worked their way north-eastward to the
relatively cool plateaus of South Africa ; they have also made
small settlements at a number of points in the belt of East
African Uplands.   Their northward advance was opposed by
Bantu tribes who, moving southward, were conquering the
same lands from less warlike inhabitants but now gave way,
in their turn, to the better-armed Europeans.

Most of the White people live south of the Tropic of Capricorn.
In the Union of South Africa they number about one-fifth of the
inhabitants ; the bulk of the population are of African descent,
but there is a relatively small group of mixed origin.   On the
equatorial side of the Tropic, white settlers are few and form
but a small minority of the population.

Over much of South and East Africa there have been attempts
at immigration from Asia—in this case from the nearer lands
which border the Indian Ocean.   On the whole, the Indians are
not welcome to the Europeans, and their influx has been
restricted ; they number only about 250,000 persons.

Australia, New Zealand and the Pacific Islands.—The occupation of Australia by the British during the past 150 years
was hindered by the difficult conditions of the continent much
more than by the resistance of the Natives, few in number and
at a low stage of cultural development.   The aboriginal people
have been driven out of most of the regions open to European
settlement, though a Native Reserve has been formed in central
Australia, and probably only about 50,000 full-blooded Natives
remain in the arid and semi-arid interior and in the hot and
wet northern coastal lands ; there are also about the same
number of half-breeds, and these seem able to maintain
themselves and even to show an increase.   The one or two
thousand aborigines who lived in Tasmania when the White

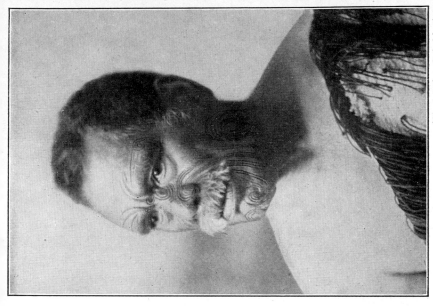

[Royal Anthropological Institute

Left: AN INDO-AFGHAN

This man of Kashmir is allied to the racial groups of Southern Europe. His ancestors migrated eastwards at a recent period in the history of mankind, and his skin colour is light brown though hair and eyes are dark. His face is long and his nose is prominent, his lips are rather thick but by no means negroid. He is well built, and taller than most Europeans.

Right: A MAORI

The Maori represent the Polynesian racial group; they obviously belong to the wavy-haired division of mankind, in spite of a limited amount of mingling with Melanesian and possibly Asiatic, earlier migrants into the Pacific region. They are generally tall and of powerful build. This Maori is of a past generation, as shown by the dress and tattooings; apart from these cultural indications he might be taken for a dark European.

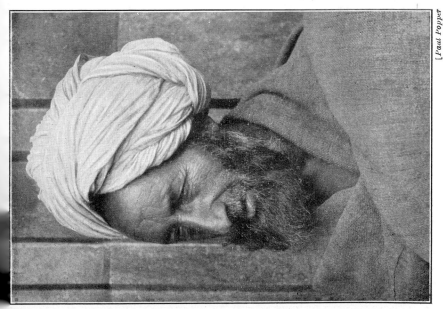

[Paul Popper

Left: AN AINU

The Ainu live in northernmost Japan and adjoining islands. They have been driven from the continent of Asia, but do not show Mongolian features and are characterised by the abundance of wavy and very dark hair on face and body. They probably evolved in north-western Asia, and their skin is lighter than that of most racial groups, often with a rosy tint over the cheeks. They are thickset, and of moderate or rather short stature.

Right: A NATIVE AUSTRALIAN

The wavy character of the hair is clearly shown, and in their general hairiness the Australian aborigines somewhat resemble the Ainu; the beard hides the prominence of the jaw. The frowning appearance is due to the forehead overhanging sunken eyes, with a deep notch above the bridge of the broad nose. The stature is generally short; this man is about 5 feet 1 inch in height. His age is only 21 years.

[Paul Popper]

Left : **TWO NEGROES**

Both live in Southern Nigeria, but the boy shows characteristics which suggest a Central African, Negrillo, element in his ancestry. The hair is of the tufted or "peppercorn" variety, in which the hairs wind round one another and thus leave patches of almost bare skin. Adaptation to the hot, moist climate is shown by a projecting mouth with everted lips, and by the nose, which has broad wings and open nostrils.

Right : **A CHINESE AND HIS GRANDSON**

The man shows the typical Mongolian characters of long, lank hair on the head but a scant beard and moustache ; his eyes are almond-shaped with the skin of the upper lids drawn down over their inner sides. The baby has the Mongolian type of eye and the commonly broad forehead, but his snub nose is a normal feature of childhood and will probably grow into the usual projecting form.

[*M. Lubinski*]

Left : AN ESKIMO

Northern Mongolian elements in the origins of the Eskimo peoples are obvious : straight, black hair ; narrow eyes, occasionally with the Mongolian fold of the upper lids ; a generally broad face with high cheekbones and rather prominent nose. Also, many Canadian Eskimo have broad skulls and flat faces, but those of Greenland, farther from the Asiatic source, have narrow heads and more finely formed noses. The stature is usually short.

Right : A MALAY

All three great divisions of mankind are represented and mingled in Malaya : aborigines have come from woolly-haired, negroid stocks ; most immigrants belonged to the straight-haired, Mongolian division ; wavy-haired groups have passed across this bridge-place. The Malay here shown appears to combine elements of the three types : nose and mouth may indicate negroid descent, eyes may suggest Mongolian ancestry, while the hair is wavy.

men arrived have been exterminated by slaughter, drink and disease.

On the Pacific coasts of Australia, as on the Pacific coasts of America, there have been Japanese and Chinese immigrants, but their settlement was met by the same kind of opposition as in North America. It was therefore checked by immigration laws which applied also to labourers brought from various Pacific islands ; in the place of these " Coloured " immigrants the east coast of tropical Queensland has now been settled by White people, mainly of British, but partly of Italian, origin. Immigration into Australia is subject to a firmly held " White Australia " policy.

The Maori of New Zealand were of finer physique and higher cultural development than the aborigines of Australia, and although during the nineteenth century wars both between the various tribes and also with the British settlers reduced their numbers, they have been able to adapt themselves to the new conditions. They have begun to take an active part in the economic and political life of the Dominion, especially in the warmer North Island, and with a relatively small number of half-breeds they are increasing in number ; yet they count only about 100,000 persons.

The Pacific Islanders seem to be dying out. On some islands the process had begun before the coming of the Europeans and was due to constant warfare and ways of life that allowed the spread of diseases and the decline of the population. New diseases brought by the white men caused even greater mortality, and the sale of alcohol and arms increased the degeneration and death-roll. The kidnapping of labourers for plantations in distant regions also decreased the native population in some parts. On the other hand, there has been a considerable influx of settlers from the Malay Region and the Monsoon Lands, especially from Japan. The number of Polynesians is only about 200,000, and that of the Micronesians half as great, but in New Guinea and the other islands of the Melanesian group, where the physical conditions do not encourage settlement of people from mid-latitude climates, the Natives number over a million and there have been relatively few immigrants.

The East Indies and Asia.—In these regions there have been no great recent alterations in the racial composition of the populations, but marked changes in the total numbers of the people. Most of the East Indian Archipelago and much of the south-east of Asia succumbed to the political dominance of Britain, France and the Netherlands, but the climate has prevented their occupation by Europeans ; the government officials, merchants, plantation managers and other white people have been mainly " sojourners " who remain only for a term of years and do not attempt to bring up their families in these regions. Two results of the European dominance were to increase production and therefore the capacity of the land to support more people, and to reduce the death-roll from disease, famine and warfare. Hence there have been some extraordinary increases in the native populations. This is the case notably in Java where the number has mounted from probably less than five millions at the beginning of the nineteenth century to nearly fifty millions at the present time, including about half a million Chinese and far fewer Europeans. India is another important example of a great increase in the native population, for while at the time of the first census in 1872 there were just over 200 million people, there are now about 400 millions, and Europeans are numerically insignificant.

In the extra-tropical parts of the Monsoon Lands European influence has been less direct. Japan has adopted many western methods, and her population has doubled in the last sixty years ; China conserved longer her old ways and, already densely populated, has experienced a smaller increase in her numbers. From both these crowded countries, as already indicated, there have been movements of people to various islands and coast-lands of the Pacific.

Northern and western Asia are, on the whole, still occupied by small numbers of people ; during the nineteenth century, Russia established its rule over a very large part of these areas and, especially during recent years, there has been an eastward movement of people of European origin into northern Asia.

Consequences of Migrations.—Some of the consequences of the movements of peoples, during man's evolution and history, may now be summarized. His physical characters have been very slowly adapted to new environments ; in early times these changes brought about the differences between the great divisions and in the racial groups of man, but recent migrations have not resulted in any comparably marked modifications in biological make-up. Yet these migrations have produced a weeding-out of individuals.   When some members of a community have sought new homes, it is usually the more active who have started off ; certainly, hardships and dangers have been encountered and as a rule only the strongest and the most enduring have survived long migrations.   If such a process is continued or repeated for a number of generations there is a stringent natural selection of the best-equipped strains.

Further, the movements commonly result in inter-breeding and the production of mixed types, and the question may be put whether the process of race mingling is " good " or " bad." What is clear is that the individuals in the new generations show a greater variety of *combinations* of physical characters, i.e. they possess greater potentialities, and from them Nature tends to select those with the greatest survival value.   There are abundant instances of individuals and of peoples who have originated from the combination of different races and have " made their mark " in the world ; pride and prejudice may urge " race purity," but science and history may make out a better case for " race mingling."   Even when it is a question of inter-breeding between representatives of widely different primary races, e.g. between Europeans and Mongolians or between Europeans and Negroes, there is no evidence that deterioration results.   It must be remembered that here it is a question only of physical qualities ; cultural and social disabilities may result, at least temporarily, from racial inter-breeding, and these will be dealt with later.

Mental Characters and Racial Groups.—It is frequently asserted that one race differs from another by such traits as bravery or cowardice, enterprise or conservatism, excitability or stolidity, etc., but it is very doubtful whether such mental characteristics have any *racial* relationship.   For example, in any racial group individuals appear to differ widely from one another in such respects.   Also, a body of people may show special mental traits, not due to race but to the environment or the way of life ; e.g. a fishing community must show bravery if it is to get its food, while in some agricultural communities bravery is not so essential as capacity for unremitting toil. In consequence, tradition counts for a great deal in determining a mode of behaviour.   Some particular kind of conduct is regarded as useful or necessary by a community, and this conduct is enforced on the rising generations perhaps over long periods ; thus it comes to be characteristic of the group. But it is not part of the biological heritage and therefore inherent ; it is a product of " nurture " and not of " nature." Under different circumstances, perhaps as a result of migration or of historical changes, the community may cease to encourage the earlier type of conduct and may display others hitherto not brought into prominence.

It is important to point out that ideas of right and wrong, and standards of moral conduct, have nothing whatever to do with racial origin.

Great caution must be employed in judging whether any race is higher or lower than another in general intelligence. Europeans, for example, may regard people of Africa or Asia as of lower intelligence than themselves, because the latter are accustomed to their own modes of thought and cannot readily deal with ideas which are strange to them ; yet few Europeans have been able to comprehend the modes of thought and ideas of men of other types of culture, as skilled anthropological research has revealed them.

Moreover, it must be remembered that a large proportion of the " backward " peoples suffer from lifelong malnutrition and chronic diseases—factors which seriously affect physical and mental health and prevent innate capacity from finding its normal expression. The hookworm disease may be cited, for it is widely spread in equatorial and tropical regions and appears even beyond the Tropics. In some inter-tropical areas almost all the population are subject to it, with the result that their vitality is lowered and their activity, endurance and persistence in effort are greatly reduced. The disease is due to a parasite which generally infects man by piercing the feet ; its extirpation, and with it the disappearance of characteristics formerly put down to " laziness " or " lack of moral fibre," is a matter of education in hygienic habits.

To get over some of the difficulties involved in racial comparisons, psychologists have tried to devise suitable forms of intelligence tests, but an experienced anthropologist [1] has summed up their results, spread over many years and affecting many peoples, as " erratic and contrary."

Finally, it must be once more emphasized that relatively

[1] Dr. F. G. Nadel, Government Anthropologist, Anglo-Egyptian Sudan, in a study of " Racial Intelligence."

great mental contrasts exist within the membership of any particular ethnic group. The conclusion of a biological investigator is : " In really important characteristics the natural differences between the races pale into insignificance as compared with the natural differences between individuals."[1] To this dictum we may add the practical deduction of another anthropologist : " In all stocks individuals differ in ability, and civilization will always be the poorer if we close the gates of opportunity to those of superior ability whatever their blood may be."[2]

[1] H. J. Muller, in *Out of the Night : a Biologist's View of the Future*.
[2] Dr. R. Benedict, in *Race and Racism*.

CHAPTER XII

CULTURAL ADVANCES—LANGUAGES AND RELIGIONS

Cultural Developments.—Distinct from the physical evolution of man are his many-sided cultural advances ; these have been made among many racial groups and in many conditions and environments, and have spread gradually among the peoples and over the regions of the world. A fundamental development of mankind was that of speech and language, and with it have grown up ideas and knowledge of all kinds. In this chapter the chief language groups will be considered first, and then the great world religions, in so far as they affect the thought and actions of large sections of mankind and have geographical results.

Throughout a consideration of cultural developments it is necessary to bear in mind that they are not limited to special racial groups, but may be accepted by, or imposed upon, people descended from any physical stock. Indeed, the spread of cultural conditions is largely determined by geographical conditions, such as accessibility, which helps contacts between particular peoples, and climate, which may or may not help the peoples to apply and develop knowledge gained by such contacts.

LANGUAGES

Languages in relation to Races and Migrations.—Although communications over considerable distances are now relatively easy, understanding between peoples is still hindered by the existence of hundreds of distinct languages ; many of these are still further divided by dialects, which may differ so much that those who speak them cannot be understood even by comparatively near neighbours.

There are two main causes for this complexity of tongues. In the first place, languages themselves evolve. As time goes on, the speech of a group of people gradually changes, particularly when their mode of life alters. Because of this evolution, a single language spoken in different areas tends to develop into different dialects or even into distinct languages.

Much more rapid changes have been brought about by movements of people from one region to another. The great migrations of peoples have been among the chief causes of the spread of languages over the world, and therefore there is a broad correspondence between the distribution of the racial groups as shown on p. 148 and that of languages as shown on p. 172. There are, however, a number of differences between the two distributions where contact of peoples has resulted in a group losing their earlier mode of speech and acquiring a new one. For example, invaders have sometimes imposed their languages upon others of different descent ; on the other hand, when the conquering group has been small, and particularly when it has consisted mainly of warriors without their families, the intruders may have been absorbed by the subject people and their language fallen into disuse. In both cases, however, there would have been alterations in the surviving speech.

To some extent, the difficulties of a multiplicity of tongues have been lessened by the spread of a few languages for certain limited purposes ; a *lingua franca* of this kind may be used over wide areas where it is understood by some, at least, of the inhabitants. Thus, English is employed in the British Colonies by merchants, planters and officials, and by those Natives who come into contact with them. A more systematic development has taken place in the U.S.S.R., for not only in Europe, but practically throughout the Asiatic territories (where attendance at school is both compulsory and free of charge), the children of the many racial groups, speaking many tongues, are all taught Russian as a second language, while this is also the one language employed in the army.

Language Families and their Distribution.—*Indo-European Family.*—Most languages have others with which they are similar because they have evolved from a common ancestor. Thus English, Dutch, German and the Scandinavian languages resemble one another in many ways ; they have spread from central Europe with conquests of Teutonic tribes and are collectively known as Teutonic languages. In their westward spread they have driven out Celtic forms of speech, which now survive in the Erse of Ireland, Gaelic of Scotland, and Welsh, together with the Breton of north-western France. Another

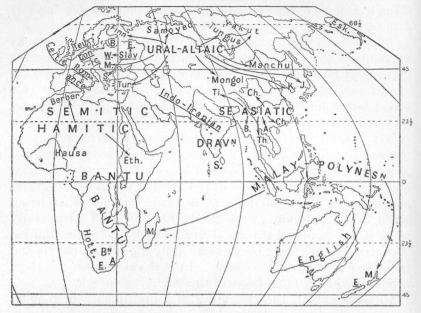

FIG. 43.—LANGUAGES OF THE EASTERN HEMISPHERE.

Note.—Languages and language groups belonging to the Indo-European family are underlined ; names of other families are in capital letters.

The arrows show the relationships of languages to their families, but not necessarily the routes by which they have spread.

European group is that of the Romance languages derived from Latin, viz. Italian, French, Spanish, Portuguese and Romanian, while Modern Greek is the representative of Classical Greek.

In some parts of Europe only one language is spoken over fairly large areas, as is the case in Sweden and in Peninsular Italy. In many parts of the continent, however, two, three or more languages are found within short distances, while quite commonly their areas are dovetailed into one another like the pieces of a jigsaw puzzle. Also, there are regions in which some people are bi-lingual, e.g. many Welsh speak Welsh and English, and there are often " islands " of alien speech within the general sphere of a dominant language. Thus only a relatively large-scale map can show the tangle of languages in such a region as western and central Europe, and the map in Fig. 43 can do no more than attempt to indicate the broad distribution of the main groups. It must also be emphasized that there is no close correspondence between the racial origins and speech of European people. Thus, although many who are largely of Nordic descent speak a Teutonic language, yet so do also many whose ancestry is largely Alpine or Mediterranean ; again, people whose physical characters are Mediterranean may employ Celtic, Teutonic, Romance or Greek speech.

All these European languages have certain similarities and form one branch of a numerous family of languages which are spoken over the region from the North Atlantic Ocean to the Sea of Bengal ; because of its distribution this great group is, as a whole, known as the *Indo-European* (or less accurately the Indo-Germanic) *family.* The likeness between these languages is due to the fact that they are all derived from the speech of the groups of wavy-haired peoples who worked their way from south-western Asia westward and northward through Europe and south-eastward across India.

Another European branch of the great Indo-European family includes Albanian, the Baltic languages Lithuanian and Lettish, and the Slavonic languages. In these last are comprised three groups : the East Slav tongues of the Russians, the West Slav group including Polish, Czech and Slovak, and the South Slav group with Serbian, Croatian, Slovene, Bulgarian and other languages and dialects.

The third branch of the great Indo-European family of languages is known as Indo-Iranian, or sometimes as Aryan.[1] The name Indo-Iranian is used because it broadly indicates the area in which the languages of this branch are spoken, comprising Iranian (i.e. Persian) and the tongues of the greater part of India. There are many Indian languages belonging to this branch ; among them Hindostani (or Hindustani) may be specially mentioned, as it has been deliberately adapted for use as a *lingua franca* over much of India. English, too, serves as a *lingua franca* for many of the educated people of India.

Quite different languages have been carried from the steppe-lands of Central Asia into the more northern parts of that continent and also into parts of northern and eastern Europe. These languages originating in the Asiatic steppes are named, after districts from which they have spread, the *Ural-Altaic family.* In Asia they include, among others, the Tungus,

---

[1] " Aryan " is correctly used only as a name for certain languages or for the people who long ago spoke those languages. The terms " Aryan " and " non-Aryan " have also been wrongly, though popularly, used in quite different senses, e.g. as applied to present-day racial groups, or to nationalities, or even to religious communities, but such usages result only in muddled thinking.

Mongol and Manchu tongues spoken by groups of straight-haired peoples, while in western regions peoples of more mixed racial origin speak the allied Turkish, Magyar (Hungarian), and Finnish languages.

In and around the great belt of arid or semi-arid country which stretches from south-western Asia through the Saharan region to the Atlantic Ocean, including the fertile river valleys of the Nile and Mesopotamia, there has spread the *Semitic family* of languages. To this family belonged the ancient Hebrew and Assyrian (or Babylonian) languages, and the most important modern representative is Arabic which, centuries ago, was imposed by Arab invaders upon many of the peoples of south-west Asia and northern Africa. Hence Arabian dialects are spoken by most of the inhabitants of Iraq, Syria, Arabia and Egypt, and by many of the people of the Saharan region and of the Atlas Lands from Tripoli to Morocco.

The *Hamitic family* of languages, which included ancient Egyptian, is still represented in the speech of the inhabitants of large parts of northern Africa. To this family belong the speech of three groups of people : (1) many of the Ethiopians or Abyssinians, and the neighbouring tribes of the Upper Nile region and Somaliland ; (2) the Berbers of north-west Africa, and a number of the tribes of the oases and marginal areas of the Sahara as far west as Senegal ; (3) the Hausa of the central Sudanese savannas. Although they speak an Hamitic language, the Hausa are themselves largely of Negro descent and their speech has been transmitted also to other Negro groups; indeed, the use of the Hausa tongue as a *lingua franca* has spread over a large area between northern and central Africa.

The *Bantu family* of languages has spread over most of Africa south of the sphere of the Hamitic tongues. Bantu-speaking tribes have themselves occupied much of the continent, and they have imposed their speech also upon other peoples whom they have dominated ; even some pygmy tribes of the equatorial forests speak degraded forms of Bantu. There are a large number of languages in this family, and they have many dialects ; among these dialects is Swahili, which was first spoken in Zanzibar by people of mixed Bantu and Arab descent and is now a *lingua franca* understood throughout the coastal districts of East Africa and even in parts of southern Arabia and in Madagascar.

The *Bushman* and *Hottentot* languages are very similar to each other but very different from those of the Bantu, although minglings of the two types have occurred. The speech of the Bushmen, and to a less extent that of the Hottentots, is peculiar in making great use of four different " clicks " or clucking-sounds, which have given to some Europeans the impression of an uncouth tongue, and the Dutch settlers compared their speech to the gobbling of a turkey-cock ; yet scientific examination has shown that " the language in its grammatical structure is beautiful and regular."

In the Union of South Africa there are two languages of equal status : English and Afrikaans ; the latter is a derivative of Dutch and is spoken mainly by people of Dutch descent.

Although Madagascar is relatively close to Africa, the Malagasy language which is spoken by practically all the inhabitants belongs to the great *Malay-Polynesian* family, for it has been brought by migrants from the East Indian Archipelago.

The many movements of peoples into and through the island groups of the East Indies and the south-western part of the Pacific have brought about a mingling and similarity of the tongues in this area. Yet, together with resemblances, there are also marked differences, as would be expected where many communities are to a considerable degree isolated in their island homes. Hence the term Malay-Polynesian family is used to cover a wide range of languages, including that of the Maori in New Zealand. The Malay language itself has spread from the neighbouring islands to the Peninsula, and related tongues have been carried northward to the Philippine Islands.

The *Dravidian family* of languages has extended over practically the whole of southern India, having been imposed upon many of the Pre-Dravidian inhabitants ; on the other side, the Dravidian tongues have been driven from northern India by the Aryan languages of later invaders, though in some transitional districts there are dialects combining elements from both sources. In southern India, besides the dialects of relatively remote tribes, the Dravidian family includes four great languages which possess their own literatures ; of these, Telugu and Tamil are spoken by the greatest number of people. Tamil has extended into northern Ceylon, but over the greater part of that island the common language is Sinhalese which has resulted from the modification of a Dravidian tongue by Aryan-speaking invaders.

The *South-east Asiatic family* of languages, of which *Chinese* is typical, stands apart from others by being monosyllabic, and having no grammatical inflexions.

The written language of the Chinese is not formed by a relatively few letters combined in various ways to make different words, but by a very large number of distinct characters ; these are like small pictures simplified in order to be produced by a few strokes of a brush, each character representing some particular object or idea or spoken sound. The Chinese language, with some thousands of such picture-words, is a difficult one to learn, and especially so to foreigners since the gradation of sounds cannot be represented by European letters. Hence the Chinese language itself has proved a hindrance to communication between " East " and " West."

The same written characters are used all over China and therefore form a means of communication among those of the Chinese people who can read and write. The spoken tongue, however, has local dialects in certain regions, especially in Canton and the south-east coastal provinces where they are so marked as to form quite distinct languages. Differences in speech have been a handicap to the unity of the Chinese nation, but this difficulty was lessened by the spread of one dialect, viz. that of Pekin, which is commonly known as Mandarin ; this is now the common form of Chinese and is understood by the people of the greater part of the country. Monosyllabic languages allied to Chinese are those of Annam, Thailand (Siam), Tibet and Burma. In India, Tibetan-Burmese dialects have spread into the province of Assam and the Himalayan borderlands.

Although Chinese ideas and modes of life have influenced the peoples of *Korea* and *Japan*, the languages of these two countries do not belong to the South-east Asiatic family ; they are polysyllabic and appear to be related to the Altaic group. The Koreans have an alphabet for their written language, though Chinese characters are also used. The Japanese have also adopted Chinese characters, but these indicate Japanese spoken words which are entirely different from those of the Chinese.

It may here be noted that printing was first employed in China, and the use of wooden blocks each bearing one character can be traced back to the sixth century. The method spread to Japan, and the Koreans used metal for this purpose in the fifteenth century, some time before printing from type was invented in Europe.

In the *New World*, the speech of the American Indians consisted of an immense number of Amerind languages and dialects which differed greatly among themselves and were not, as a whole, related to those of the Old World. Over much of the continent they have been displaced by European tongues, and here it can be noted only that in the extreme north all the Eskimo of the tundra speak dialects of the same language ; this is quite distinct from the dialects of the Indians of the adjoining forests.

Three European languages have now spread over much of the New World. North of the Mexican border English is the dominant speech, and the United States and Canada together are often referred to as " English-speaking America " ; the chief exception is that French is the language of most of the people of the Canadian province of Quebec. South of the United States is " Latin America," where Spanish and Portuguese are the most important languages. In most of the South American States Spanish is the official speech although in the more remote areas of the interior Indian tongues have persisted. In Brazil the dominant language is Portuguese, though in the south of that country many people of German and Italian origin retain their own speech.

English has spread to some of the West Indian islands, into the cooler parts of eastern and southern Africa, and over Australia and New Zealand.

RELIGIONS

The religions of peoples have geographical relationships ; e.g. on the one hand the spread of particular religions into certain regions was influenced by position and other natural conditions, while on the other hand the beliefs of a particular group of people may have a great effect on their work, mode of life, government and relations with other groups. It is such geographical aspects of religions that are considered here.

Primitive Forms.—The religious ideas of mankind, like languages, have evolved in the various parts of the world in

diverse ways and to different degrees.   In climatically unfavourable regions of inter-tropical and sub-arctic latitudes and also
in remote districts where people have been isolated from contact
with others, man's advance has been slow and primitive forms
of religion still remain (see map on p. 180).   These forms are very
numerous, but many of them may be grouped under the term
" animism."

Animism connotes a belief in spirits which dwell in many
or all the objects forming man's environment—both animate,
such as plants and animals, and inanimate, such as rocks and
rivers, fire and water, the earth and the weather.   Spirits or
evil influences are regarded as the cause of illnesses and acci-
dents which may befall men and beasts.   A very widely held
belief is that of the transmigration of souls, according to which
the souls of men and the spirits of animals are transferred at
death to the bodies of other men or animals ; it may be into a
lower form of life as a punishment or into a higher form of life
as a reward.

Commonly, spirits which bring good fortune are worshipped
as gods, while those which have evil effects are feared as devils.
Men therefore seek to propitiate the spirits by various means :
sacrifices are made, charms are devised and incantations are
performed.   Practically all the activities of people are involved
in these animistic beliefs, and their actions are regulated
accordingly ; often the ordinary work of tilling the soil and
tending the animals must be carried out with a fixed ritual
having a religious compulsion.   Hence the beliefs and the
everyday life are bound up together in a complicated system
which hinders religious advance and mental development in
general, and also material improvements.

Hinduism.—This term is used to cover the multitudinous
religious beliefs and the connected social organizations of the
Hindus who form the majority of the population in the greater
part of India.   These ideas and customs have developed over a
period of nearly 4,000 years, in connection with the migrations
into India of the Aryan-speaking people and with their contacts
with the other inhabitants of the region.

At a very early time, about 1,000–1,500 B.C., the Vedic
hymns already showed lofty philosophic, religious and moral
ideas.   At a later stage the Brahman religion evolved with its
conceptions of one spirit pervading the whole universe and a

trinity of divine personalities ; at this period, too, grew up myths of many lower gods and heroes and other manifestations of the divine essence. Bound up with these ideas and legends was the doctrine of " karma," i.e. the inevitable consequence of good or bad actions showing itself in the fate of individuals and in the transmigration of their souls into a higher or lower state. Hinduism suffered further changes over many centuries, and was corrupted by the fusion of beliefs held by the animistic tribes whom the Aryan-speaking peoples conquered.

Hence the forms of the religion now differ greatly among the population of India, and many deities are worshipped. The religion of large numbers of the people has been described as a religious chaos. The observances, rites and customs dependent upon these beliefs are equally numerous and complicated ; indeed, the lower types of Hinduism cannot be distinguished from animism. Yet, at the other extreme, educated Hindus have developed the earlier Brahman ideas into philosophic conceptions of a high order.

Essentially bound up with the Hindu religion is the caste system which probably had its origins in primitive beliefs and practices. In India it was sanctified and strongly enforced by religion, and it was used as a means of keeping apart the lighter-skinned Aryan conquerors from the earlier inhabitants, and of ensuring special respect for the priestly and warrior classes of the invaders. The early caste system divided the people into four distinct groups : (1) the Brahmans—the priests and spiritual leaders ; (2) the warriors and nobles—from whom the modern Hindu Rajputs claim descent ; (3) the traders, pastoralists and cultivators ; (4) Sudras, the low caste of the labourers, descendants of the darker peoples whom the immigrant rulers admitted into their society to perform necessary menial tasks. In connection with their work, the Sudras are now divided into more than 2,000 minor castes and sub-castes, and they form a large proportion of the population.

In this way the people of all India where Hinduism is practised are divided into distinct compartments or strata, far more rigorously separated than any classes in the Western world. The castes are hereditary, and in general marriages are restricted to those within each caste. The members of each caste are distinguished by their clothing or some obvious badge, and they may not closely associate nor eat with those of other castes.

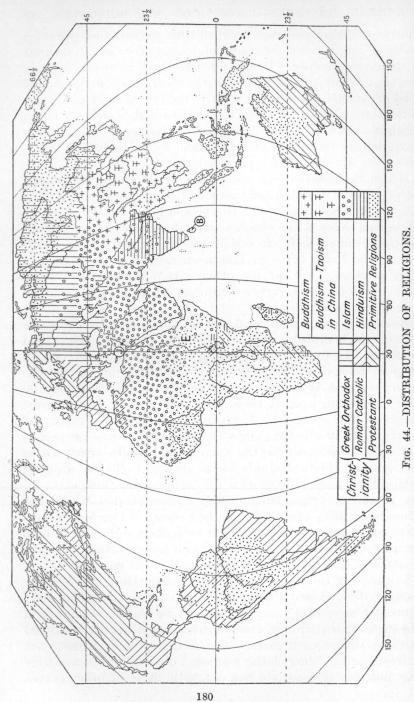

FIG. 44.—DISTRIBUTION OF RELIGIONS.

Note.—Markings indicate the most commonly held beliefs; it is not possible to show intensity of feeling, indifference, or many overlappings. J = Judaism in Palestine;
P = Buddhism in Ceylon; E = Ethiopian forms of Christianity and also Judaism and Islam.

Frequently the castes are identified with particular occupations, and the work which men do is therefore fixed from generation to generation.

There are also the " depressed classes," who number about one-fifth of the Hindus. They are largely the descendants of pre-Aryan peoples never admitted to the ordinary caste system although they have their own caste groups ; even though they may worship some of the Hindu deities they are excluded, as a rule, from the temples. They have been known as the " untouchables " to most of the high-caste Hindus because contact with them causes religious pollution, and to them the most " unclean " tasks are assigned. British officials preferred to call them the " scheduled castes," but British insistence upon their legal rights, e.g. to attend state-aided schools, sometimes broke down before religious ideas and traditional customs.

The " outcastes " are the people regarded by Hindus as quite outside their community : members of sects which have broken away from the common Hindu faith ; those who practise some other religion of India—Muslims, Parsis and Buddhists ; primitive tribesmen of animistic belief, such as Gonds, Bhils and " pariah " groups ; British and other recent immigrants.

It is easy to see how the caste system imposes upon Hindus a strict conservatism in many spheres of life. Economic changes are made very difficult, e.g. the fixing of occupations according to caste hinders all except members of the lower castes or the depressed classes from doing much of the work necessary in newly introduced industries ; again, developments in the practice of the older means of livelihood are hampered. Other Hindu beliefs and customs have economic results. Thus the veneration of the cow, a sacred animal to all Hindus, allows great numbers of cattle to exist but prevents them being effectively utilized, for although their milk may be used their flesh may not be eaten ; also, because of grazing by animals which have no economic value yet must not be killed, effective utilization of the land is considerably limited.

In various ways the caste system checks production and hence keeps down the standard of living, while other Hindu institutions raise difficulties in the way of social and political reforms.

At various times, followers of the Hindu faith have taught purifications of doctrine and urged new practices ; in the sixth century B.C. the *Jains* broke off as a reforming sect. Another movement was the rise of the *Sikhs* in the fifteenth century A.D., teaching the unity of God and the brotherhood of man, and abolishing the caste system within their community. They began as religious reformers but became imbued with the military spirit and rebelled, but unsuccessfully, against the Muslim, and later the British, power in India ; at a later time many Sikhs willingly accepted service in the Indian army under the British administration.

Buddhism.—Rather more than 500 years before the birth of Christ, Gautama, a young chieftain of an Aryan clan in northern India, observed the miseries of life and went into retirement to seek their cause. This he thought to be the insatiable selfishness of man, and he taught that one's aim should be to attain " Nirvana," by which was meant not death but deliverance, for example from evil desires ; to attain Nirvana, man should follow the " Aryan Path "—see the Truth, aspire to the Good, free the heart through Love. By his followers Gautama was called Buddha, the Enlightened One, and his teaching was the basis of the Buddhist religion.

A number of other, commonly held, beliefs were later incorporated into Buddhism ; one of great importance was that of the immortality and the transmigration of souls.

Greek influence, through the descendants of Greeks whom Alexander the Great had brought to India, first created the figure of Buddha familiar in sculpture.

Aided by a great monarch, Buddhism extended over all India, but it became affected by Hindu beliefs and practices and after a time, like other religions, lost much of its original noble simplicity and value. Later, it spread over a great part of Asia, and became distorted in varying ways as it became the popular faith in Tibet and part of Turkistan, China and Indo-China, Burma, Ceylon and the East Indian Islands. In most of India itself, however, it became absorbed into Hinduism, though still remaining as the dominant religion in the Himalayan borderlands.

Buddhism rejected the ideas of caste, and hence the regions in which it is now held escape evils arising from that system ; yet they tend to suffer from a great development of the Buddhist priesthood which has a retarding influence upon any kind of advance. Also the Buddhist objection to destroying animal life has an obvious effect in countries where wild beasts abound and do great harm, while it also militates against the rearing of cattle and other domestic animals, as these may not be killed without committing an irreligious act.

Tibet, in particular, is greatly affected by its religion. A degraded form of Buddhism is practised, for it has incorporated much of a primitive and crude form of devil-worship. Also, popular ignorance and superstition express themselves by the use of small windmills and banners on which prayers and charms are written; as these are moved by the wind, they are supposed to take the place of praying to spirits and uttering charms against demons. Monks number nearly a quarter of the population of Tibet, and the monasteries own much of the property. The higher ranks of the priesthood are formed by the lamas, the effective rulers of the country. The head of the Tibetan government is the Dalai Lama, the Grand Lama, who is regarded as a reincarnation of the Buddha.

Religions of the Far East.—*China.*—From very early times, the religious ideas of the Chinese people combined animistic beliefs in many deities with *ancestor worship*. This is still a powerful factor in the faith and life of the Chinese ; among the less educated, sacrifices are regularly offered in order that the spirits of ancestors should protect and aid the living, and funeral rites include presents to supply the needs of parents in the spirit world. Therefore a man both reveres his forerunners and also regards it as essential that he should have successors to make provision for his own future after his death.

Three very important consequences follow from ancestor worship. First, the Chinese have looked upon the family— past, present and future—as the essential unit of which they form part ; to some extent the family has taken the place that is held by the nation among many Western peoples, and the idea of nationality in a political sense has only recently become strong and widespread among the Chinese. Secondly, ancestral traditions and the decision of the living head of the family act as a powerful brake upon the wheels of progress, even among educated Chinese ; thus, only after rejecting the most binding conceptions of filial piety can the younger men accept new ideas and practise new methods in almost any department of life. Thirdly, the necessity of continuing the family succession is an incentive to the maintenance of a high birth-rate and, together with the practice of polygamy, it has been one of the causes of the dense population of China.

Confucianism has had wide influence in China. Confucius, like Buddha, lived in the sixth century before Christ ; he made no claim to divine revelation but, like Buddha, taught a way of life based on a number of moral principles, among which he ranked highly filial piety and the golden rule : " What you do not like when done to yourself, do not do to others." He was much concerned with the conduct of men in public life ; indeed, his teaching is a system of ethical and political rules of conduct, but it is not a religion.

Taoism. At the same time as Confucius there lived another great Chinese—Lao Tse ; the two men approved each other's work, for in their fundamental ideas there was much in common. Also, like Buddha, Lao Tse taught a " way," i.e. " Tao," and his teaching is therefore known as Taoism. It became a religion, and it has borrowed ideas and rites from Buddhism to such an extent that these two forms of religion in China became very similar.

Buddhism was introduced into China in the first century A.D. ; it has greatly influenced Chinese ideas and it is sometimes said to be the religion of China. Yet, in the minds of most of the people, some forms of Buddhist teaching are now merged with other beliefs and practices, including ancestor worship, together with local superstitions and customs. It is to be noted that in China the various beliefs, instead of being a cause of conflict as in some countries, even aid one another in promoting feelings of tolerance among the people.

Korea.—Buddhism spread from China to this country, but here as elsewhere the faith and its priesthood suffered corruption. Confucianism became the official cult ; yet some form of animism has remained the belief of most of the uneducated Koreans, and ancestor worship is almost universal.

Japan.—The primitive religion of Japan was Shinto (the Way of the Gods), a mixture of nature worship and ancestor worship. It did not have a system of doctrine or a definite code of morals, but it contained two elements which later affected the relations between Japan and other States. One was the belief that the first sovereign of Japan was the grandson of the sun goddess, and that consequently the Emperors of Japan were themselves divine, and were the source of all authority within their realm.

The other belief inherent in Shintoism was that of the superiority of the Japanese above all other peoples.

In the sixth century A.D., Buddhism spread into Japan, and for some hundreds of years Shinto became absorbed into the new religion. But in the middle of the nineteenth century, a Japanese policy of seclusion and of isolation from the rest of the world was broken by American intervention. Then, in order to ensure the concentration of political power within the State and to strengthen the feeling of nationality and national superiority, Shinto was revived, organized and established as the State religion ; its tenets were taught to the children, and by every possible means obedience to its injunctions was enforced upon all Japanese citizens.

The effects of Shintoism upon internal and external politics were so far-reaching and so great a factor in military strength, that in 1945, after the defeat of Japan which ended the war which Japan had waged to obtain supremacy throughout eastern and southern Asia, the Allied Powers ordered the abolition of Shinto as a State religion. It might still be held by individuals, though shorn of direct political and military influence, and it must now take its place with Buddhism or other religious faiths.

Judaism.—The religions hitherto considered have arisen among, and have mainly influenced, that part of the world's population which lives in Asia on the eastern side of the great desert-belt of the Old World. Three other great religions have arisen within, or on the margins of, the desert-belt itself, and these three have had world-wide influence.

On the uplands of Judah, between the Syrian desert and the Mediterranean coast-lands, a succession of prophets early taught obedience to the tribal god of the Jews and later developed the idea that He was the one and only God ; at the same time their ideas of the moral attributes of God and the corresponding duties of men were raised to successively higher planes. In this evolution of religious thought, a critical period was the sixth century B.C. (the century, it will be remembered, of Gautama, Confucius and Lao Tse), when for about two generations the Jews were taken into captivity in Babylon. The national disaster was associated with religious backsliding, and with the return to Jerusalem came religious revival ; also, from the Babylonian contact came elements which now form part of the scriptures, such as accounts of the Creation and Deluge.

In Judaism there has always been a close connection between religion and nationality : the Jews regarded themselves as the Chosen People of God, and the closest bonds binding Jews together are the worship of their God and reverence for their national traditions. After the Romans destroyed the Temple at Jerusalem in 70 A.D., the Jews no longer formed a nation occupying its own territory. They have suffered dispersal, time after time, into many lands, and from the racial point of view have experienced great changes ; yet they have maintained a continuity of religious tradition, and the Hebrew language is still enshrined in their scriptures. In recent times persecution in Europe has caused the death or flight of millions of Jews. A considerable number have returned to develop their " National Home " in Palestine, but many who desired to do so found it impossible ; others, however, prefer to be accepted on terms of equality as citizens of the States in which they live. The number of Jews in the world at the present time is estimated at less than twelve millions, and of the total more than one-third live in the United States of America and almost as many in the U.S.S.R.

Christianity.—Christianity developed from Judaism, and in its early growth was much influenced by the ideas then current around the eastern Mediterranean Sea. The wider spread of Christianity has been closely bound up with the political power of the States in which it has been accepted. Its early centre was Rome whence, as the " Roman " or " Catholic " Church, it extended with relative rapidity within the Empire and more slowly over the rest of western and central Europe. The " Orthodox " or " Greek " Church developed along different lines at Constantinople (earlier called Byzantium and now Istanbul), and it was much later before it spread over the east of Europe. Thus Peninsular and Trunk Europe were dominated by variant forms of Christianity, and have been affected by a number of cultural differences connected with their religions, including the use of the Roman alphabet in the former and the Greek alphabet in the latter.

After the close of the Middle Ages, several " Protestant " churches were formed in the northern part of central and western Europe, their extent coinciding largely with that of the dominions of the princes who desired political independence of the Roman power. Even yet, in several parts of Europe religious and political factors are closely connected ; e.g. the mutual antagonism between the Protestants of Northern Ireland and the Roman Catholics of Eire is one of the hindrances to their closer co-operation.

With the migration of Europeans to the new lands overseas during the last two or three centuries, Christianity has enormously extended its sphere of influence. In the English-speaking northern part of America the dominant form is Protestantism, while south of the United States Roman Catholicism prevails. The white inhabitants of South Africa, Australia and New Zealand, having come mainly from northern Europe, are largely Protestant.

Islam.—The last faith which has so spread as to be regarded as a world religion is Islam, for there are about 250 million Muslims forming the majority of the population in regions extending from northern Africa through south-western to central Asia, and even to India and the East Indies.

Muhammad (whose name is variously spelt) lived in the seventh century A.D., first in Mecca and then in Medina, two oasis settlements near the western margin of the Arabian desert. Mecca was then, as now, a pilgrim centre, but in the time of Muhammad the sanctuary was the abode of a god who was merely one of some hundreds of gods of the many Arabian tribes. Muhammad rejected the current polytheism, and taught that there was but one God and that he was His prophet. Muhammad was influenced by Jewish teaching and admitted Abraham and Jesus into the ranks of the prophets. He taught also the equality of all true believers in the faith of Islam, no matter of what race or country ; he enjoined peace between them, and required of them considerate treatment of their wives and slaves.

Threatened with assassination in Mecca, Muhammad fled to Medina, and thence he and his successors spread their faith by the sword. Islam is essentially a proselytizing religion and before long the nomadic and warlike fanatics had extended their conquests and their faith over Arabia, the south-west of Asia and even the heart of that continent, together with all northern Africa. For a time the Muslim Moors of the Atlas Lands conquered Spain, and still later the Turks advanced through the whole of the Balkan region ; the invaders were, however, eventually driven back from these outposts, and in Europe the only considerable number of Muslims are in parts of the Balkan countries.

On the eastern side of the desert home of Islam, Muslim chiefs from central Asia invaded India, and in the sixteenth century Moghul, i.e. Mongol, emperors established their rule over much of that country. As a result, the bulk of the population in the north-west of India, where the newcomers settled in large numbers, is now Muslim. This is also the case in eastern Bengal, where the low-caste aboriginals found that the Islamic doctrine of equality relieved them of the disadvantages with which Hinduism oppressed them ; in other parts of India, too, there are Muslim minorities. Because of the religious differences between Hindus and Muslims, and the resultant social cleavage and sometimes economic competition, there have been repeated " communal " conflicts between them in many places in northern India. Even in China, both in the south-west and also in the north-western borderlands, there are outposts of Islam ; here, however, there is mutual tolerance between Muslim and other Chinese. The Arabs extended their influence by sea round the Indian Ocean ; hence in the north-eastern coastlands of Africa, the Malay Peninsula and the East Indian Islands, Islam has largely displaced earlier beliefs.

Together with their religion the Arabs introduced other cultural factors, e.g. mathematical science and improvements in irrigation ; in central Africa, however, slave trading has often accompanied their incursions. As a rule, where Islam has been imposed it has been tenaciously held, and today it is a strong bond between most of the peoples who live in or near the great desert belt. One factor in this Islamic unity is the annual pilgrimage to the Holy Cities of Arabia, and it is worth noting that about one-half of the pilgrims come from Malaya and the East Indies and one-quarter from Pakistan. The political effect of the Muslim religion can be paralleled only by that which was formerly exerted by Shinto, but in the case of Islam it goes far beyond the boundaries of a single State. In this connection it must be pointed out that the " Arab League " of States, which will be further referred to in a later chapter, is based not only on a common language and interests, but also on a common culture and law derived from Islam.

CHAPTER XIII

MODES OF LIFE—THE SIMPLER FORMS

In many parts of the world, people have their modes of life determined largely by the ways in which they earn their livelihood. The regions in which the main types of occupation respectively dominate are broadly shown in maps on pp. 192, 206, and 246. It will be noted that to some extent they correspond with climatic or vegetation regions, since particular occupations can be carried on only where nature offers suitable conditions. For example, the growing of plantation products requires a much moister climate than the keeping of animals such as sheep, goats and camels ; hence the former kind of work has extended over certain parts of the hot and well-watered inter-tropical regions, while nomadic pastoral peoples utilize semi-arid areas. Again, the hunting of wild, fur-bearing animals can be carried on in the cold, sub-arctic forests or even the tundra lands.

Yet while nature must permit, it does not determine, the kind of work and the mode of life in a given region, for the character of the people concerned is an essential factor. The will of man, based upon his knowledge and his desires, is the driving force by which he adapts his modes of life to his environments, and also his environments to his modes of life.

Particular groups of men have learned the arts of hunting, of carrying on various forms of agriculture, of domesticating animals and using their products, and of developing industries and commerce ; such knowledge has been acquired in favourable regions and may then spread to other peoples and other areas. But the spread has been gradual, and even now in some regions which are in themselves suitable for relatively advanced agriculture, primitive peoples may merely collect plants which nature provides or at best may grow a few crops in a simple and ineffective manner. Again, some of the simpler forms of pastoral work are at the present time giving way to more developed methods or are being replaced by cultivation.

The main types of occupation will now be considered in turn, in this chapter taking those connected with the simple collecting of plants, and with hunting and fishing, and then various forms of utilizing animal life by pastoral work ; the following chapter will deal with certain kinds of agriculture.   This order, however, was not the normal one of human development, for the arts of agriculture were well begun before man advanced from the hunting to the pastoral stage.

Primitive Gathering and Hunting.—A very simple mode of life is that of the peoples who satisfy their needs by collecting parts of plants, especially roots, tubers, seeds and fruits, by catching animals—sometimes larger game but usually small kinds as rats, monkeys, or lizards—and by fishing if opportunity offers.   Many of the people who get their living in this way are those who appear to be of earlier racial types and to have been driven by more developed groups into the equatorial forests of the Old World or the semi-deserts of South Africa and Australia.   The pygmies of Central Africa and the East Indian Archipelago, the Semang and Sakoi of the Malay Peninsula, the Bushmen of South Africa and the Australian aborigines are well-known examples.   There are also some Amerind tribes who still live in much the same manner, as in the Amazon valley and forested uplands of Brazil.

Although these gatherers and hunters have made but small advances in most ways, they have had to develop considerable ability in their particular means of getting a living in such unfavourable or even hostile environments.   Their digging-sticks, weapons, clothing and shelter are crude but serve their purpose.   The need of moving about for fresh supplies of food prohibits a settled life and prevents the possession of any conveniences or even any surplus necessities.   With practically no possibility of storing food, they suffer alternations of occasional abundance and periods of hunger.   They are also much subject to disease and their life is normally short.

The family is the economic unit, the men hunting or fishing and making weapons while the women gather plants, prepare food and look after the children.   Related single families may be associated into family-groups,[1] and these are regarded as

---

[1] Throughout this book the term " family-group " is used to denote a group formed by several closely related families, e.g. those of the married sons, or of the brothers, of the head of the family ; in China some family-groups are of even wider formation and yet in many respects act as a social unit.

having the right to occupy a certain territory, though private ownership of land is an inconceivable idea to them. In some cases the families are united into tribes, but when there are organizations of this kind they are usually loose and there is little common action. Commercial intercourse with more advanced peoples does not go beyond small exchanges. The general outlook of these folk is limited : it is " here and now."

Their numbers are necessarily small, and as their lands are still being encroached upon, while their ways of life and their health are endangered by contacts with other peoples, they seem doomed to disappear. The only hope of their survival, as independent groups living in much the same way as their ancestors, seems to be in the creation of " native reserves " where others may not settle or acquire land.

In parts of the world where game or fish were relatively abundant, peoples developed hunting or fishing modes of life to a higher stage than that described in the preceding section. This was especially the case in the mid-latitude grasslands, but as these areas were capable of more effective utilization the hunters have given way before peoples who had acquired other ways of life ; the buffalo-hunting Indians of the Prairies and Great Plains of North America may be cited as a large group which has but recently disappeared.

Commercial Hunting and Trapping.—Now, the only large regions in which hunting is the characteristic occupation are the sub-arctic forests and tundras in North America, in the extreme north-east of Europe and in northern Asia. Even in the remote northern forests and tundras, the mode of life has been changed in some important ways by the influence of people from other regions, for most of the hunting folk are no longer dependent directly upon the products of the chase ; they sell valuable furs and skins to traders and in return obtain a considerable part of their requirements, including more effective weapons, manufactured clothing and blankets and perhaps material for tents, as well as comforts such as tobacco and even some kinds of food. In this intercourse there is a two-fold danger to the hunting communities : in the first place, peoples of simpler outlook and habits usually suffer from contact with others to whose ways they cannot adapt themselves ; in the second place, the increased demand for furs and the greater efficiency of the new weapons lead the hunters to reduce the

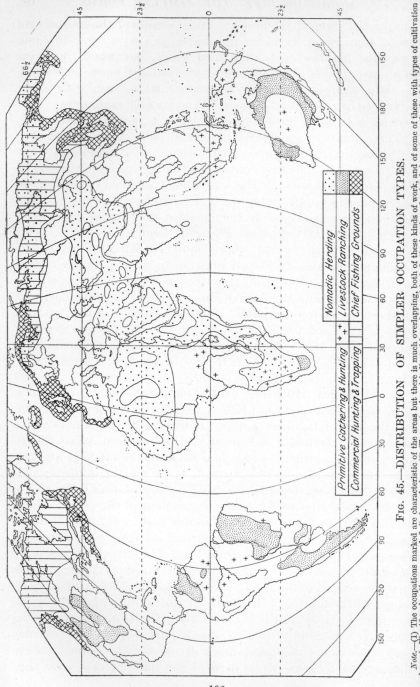

FIG. 45.—DISTRIBUTION OF SIMPLER OCCUPATION TYPES.

Nomadic Herding

Livestock Ranching

Chief Fishing Grounds

Primitive Gathering & Hunting

Commercial Hunting & Trapping

Note.—(1) The occupations marked are characteristic of the areas but there is much overlapping, both of these kinds of work, and of some of these with types of cultivation shown in Fig. 46 ; also, there are no definite boundaries. (2) The pastoral work indicated here does not include the keeping of animals in systems of mixed farming.

192

numbers, and even to threaten the survival, of the animals on which they depend. These dangers have shown themselves so markedly among the Indians and Eskimo of North America and Greenland that the governments—Canadian, United States, and Danish—who now control these peoples have restricted the killing of the game. Although the hunting communities may be considered as less advanced than those of some of the agricultural and industrial peoples, they may show a high degree of adaptation to their environment. There is usually no close organization among the hunting peoples, though family units may join into bands for hunting expeditions ; in the past, however, the tribes in some regions used to act as a whole in warfare.

Fishing.—Shore dwellers in many parts of the world have in the past obtained their sustenance entirely or almost entirely from fish and other forms of animal life in the sea. These people are now few in number, and are represented mainly by inhabitants of the inter-tropical Pacific islands from the Malay Archipelago to Polynesia.

Far more important is the fishing that has developed on a great scale to provide food, oil and other products as articles of commerce sold by the fishermen for use largely in densely populated industrial and commercial regions.

The bulk of the world's supply of fish products comes from four great fishing-grounds ; these are formed by the shallow waters of the continental platforms on both sides of the Atlantic Ocean and on both sides of the Pacific Ocean in the mid-latitudes of the northern hemisphere (see the map in Fig. 45). In these situations the conditions of the ocean waters allow the existence of fish in very large numbers, as the drifting plankton, the basis of all marine life, appears to develop most abundantly on the polar sides of mid-latitudes, especially where currents meet, bringing waters from warmer and cooler areas respectively. Moreover, in all these four great fishing-grounds the shallowness of the sea facilitates the capture both of the surface, pelagic fish (e.g. herring and mackerel), which live more directly upon the plankton, and also of the demersal fish (e.g. cod and halibut), which dwell on or near the bottom over the continental shelves.

Thus in these regions there is an abundant supply of fish for a fishing industry, while the other requisite, that of a corresponding demand, exists among the great populations of the neighbouring countries. Further, the actual coasts adjoining the fishing-grounds are to a large extent infertile, and the people find it a relatively paying occupation to catch the fish of the sea on the one side of their homes and to sell them to the people on the other side. They use not only the grounds nearest to them but also more distant ones ; for example, the European fishermen visit the Banks off Newfoundland, and the Japanese go to the seas off western North America.

In the southern hemisphere, neither the supply of fish nor the demand for it is as great as in the northern hemisphere. The Antarctic, however, has attracted whalers from the northern fishing communities, and to such an extent that international restrictions have become necessary to prevent the extermination of the whales.

The fishing communities of the present time are different in many respects from primitive fishers, for they use scientific methods and equipment. Although it is a convenient arrangement to deal with their means of livelihood in this chapter entitled " simpler forms," their general way of life tends to resemble that of the neighbouring industrial and commercial peoples as closely as their occupation permits.

Forestry.—The utilization of the products of forests, as of fisheries, has become largely the concern of people closely connected with those of industrial and commercial regions.

In both equatorial and tropical forests, the work is carried on by natives of the regions who generally work under the direction of European or other relatively well-off business men dealing in timber for export. In the dense equatorial forests the procuring of the timber, and also of resins, nuts and dyestuffs, is hindered by several factors : the scattered growth of particular kinds of tree ; the difficulties of transportation ; the climate ; the lack of adequate labour. Therefore, although the timber is mainly hard wood with useful properties, only the most valuable kinds are cut and exported, e.g. mahogany from Central and South America, and ebony from Africa and southeastern Asia. The collecting of the latex from the " wild " rubber-producing trees in the equatorial forests of South America and Africa has given way to the production of rubber from plantations—a branch of inter-tropical agriculture. The tropical forests in which there is a more uniform growth of particular kinds of tree are easier to exploit, and labour is generally more abundant and more efficient ; hence there is a greater development of forestry in some of these regions, e.g. the teak-producing areas of Burma, Siam and the Malay Region.

Nine-tenths of the world's supply of timber comes from the forests of mid-latitudes ; of this, less than half is " hard wood " and more than half is " soft wood." The hard wood includes oak, beech, elm, ash, maple, chestnut, walnut and the Australian eucalypts ; it is obtained mainly from the mixed forests in central Europe and the east of North America. As most of the land in these regions has now been cleared for cultivation or pasture, the forested areas are scattered over the uplands and are relatively small ; the men engaged in forestry therefore live among, and in much the same way as, the agriculturists.

Soft wood is increasingly utilized, notably for the production of pulp from which paper, chemicals, rayon and other commodities are obtained. The regions in which it is cut fall into two groups. In the first group are mid-latitude areas in which conifers, especially pines, firs, spruces and cedars, are numerous. The belt of great trees along the north-western coasts of North America is one of the most important areas ; another area is on the opposite side of the continent in the south-east of Canada and the east of the United States ; a third is in east-central Europe. On the whole, these soft-wood forests are less cleared for farming than mid-latitude hard-wood areas ; hence forestry is in some cases the main occupation, though elsewhere the workers may follow a seasonal change of work, going into the woods in the winter but farming in the summer.

The second group of regions yielding soft wood are the sub-arctic forests ; over considerable areas of these the cutting and transporting of timber is one of the main occupations of the inhabitants. Although these coniferous forests have an enormous extent in North America and Eurasia, they include large tracts of bog and swampy land in which there is little valuable timber, as is the case over 30 per cent. of the forest area of northern Sweden. There are also great expanses, as in northern Canada and Siberia, where the severity of the climate allows but a poor and thin growth of trees ; in Siberia little more than half the forested region is really timber country.

Moreover, the factor of accessibility is of primary importance, and at the present time the sub-arctic forest areas from which soft wood is exported are mainly limited to the south-eastern border of the North American region, viz. in Canada and

Newfoundland, and to the western border of the Eurasian region, viz. in Scandinavia, Finland and European Russia. These areas are in relatively close touch with the industrial and commercial regions where the wood is used, while the rest of the forests have very poor communication. The northern drainage systems are of little value, for most of the rivers lead down to the Arctic Seas ; also the spring flooding of large expanses of the upper basins and the formation of ice-jams in the lower courses present almost insuperable difficulties in some cases.

Forestry is now changing its character ; in many parts it is ceasing to be an example of " robber economy." It is widely realized that the earlier practice of simply cutting down the trees resulted in the total destruction of the forests, which might be replaced only by a poor growth of brush or tough grass ; also there frequently followed soil erosion and its attendant evils. Hence this wasteful method is being replaced by a careful utilization of the forest—a co-ordinated system of felling selected trees and arranging for the better growth or the replanting of others ; the result may be illustrated by the fact that in Sweden even in the slow-maturing sub-arctic forest the growth more than compensates for the cutting.

Nomadic Herding.—This is the simplest form of pastoralism and the migratory peoples who travel with their flocks or herds from one place to another occupy three great areas in the eastern hemisphere. The main one is that which extends over the semi-deserts of northern Africa and thence north-eastward across the semi-deserts of south-western and central Asia, together with the adjoining dry steppe-land of the U.S.S.R. Other areas, in which different forms of pastoralism are carried on, are the tropical grasslands south of the Sahara in Africa, and the sub-arctic forests of Eurasia. Since the people depend almost entirely upon their animals, directly or indirectly, the mode of life is bound up with the requirements of the animals and with the products they supply.

The Nomads of the Old World.—In the main pastoral area of northern Africa and south-western and central Asia sheep form the chief stock, for they can graze upon the poorer kinds of grass and shrubs, and with them are usually goats which can exist on even poorer pastures and more scanty water-supply. Most of the needs of the people are satisfied by the products of these animals : the milk, and generally to a less extent the meat, give the staple food, while the wool and skins provide much of the material for clothing and tents. A much smaller number of horses is usually kept, both for the sake of their milk and their flesh and also for riding ; in some parts camels also are bred, for their milk and hair as well as for riding and the transport of tents and gear. On the cold Tibetan plateau the nomads make use of yaks.

Because of the generally scanty nature of the pastures, constant movements of the flocks are necessary, and the people live in tents grouped in encampments. Around these as centres the animals are driven from one spot to another until the available grazing, or drinking water, is exhausted ; the whole encampment is then moved to a neighbouring place.

With the seasonal changes of temperature and rainfall, and the consequent disappearance of plant life in some areas, more extensive migrations are compulsory to take advantage of the growth of pasture in regions of different climatic conditions. On the north-western side of the Sahara there is a southward movement into poorer areas when winter rains make their grazing possible, while the drought of summer necessitates a northward retreat to the Atlas Lands. In the Arabian Peninsula the Bedouin (or Badawin), who depend mainly on camels, live for much of the year on the semi-desert areas and take advantage of rains to go even into the true desert, but on the other hand they migrate to the better-watered margins in times of greatest drought. In Russian Turkistan Kazak herdsmen spend the cold winter on the southern margin of the dry region, where valleys at the foot of the Tian Shan mountains give shelter and supplies of water, and in early summer go northwards to the steppes where at that season there is rain and consequently pasture.

Another type of movement is that which alternates between highland in summer and lowland in winter. For example, the Kirghiz of Turkistan have winter quarters near those of the Kazak at the foot of the Tian Shan mountains but in summer go southward to the mountain pastures.

The nomadic life prevents much accumulation of equipment and limits the material aids to cultural development. Until recently, there had been little change in the mode of life for hundreds or even thousands of years, for the customs of the people had to be closely adapted to the same physical conditions and to the needs and products of the animals. The introduction of the camel, however, did make possible a new way of life to the people by whom it was employed ; e.g. by its means some of them engaged in trade and transport across the desert, though recently the building of roads and the use of motor vehicles have threatened this occupation.

The nomadic pastoral peoples have a simple social organization into family-groups which work together ; in these the women do most of the labour within the camp, including care of the animals, while the men's work is mainly outside the settlement. The men have the easier life and a superior position, and the head is the patriarch, to whom all owe obedience. The families possess their own animals, but do not own their grazing-lands ; the right to use these is the common possession of clans or tribes formed by related family-groups.

A transition to a more advanced type of occupation is shown where pastoral people also carry on a certain amount of agriculture. They usually have well-constructed winter quarters where there is a sheltered situation and where water can be obtained with fair regularity, and here some crops such as hay, grain and potatoes can be grown by those of the community who remain through the year, while the rest migrate with their animals to the summer pastures ; this mode of life, dependent upon a combined economy, is known as transhumance. In Russian Turkistan the Soviet government has developed systematic transhumance in connection with very extensive collective farms, and has organized " bases " along the lines of migration to aid travel. Another advance upon the simple, practically self-sufficing, form of nomadism is the addition of trading, animal products being regularly exchanged for goods obtained from agricultural peoples.

In general, nomads have an uncertain or even precarious existence, for their animals may perish in times when rain and pastures fail or when winter snow and ice prevent grazing. In such circumstances they may trespass upon the pastures or raid the flocks and herds of other pastoralists ; thus arise frequent clashes between the nomads themselves. Also they may attack their agricultural neighbours who, being of sedentary habit and unused to warfare, are commonly unable to resist the sudden onslaughts of bands of horsemen or camelmen.

Occasionally, too, large numbers of nomads may leave their region altogether and settle elsewhere.

Such raids and permanent migrations acted as safety-valves for pastoral communities, but they are no longer possible because of the growth of more powerful governments in the adjoining regions. In fact, a reverse process has now become common, viz. subjugation of the pastoralists and occupation of part of their traditional lands. This is the case, for instance, in the Turkistan region, where the Russians from Europe some time ago settled and cultivated the better steppes, and then greatly extended oasis cultivation along the line of foothills which the Kazak and Kirghiz had used as their winter quarters. Nevertheless, it is doubtful whether the main area of pastoralism in the Old World is capable of being utilized in a way greatly different from that of past ages, and it is therefore likely to remain very scantily populated.

The Reindeer Herdsmen of the North.—Although some of the herdsmen of the sub-arctic forests of Asia, e.g. some of the Yakut tribes who have migrated northward, have tried to keep horses and cattle, most of the pastoralists of the north of Eurasia have domesticated reindeer which are naturally adapted to the conditions of the coniferous forest and the tundra. Several groups of people are dependent, to a greater or less degree, on tame reindeer for their living, including the Lapps in Europe and the Samoyed and Northern Tungus in Asia. Recently, attempts have been made to give the American Eskimo an additional and relatively stable means of livelihood by introducing reindeer from Asia.

Among the herdsmen of the north a habit of migration is necessary, viz. to the tundra for the relatively abundant fodder during the short summer, and to the forest during the winter when constant moving is required for the scanty supply of lichen which has to be scraped from beneath the snow. The reindeer are used in several ways and to varying degrees by the different peoples—for the milk, flesh and skin ; for pulling sledges ; for riding. Moreover, the herders are also hunters to varying degrees, and often fishing is a supplementary resource ; hence the overlapping of the markings on Fig. 45.

The Cattle Herdsmen of Africa.—The grasslands of Africa south of the Sahara are better watered than the main pastoral region of northern Africa and Asia, and the pastures are therefore both richer and also less liable to disappear because of drought ; hence there are three differences between the modes of life in these two areas. First, in the southern region as a whole, cattle form the most important part of the livestock, though sheep and goats are also kept ; secondly, migration is more limited than in the north, settled habitations being common even though they are left for a time when the herds have to be taken to distant areas ; thirdly, agriculture is widely possible and its products are already used to a considerable extent by the cattle rearers, being obtained either by the pastoralists themselves or by exchange with cultivators.

The pastoral peoples entered Africa from Arabia in the neighbourhood of the strait of Bab el Mandeb and migrated along the grasslands in two directions—westward along the Sudanese savannas and southward over the East African plateaus ; they were typically nomadic warriors who often subjugated or displaced agricultural tribes previously in possession of these lands. In East and South Africa the Bantu include tribes of both modes of life, e.g. in Kenya are the Masai who are herdsmen and the Kikuyu who are cultivators ; in some cases the two occupations are combined.

In northern Africa pastoral Hamites have occupied both the semi-deserts in the Sahara region, as for example the Tuareg have done, and also the drier parts of the adjoining savanna lands. Among the peoples of this latter region may be mentioned the Hamitic Fula ; originally cattle-men of the poorer country, they have penetrated southward into the better savannas inhabited by agricultural Negro tribes, and these migrations have led to modifications in the modes of life of both types of people. For example, the previously nomadic Fula have formed the ruling class in the towns and villages of the negroid Hausa of Northern Nigeria, while farther west other Fula have become semi-nomadic in their habits.

Although the African grasslands are not subject to drought to the same extent as the more northerly pastoral regions, they have been seriously harassed by another danger—insect pests ; thus in one area after another the tsetse fly has caused the loss of the animals and the mass-migration of their owners.

Livestock Ranching.—In some of the grasslands and scrublands of continents recently opened to European development, a more advanced form of pastoralism is carried on. In this work a large number of the people, like most of the present-day fishers and hunters, are engaged in supplying the needs of great industrial and commercial regions. Their method of keeping the animals, and therefore much of their mode of life, has been derived from European practices; moreover, many of these more advanced pastoralists are of European descent. They are not nomadic, but have settled homes, even though they leave these for a time to supervise limited migrations of their charges. It must be made clear, however, that what is here considered is not the keeping of animals in mixed farming but the grazing of animals entirely or largely on the natural vegetation.

The regions in which this type of work is the main occupation are shown in Fig. 45, and it will be realized that they are generally unsuited to more intensive means of utilization. There are two groups : the first are tropical savannas, including the llanos and campos of South America, and part of the Northern Territory and Queensland in Australia ; the second group are extra-tropical grasslands or semi-deserts in the west of North America, in Uruguay and Argentina in South America, in the interior of South Africa, and in the more southerly parts of Australia. In the tropical areas cattle form the main livestock, and in the cooler, extra-tropical regions sheep are much more numerous, though cattle and in some cases goats are also reared.

The regions differ greatly from one another in the number of animals they can support and consequently in the value of their products ; e.g. in Australia the rather better-watered areas have over 300 sheep to the square mile but the poorer ones have less than one-fifth of that number—in other words, about ten acres are necessary to support each sheep. The quality of the animals also differs considerably, but because the products are largely destined for European use, improved breeds of animals and better methods have been introduced ; consequently this type of pastoralism is much more productive than that of the nomads of Asia and Africa.

Migrations of flocks and herds are not as important as in the Old World ; for instance, in summer the animals may be moved to near-by higher lands to fresh pastures or to avoid floods in lowland districts. A lack of pasture in dry seasons is in several regions met by the use of fodder such as alfalfa (i.e. lucerne) grown with the aid of irrigation, and in Australia the boring of deep artesian wells is a partial safeguard against the drying up

of supplies of drinking-water. These artificial means of procuring food and water mitigate the effects of climatic variations,
but droughts may nevertheless be both frequent and serious.
At such times the owners of the flocks may lose a considerable
proportion of their animals and some may face the ruin of their
business ; yet the people themselves are not in danger of their
lives nor are they forced to mass migrations as in the case of the
Old World nomads, and in a few years there is a recovery in the
number of sheep in the country and the value of their products.

The cattle of the savannas are kept mainly for their hides,
which are to a large extent exported, and for their flesh, which
is in part consumed in the countries where the industry is
carried on and in part sent overseas to Europe in the form of
chilled, frozen or tinned beef. Dairy cattle, on the other hand,
are reared on the better pastures of the regions of mixed farming which will be considered in the next chapter. There is a
similar distinction between the types of sheep : while those
bred mainly for mutton can be best fed on the more abundant
resources available in the mixed-farming areas, those bred for
their wool are largely supported on the poorer resources of the
pastoral regions here described. Hence these are the main
sources of the wool which is sent overseas to the great manufacturing districts of North America and Europe, the greatest
amounts coming from Australia, Argentina, New Zealand and
South Africa. In the driest parts of the pastoral regions, but
not in Australia or New Zealand, many goats are kept ; mohair
obtained from the Angora breed is exported from the South
African area.

For livestock ranching, little labour is required ; for the
greater part of the year the animals wander freely over wide
ranges, being rounded up for branding with the marks of their
owners, and later for shearing, for driving to other areas or to
ports, or for slaughter. Hence the herdsmen live on small
stations at considerable distances from other communities, and
the population of the pastoral regions is scanty. More intensive
utilization of these regions in the near future appears unlikely.

A recent extension of the pastoral industry may be noted in
the breeding of furred animals in captivity, instead of hunting
or trapping in the sub-arctic forests ; for instance, farms of
silver foxes have been established in the United States and in
eastern Canada, and farms of minks and foxes in Lapland.

CHAPTER XIV

MODES OF LIFE—AGRICULTURE (1)

Introduction.—The cultivation, as distinct from the simple gathering, of plants probably arose independently in several parts of the world and in various ways. For example, the custom of putting food into graves for the use of the spirits of the dead may have resulted in the appearance of new shoots, and thus suggested deliberate planting ; the same result may have followed from observing the growth of roots or seeds which had been accidentally left in soft, moist earth near dwellings.

When once agriculture had become even a partial means of obtaining a food supply, it brought with it other advances in man's modes of life. A settled dwelling near the cultivated patch would be essential and this, in turn, would allow both the construction of more permanent habitations and the accumulation of various tools and other possessions. A surplus of food might be obtained, and with it the possibility of leisure time in which agricultural implements and also hunting weapons might be improved. Moreover, forethought as well as constant work is required for the successive processes of clearing the ground, planting, keeping the ground clear of the quickly growing weeds, protecting the crop from raiding birds and animals, and harvesting. Crops which come at definite seasons have to be stored and receptacles provided ; this need must have stimulated the arts of weaving baskets and making pottery. In such ways agriculture encouraged both mental and material progress, and with its further development many other cultural advances were brought about.

Inter-tropical Shifting Tillage.—The most primitive form of agriculture is that now carried on in equatorial regions of constant heat and rain and in those of the Tropics which have hot and rainy summers. Clearings are made in the inter-tropical forests and savannas by the simple method of burning the natural vegetation without removing the roots, and usually with very little cultivation of the ground. Under these conditions the soil is quickly impoverished, especially when it is of the infertile, lateritic type, and after a few seasons at most the clearing has to be abandoned. A new one is then made, if possible near the village ; after a time, however, the suitable land may be used up and the whole settlement then has to be shifted some distance, to a place where cultivable land and drinking-water are obtainable.

The making of a clearing is commonly carried out with the help of all the men of a village, after which each family cultivates its particular patch and lives on the produce. Women are responsible for much of the labour as well as for the preparation of the food and the care of the children, while the men often engage in some hunting or fishing. Because of the small yield of the land and the repeated shiftings, relatively large areas can support only a small number of people ; as contrasted with the luxuriance of the natural vegetation of much of the inter-tropical lands, their agricultural productivity is small.

There are three main regions in which this kind of cultivation is carried on, viz. Central and South America, inter-tropical Africa, and the area which extends from Indo-China and the East Indian Archipelago to the Pacific Islands ; these regions are broadly distinguished from one another by their typical implements and by their products. (Refer to map on p. 206.)

In the American region the simplest tool is employed—the planting-stick ; this, like the dibber of our country, is used to make holes into which seeds, tubers, roots or cuttings are dropped and then covered up. Where the planting-stick is employed there is little or no cultivation of the soil, and sometimes only one crop can be obtained before the patch has to be abandoned and, as a rule, five or more years elapse before it is again utilized. The chief food plants of the inter-tropical American region are manioc, from which cassava bread is made (and also tapioca for export), sweet potatoes and maize.

In the Malayan–Pacific region the digging-stick is employed ; this is a heavier tool than the planting-stick, and because it digs up the ground it brings the soil into better condition and makes possible longer or more frequent periods during which the patch may be utilized. The yam is grown for its tubers and the taro for its underground stems, and in some parts upland or hill rice —a variety which does not require irrigation. Near the sea, trees are cultivated : the coconut palm, bread-fruit tree and banana and plantain trees yield their fruits, and sago is obtained from the pith of the sago palm.

In the African region the hoe, a still more effective implement, is commonly employed ; with this tool the soil is more thoroughly worked, and in some parts the cultivation is as efficient as under the plough of middle latitudes. The patches may be utilized for two, three, or even more seasons before a shift becomes necessary. The variety of products is fairly great : among the " root " crops yams are important, the cereals include millets and sorghums (the " Guinea corn " or " Kaffir corn " of Africa is a sorghum) and of the trees special mention may be made of oil palms, bananas and plantains.

Tropical and Inter-tropical Fixed Tillage.—More efficient cultivation, generally applied to soils which have been less leached and are therefore naturally more fertile, enables the land to produce a greater yield and to be used for a longer time before it requires a period of fallow. Hence the cultivated area can be kept within working distance of the village, and permanency thus becomes a characteristic both of the farmed land and of the settlement. A common feature of this fixed agriculture is the keeping of domesticated animals which by their manure aid in maintaining the fertility of the soil, and in some cases are used for such work as threshing grain, transport, and even for simple forms of ploughing.

In some areas this advance has been stimulated by natural conditions. For example, on highlands the vegetation is relatively easily cleared and the land can be more easily kept free of weeds ; moreover, the area of useful land is limited and therefore careful cultivation is a necessity if any considerable number of people is to be supported. The Andean Highlands have for long been the homes of advanced cultivators employing irrigation, and here the Spanish invaders found the Aztec civilization. Maize was grown at moderate altitudes, while at greater heights was the original habitat of the potato which has since been introduced into many lands of middle latitudes. On the plateaus of Africa millets are specially important. Upland rice is the characteristic foodstuff of many mountainous districts of the East Indian Archipelago. Moreover, in Java, even before the Dutch established their plantation system, the natives had learnt from Asiatic immigrants the art of growing rice by irrigation, and for this purpose had constructed terraces on mountain-sides and led streams from higher to lower levels.

Another group of regions where fixed tillage was encouraged

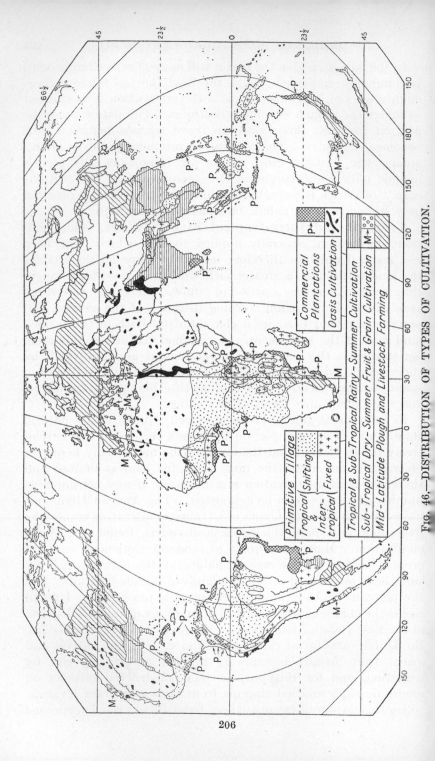

FIG. 46.—DISTRIBUTION OF TYPES OF CULTIVATION.

Commercial Plantations P

Oasis Cultivation

Primitive Tillage
Tropical & Inter-tropical { Shifting
Fixed

Tropical & Sub-Tropical Rainy-Summer Cultivation

Sub-Tropical Dry-Summer Fruit & Grain Cultivation

Mid-Latitude Plough and Livestock Farming M

by natural conditions lies near the margins of the inter-tropical zone, where heat and moisture form less of a handicap to cultivation ; here, too, the alternation of a hot, wet season with one of cooler and drier weather makes possible a relatively wide range of products which have differing climatic requirements.

In some regions the human element has been the determining factor in the development of the fixed type of agriculture. For example, the families of native workers on many European-managed plantations grew their own food on adjoining land and adopted European methods. Again, the European governments of some tropical dependencies stimulated the production of commodities intended for sale.

Areas in which cultivation of varied crops occupies a large part of the ground may be concisely labelled " crop-lands." Accordingly, some parts of the tropical and inter-tropical regions have been transformed by fixed tillage into crop-lands, but the greater areas remain as forests, woodlands or savannas.

Oasis Irrigation.—The term " oasis irrigation " is here used to include any form of cultivation which depends upon supplying water to otherwise unproductive land ; the supply may be obtained from wells or springs in small oases, by the regulation of rivers which at times flood their valleys, or by the construction of canals which take water into an arid district. Thus, irrigation as considered in this section is distinct from that which merely helps cultivation in regions where the rainfall is the main source of the water-supply. The importance of irrigation may be realized if it is recalled that the earliest civilizations were based upon it, and at the present time the total area under irrigation is over 200 million acres; moreover, large-scale projects for bringing water to barren lands are still being carried out while others are being planned.

Oases (always including the irrigated river valleys) are to be found in the dry regions of tropical and middle latitudes and in a relatively few cases in the less-watered parts of the mid-latitude, light-rain regions. In these irrigated areas, temperature and soil conditions are favourable for cultivation, but man must organize the water-supply. The particular products which can be obtained depend on the amount of heat, and therefore belong mainly to two classes : those which require high temperatures and those which mature with less heat. The former, such as dates, cotton, sugar-cane and rice, can be obtained only in the hotter oases ; the latter, such as maize, wheat, barley, and a considerable number of fruits, can be grown either in the cooler season of the tropical areas, or in the summer of the extra-tropical oases.

The most important tropical and sub-tropical oasis regions are in the river basins of the Nile, the Euphrates-Tigris (Mesopotamia) and the Indus ; it was in these regions that three of the first civilizations developed, from about 7,000 to 5,000 years ago, and today they are the homes of dense populations amounting in each case to several millions of people.

Successive improvements in irrigation may be illustrated from the case of the delta and lower valley of the Nile, where the autumn floods gave an annual supply both of water and of fertile alluvium ; the natural conditions encouraged agriculture and stimulated the control of the water, thus giving rise to the great irrigation system of ancient Egypt. The simple " shaduf," a long cane or pole suspended above the river bank, tipped buckets of water on the adjacent land, but could supply only small areas. This method was supplemented by " basin " irrigation, by which canals led water from the river into large and small basins enclosed by dykes ; the basins could be filled only during the autumn period of high water, and therefore could be used for the subsequent cool-season crops such as wheat and barley, but not for summer-growing crops such as cotton. For this reason, " perennial " irrigation was introduced about a century ago ; reservoirs were made and water brought from them whenever required, and cotton became the great export production of Egypt. Today, engineering works include huge barrages across the Nile to regulate the floods at several points, reservoirs which store thousands of millions of cubic feet of water, and innumerable large and small canals which distribute the water, as and when needed for the various crops, over several thousand square miles of cultivated land. In the Sudan, recent works have irrigated the Gezira area between the White Nile and the Blue Nile ; here the summer heat is so great that the cotton crop is grown during the cool season and picked in spring.

In Mesopotamia, the different natural conditions present different problems for the utilization of the waters of the Euphrates and the Tigris ; also, the ancient works fell into ruin as a result of the incursions of Bedouin nomads, and quite recently modern engineering made a new start in almost un-inhabited districts. In Iraq there is a smaller population than in Egypt, and the chief productions are grain in the northern part, and rice and dates in the southern part.

In the north-west of India, as in Mesopotamia, much of the ancient irrigation disappeared, and the British government constructed enormous new works and organized the settlement of millions of people in what was barren country. In the Punjab, wheat, millet and other foodstuffs are grown, and in the lower Indus valley, grain, rice and cotton are obtained.

The very numerous oases of the desert belt of northern Africa and south-western Asia are watered from wells, springs or small streams. They are of various sizes, but no large works are required for their irrigation ; the peasants grow grain, vege-tables and fruit for their own use, and dates both for home consumption and for export. The date palm is characteristic of these oases ; with adequate water at its roots it can flourish even when the water and soil are too saline for other productions. On the cooler plateaus of Iran and Turkistan, grain, vegetables and some fruits can be grown ; the cultivation of the vine has spread even to the oases of Central Asia where it must be protected from the winter cold by being buried under mounds of earth. In Russian Turkistan large amounts of cotton are grown by irrigation from the Syr Daria and the Amu Daria.

Similar productions come from the irrigated areas of the New World. In the United States and Mexico, engineering works lead water from the Western Cordillera into arid and semi-arid highland basins which yield grain, vegetables and fruits, and also alfalfa for feeding cattle ; the coastal areas of the south of California also depend upon water from the Cor-dillera. In South America, the Andes supply the Atacama–Peruvian desert for plantations of sugar-cane and the arid region of Argentina for sugar, rice, alfalfa and fruit. In Aus-tralia, also, there is production of fruit and cattle fodder ; here, most of the irrigation is in the central and lower courses of the Murray-Darling river system.

In many regions irrigation is complicated by the need for adequate drainage. This is obviously the case in delta lands where the ground is apt to be waterlogged ; in inland basins, too, a problem arises when the water brings with it dissolved salts and alkalis and, after evaporation, leaves on the surface crusts and efflorescences which prevent further utilization of the ground. On the other hand, in several areas surplus water is used for power ; it turns turbines which generate electricity, and this can be carried by cables to considerable distances and employed for lighting, heating and mechanical power.

Oasis irrigation was one of the most important factors in the cultural advance of mankind. From the primitive use of flood water, the art of agriculture developed in many ways, growing new crops and utilizing improved implements ; domesticated animals were employed to draw the plough as well as to transport goods in wheeled carts. From the irrigated river valleys, such improvements in methods spread to distant regions.

In other matters, too, developments in irrigation brought advances. Thus in ancient Egypt each family could no longer live and work by itself on its own plot of land ; the waters had to be controlled over great stretches of country, and this involved the formation of a State in which the water, the land and the people were organized by officials so that large numbers of men worked in co-operation on the irrigation schemes. Several branches of science owe their early development to the problems which had to be solved : the construction of the irrigation works and the utilization of water- and wind-power led to engineering, and this also achieved the building of great roads and of the palaces and pyramids of the Egyptian kings ; systems of writing, measuring and calculating had to be devised ; astronomical observations of the sun, moon and stars were necessary to foretell the time of the return of the floods ; the invention of geometry was required to mark out again, after the floods, the boundaries of land-holdings on the flat, featureless ground. The necessary division of labour among the specialized groups and classes of people meant that the productions had to be distributed, and commerce was organized to deal with the surplus. To accommodate the rulers and officials and to give centres for industries and trade, cities were laid out.

The numerous cultural advances related to irrigation effected such radical changes in the appearance of the lands that a new phenomenon appeared on the earth—a " cultural landscape." In this the larger features of the relief remained, but much of the natural vegetation was replaced by cultivated plants ; also, as far as man had occupied the country, the buildings and many results of his labours formed elements in the cultural landscape, and manifested even the workings of his mind.

In most oases of the present time productivity is so great that a large number of people can be supported on a given area ; dense populations are the rule. The ways in which the land is owned or rented, i.e. the methods of land tenure, vary greatly because not only the land itself but also the provision of water is involved. In the case of the oases proper the owners of small patches of land may have their own wells or springs ; peasant proprietorship is common. Where river or canal engineering is necessary, this may be undertaken by commercial enterprises which sell the water to the owners of the land, and might in some cases hold them almost at their mercy. Hence some large irrigation schemes are under the control, and some are under the direct management, of the State, which determines the conditions both of the supply of water and of its use. Elsewhere, farmers may be authorized to form co-operative societies of their own to supply their needs.

Plantation Agriculture.—Three hundred years ago, Europeans had begun to establish colonies, known as plantations, in inter-tropical and tropical regions in order to obtain commodities, e.g. cane sugar, tobacco and cotton, which were sent back to European countries. Although the word " plantations " originally referred to the settlements which were " planted " abroad, the term also suits the kind of crops obtained, for practically all are obtained from trees or shrubs planted, not sown ; they now produce also tea, coffee, rubber, bananas, cacao, copra (dried coconut kernels from which oil is pressed) and sisal (yielding fibre for twine and rope).

By no means the whole supply of these commodities comes from plantations, for some part is obtained under other systems of cultivation ; all plantations, however, are carried on with the main object of exporting their production. Hence it follows that plantations are business concerns and the type of cultivation is essentially different from the subsistence agriculture of the forms of inter-tropical agriculture already described. As a rule the plantations are on relatively large-scale holdings which require a considerable amount of capital, expert knowledge and skilled supervisors ; in general, the capital and organization were first supplied from European or American sources, and the supervisors were White men who remained only for a period of some years on the plantations. Most of the considerable amount of labour required on plantations is drawn from the local inhabitants or from immigrants from other inter-tropical or tropical regions ; moreover, the heavy seasonal needs such as planting and picking (for effective machinery for gathering tea, coffee, sugar and rubber is not yet devised) often have to be met by bringing in workers from neighbouring areas.

In the early days the labourers were often slaves, and even later they were recruited in a form not very different from slavery ; now their condition has generally improved, though an indirect form of compulsion may still exist, as for instance where Natives have to pay a tax to the governments of colonies and the only way to obtain the money is to work in alien enterprises such as plantations and mines.

In recent years, a development has become widespread in which the Natives have undertaken the production of one special commodity for export ; for example, two-thirds of the large amount of cacao obtained from the Guinea coast of West Africa comes from the holdings of African growers, encouraged by manufacturers of cocoa and chocolate and aided by the advice and assistance of the governments of the colonies concerned. Other examples of commodities produced under this kind of native cultivation are cotton from Uganda, copra from the Pacific Islands, yerba maté from Brazil and sugar from Mauritius and Fiji. In such cases holdings are relatively small.

Some plantations have been made in order to substitute scientific growing of the trees and efficient collection of their yield for the often haphazard procuring of wild products, generally of poor quality ; examples are rubber now grown in Malaya, Ceylon and the East Indies, and cinchona (for quinine) in Java, the plantation yield of both commodities having practically superseded the natural growth in South America.

It may be further noted that both rubber and cinchona, after having been planted first under the direction of White men, are now obtained also by coloured people in the Malay region. Other commodities, too, are obtained both by alien and by Native owners ; e.g. tea is produced on large-scale European- or Native-owned plantations in India, Ceylon and the East Indies, while it is grown also on the small-scale holdings of the peasants of China and Japan. Cane sugar is another example of a commodity produced under different types of ownership.

The common characteristic of plantation agriculture is the concentration upon one main crop, and as this is destined for sale, the enterprise is liable to suffer from changes in the market price ; a glut in a particular commodity means a heavy fall in the world price, and perhaps bankruptcy of planters, reduction of the producing areas and loss of the means of livelihood of the workers. Most forms of monoculture (one-crop farming) face commercial risks which are due to conditions in distant parts of the world, in addition to climatic variations and consequent bad harvests in the producing regions.

Some plantation commodities are produced within a markedly limited area : e.g. bananas are exported mainly from the mainland and islands bordering the Caribbean Sea ; quinine from Java ; cloves from the islands Zanzibar and Pemba ; coconuts and their products from the islands bordering or within the Pacific Ocean. On the contrary, other commodities have an unusually wide range of production. Cane sugar is exported largely from several groups of islands : the West Indies, the East Indies, and the Pacific Islands near the Tropic of Cancer ; smaller amounts come from mainland coastal belts, e.g. in Brazil, Guiana, Peru, Queensland and Natal. It must be noted, however, that the considerable production of cane sugar in India and China is not obtained from plantations, as the term is here used, nor does it even satisfy the home needs of those countries. Coffee is another widely distributed commodity ; although the greatest centre is in eastern Brazil, it is also a " Caribbean " production, and several other areas lie on uplands around the Indian Ocean.

By reviewing the regions in which plantations have been formed, it will be seen that some of them have the equatorial type of climate and others the hot, rainy-summer type. Most are fairly close to the sea, though there are marked exceptions in the relatively recent developments on the inland plateaus of East and South Africa.

The maritime position of most plantations, besides satisfying the special climatic requirements of particular crops, has two general advantages : it tempers the heat for the managers and workers, and it facilitates the export of the products and the import of equipment and food.

The sugar plantations of coastal districts of Queensland between latitudes 16° and 26° S. are exceptional in being carried on entirely by white labour under a tropical climate. There is also some production of cotton by white labour in tropical areas of Queensland. It may be noticed that in this section cotton-growing in the south of the United States has not been included ; like the sugar production of Australia, cotton-growing in North America began under the usual plantation system, but the abolition of slavery led to such modifications that it is now better described as a form of sub-tropical cultivation.

Tropical and Sub-tropical Rainy-summer Cultivation.—*South-eastern Asia.* No sharp dividing line can be drawn between the more productive kinds of inter-tropical and tropical fixed tillage (e.g. some of the native agriculture in the East Indies) and tropical small-holding cultivation like that of India and southern China. Here much of the farming is of the subsistence type meeting the direct needs of the dense populations, and it produces rice, cotton and other crops requiring considerable heat and rain at the same time. In the transitional Indo-Chinese Peninsula, agriculture shows several stages of evolution, while the more easily cultivated parts have products similar to those of southern China. Except on the forested highlands and wooded slopes, there is a sufficient amount and variety of production for the Peninsula as a whole to be grouped among the tropical crop-lands.

It is in China and Japan, however, that intensive methods of cultivation and the associated mode of life show themselves in most pronounced form. One of the earliest civilizations was that of China ; it probably arose in connection with the cultivation of the loess in the North China Plain, and the arts of agriculture gradually spread from there throughout the Far East. In southern China with the tropical rainy-summer type of climate, and in central China and southern Japan with the sub-tropical rainy-summer type, a most intensive form of cultivation is carried on by families owning several extremely small and scattered plots of land, together amounting to about two acres on an average ; on the produce of these they live a hard and often precarious life.

The ground is very thoroughly worked, largely by hoeing and by spade digging, and also by " wet ploughing " of the rice-fields, the ploughs being often drawn by water-buffalo. Irrigation is a necessity for rice-growing and is used also to supplement the rainfall for other crops. The soil is kept in such excellent condition, by very careful manuring and an ancient system of rotation of crops, that periods of fallow are not necessary even though the yields are great.   The long series of operations involved in the cultivation of rice makes heavier demands on the industry and patience of the workers than most crops, and men, women and children must all take their part ; on the other hand, the yield of rice is correspondingly high, and as it is the main food of China and Japan, it makes possible the extraordinarily dense farming population of these countries.   Because the temperatures over most of the region are sufficient for the growth of plants throughout the year, it is possible by skilful alternation of plants which ripen at different seasons to practise double-cropping, i.e. two crops may be obtained from the same ground in the course of a year ; wheat and beans are grown after rice over central and southern China, southern Korea and most of Japan.   Few animals are kept in this tropical and sub-tropical agricultural region of Asia, with the exceptions of water-buffalo, and of pigs and poultry which form an important though relatively small element in the diet of the Chinese ; recently cattle-rearing has been slowly increasing in Japan.

It may be pointed out that on the map on p. 206, the northern limit of this type of cultivation is drawn to coincide approximately with that of the main production of rice in China, Korea and Japan.   It also marks the area in which cotton is one of the chief crops, although in China cotton cultivation overlaps northward into lowlands of the Hwang Ho Basin, while in Japan the land is used predominantly for growing food, cotton being largely imported from other lands.   In central China, the southern part of Korea and much of Japan, the production of silk has been of great importance, though artificial silk is now a serious menace to the industry.   The growing of the mulberry trees, the care of the silkworms and the preparation of the fibre together constitute a very intensive form of farm-work.

In China a distinction may be made between the south—i.e. the basin of the Si Kiang and the coastal lands on both sides of Canton—and central China—i.e. the basin of the middle and lower Yangtze Kiang with the adjacent coastal districts. Central China has a sub-tropical climate and its type of farming is that described above, but in southern China the climate is tropical and the cultivation has some distinctive features. With a longer period of hot weather, two harvests of rice can be obtained in a year on the same plot, in addition to another of a grain or other crop during the cooler season. The greater production of rice makes possible an even further reduction in the size of the peasants' holdings than in the central areas. Another common food crop in the tropical south is the sweet potato, and sugar-cane and citrus fruits are important products.

In India there are various types of agriculturists in the south, including those who practise primitive forms of cultivation as well as those who can be classed with the skilled farmers of the Far East. Cultivation in India is most developed in the north, partly because the later immigrants into this region are at a higher level of general advance, and partly because in recent times the British government aided farming by provision of large-scale irrigation apart from that described earlier as of the oasis type. On smaller scales, irrigation has been long employed in other districts occasionally subject to drought.

Taking India as a whole, rice occupies a far greater area than any other crop, though it is mainly grown in the wetter parts. Cotton has a different distribution, being obtained from areas of less rainfall ; wheat, too, is a product of drier parts of the country and much of it is grown under irrigation. An important part of the food-supply of India comes from other grains, which include millets and the sorghum known as " jowar," and from pulses comprising peas, chickpeas or " gram," beans and lentils.

In general, cultivation in India is not so efficient as in China and Japan, and the yields are consequently lower. Hoeing is less practised and there is less careful manuring. Rice-growing in particular does not receive the minute attention given to it in the Far East ; on the other hand, where cotton is grown for export it is more effectively tended than in China. In India there is always a considerable amount of ground lying fallow, and in addition there are large areas of unused land—the " jungle " especially common in the south.

In the north of India, climatic conditions, aided by irrigation, allow the cultivation of two contrasted types of plants which may be grown in rotation during the same year. The hot-weather or " kharif " crops which are reaped in autumn include rice, cotton, sugar-cane, jute, millets and some pulses ; among the cold-weather or " rabi " crops which are reaped in spring are other pulses, wheat and barley.

In contrast to the Far East, India lacks pig-keeping, but has very large numbers of cattle, sheep and goats which are often pastured on the fallow and unused lands. Bullocks and buffaloes are used for transport and ploughing, and the cows yield milk from which is made " ghi," i.e. butter clarified to the consistency of thick oil. Indian cattle-keeping and dairying is in special need of development, for production is small in comparison with the number of animals, it is often of poor quality and sometimes injurious to health, and its cost is probably higher than anywhere else in the world. The reasons are complicated : ignorance of hygienic principles, the influence of religious ideas, the consequent reluctance of the government to intervene, and the impossibility of large-scale improvements such as are possible in crop-raising through irrigation systems.

In China, Japan and India agriculture is the main support of a dense population, which normally has a very low standard of living and is subject to famine when the monsoons fail. Apart from the highlands on which forests still remain, these countries are tropical or sub-tropical crop-lands.

South-eastern United States.—In North America, the region of sub-tropical, rainy-summer cultivation is situated in the south-east of the U.S.A., and corresponds broadly with the area politically known as " the southern States," or simply " the South." On a map showing the smaller agricultural regions of the United States it would include in its northern part the " cotton belt " and in the south the " humid sub-tropical zone." This latter zone produces rice on floodable land in the western coastal area of the Gulf of Mexico, sugar-cane on the delta land of the Mississippi, and in Florida citrus fruits and " truck-crops," i.e. vegetables sent by truck in express trains for the winter supply of the cities of the northern States.

The cotton belt of the United States is the greatest cotton-producing region in the world ; till recently it was a one-crop area, but cotton is now grown in rotation with other crops, especially maize and hay for cattle and pigs. Negro slave labour was the basis of the early cultivation of cotton, and still much of the work is done by Negroes.

In connection with the important matter of land tenure, it must be noted that after the abolition of slavery the large plantations disappeared, and most of the farms were held on a tenancy basis, either by White people or by Negroes. There were two systems of tenure : one by the payment of a fixed rent, the other by " share-cropping," i.e. the sharing of the crop return between owner and farmer. The farms of the southern States (although at least twenty times as large as the holdings of the peasants in the corresponding region in China) were generally considerably smaller than those of the northern States ; the land was often worked with the aid of a plough drawn by a single mule—an exceptional state of affairs in the U.S.A., where machinery and large-scale working are typical. Exceptional, too, was the low standard of living, for there was much poverty both among the coloured population and among the " poor Whites."

Now, however, a further change is proceeding rapidly, stimulated by the Second World War. Many of the poor Whites and Negroes were required for army service or went north into war industries, and to make up for lack of labour, agricultural machinery was widely introduced—notably the mechanical cotton-picker. For mechanization there were two requisites : the provision of capital and the formation of large farms by the joining of small ones, and both needs were supplied by companies largely of northern origin. Partly as a result of the changes, many of the Negro and White workers did not return to the region and the rural population tended to diminish ; yet the productivity of the South increased.

The farmers of this North American sub-tropical crop-land do not suffer from floods and droughts to such a degree as those of the regions of the same type in Asia, but their great scourge is the cotton boll weevil—an insect pest which did much to break down their dependence on one crop, and is still serious.

South Brazil.—South of the Brazilian region of tropical plantations is a sub-tropical area which as yet is relatively undeveloped, and therefore may make a larger contribution to the world's food-supply. In the coastal and lower parts, some crops which need considerable heat are grown, e.g. rice, bananas and sugar-cane ; on the cooler plateau are the chief crops, which include maize, vines, beans and potatoes, while large numbers of pigs are kept. The farmers, largely of German and Italian descent, possess small properties cleared from the forest ; they use rather crude methods, subsist largely on their own products and in a number of ways lead a pioneer-like life. As a whole, the region is in process of evolution into a crop-land.

Australia.—In the eastern coastal areas of Australia, south of the belt of tropical plantations, there is a crop-land of sub-tropical rainy-summer type of cultivation in which some of the production is for sale in other districts and some for home use. The region extends from the south of Queensland where, in the neighbourhood of Brisbane, sugar, cotton and fruits, such as bananas and pineapples, are obtained (of course, entirely by White labour) ; it continues along the coast of New South Wales, where oranges are grown north of Sydney, while from the south come peaches, plums, pears and apples. Throughout this belt, however, most of the cultivated land is given over to sorghum, maize, millet and lucerne, with other crops for cattle for the dairy industry and for pig and poultry keeping.

Sub-tropical Dry-summer Cultivation.—In regions with the " Mediterranean " climate, the warm and wet winters followed by hot, dry and sunny summers permit the growth and ripening of warmth-loving fruits which have become the typical production of regions of this type ; of great importance are the olive, vine, and citrus fruits—especially oranges and lemons. Wheat and barley grow during the winter and are harvested in early summer. Irrigation is often employed to supplement the rainfall, and this makes possible not only better and safer yields of the usual " Mediterranean " fruits and grain, but also the occasional production of rice, cotton, maize and other crops of summer-rain regions. The lack of natural grasses, save on the more mountainous areas, often prevents the pasturing of cattle and limits that of sheep and goats.

A short label applicable to the regions with this type of cultivation is " sub-tropical fruit- and grain-lands."

In the *Mediterranean region proper* are the lands where " wheat, wine and oil " have provided the main sustenance of the people from time immemorial. In the coast-lands bordering the Mediterranean Sea, the lowlands are not extensive and the hillsides are commonly terraced. The individual plots of land are therefore small, irrigation by small streams from the uplands is simple, and by intensive work with the hoe the peasants from their small properties obtain quite a variety of grain and fruit crops, besides vegetables. Yet the total yield is not great and often a rather low standard of living is their reward. There is also a considerable export of olive oil, wine and grapes, citrus fruits and figs. Milk from sheep and goats is used as food, commonly in the form of sour milk and cheese. Some animals are driven up to the better-watered mountain pastures during the dry summer and brought down to the villages for the winter; this transhumance, with summer upland huts for those of the people who tend the flocks and herds, is characteristic of the Mediterranean Lands.

In *North America*, the Central Valley of California is a very productive region of this type; it specializes in growing for export and uses most efficient methods. In the New World, the early settlers acquired much larger areas of land than those possessed by farmers or peasants in the Old World, hence many of the land-holdings in the " Mediterranean " region of America are relatively large; also large-scale irrigation is utilized, abundant water being brought from the adjoining mountains. Wheat and alfalfa are grown, but the great production is of fruit and vegetables, especially those which can be sold at prices able to cover the cost of transport by rail or ocean carriers. A high degree of commercial development has been attained, for example in drying and canning the fruit and vegetables in plants operated by machinery.

In *South America* the Central Valley of Chile has several similarities to the Central Valley of California, including the supply of irrigation water from the mountains. But in Chile, as a legacy of the past, large landowners hold their workers in a semi-servile condition; these people toil hard and live miserably. Moreover, the production is largely for consumption within the country, and hence generally lacks the stimulation of competition in export trade. Wheat is the principal crop, and barley and maize occupy much land; alfalfa is grown as cattle feed. Fruit trees, too, are cultivated, and vines yield grapes used mainly for making wine for home consumption.

In *South Africa*, the south-west of the province of the Cape of Good Hope has, from the first days of European occupation, been a region where wheat- and vine-growing have been characteristic. Its main developments have been in the use of irrigation from the Cape Ranges, in the export of wheat and wine to Britain and elsewhere, and in the cultivation and export of the " Mediterranean " fruits. In exporting to Europe, South Africa has an advantage that its grain and fruit ripen at different times of the year from those of the northern hemisphere, and reach Europe during periods of relative scarcity in the markets.

In *Australia*, regions with this " fruit and grain " type of production are found in the south-west corner of West Australia and the south-east corner of South Australia.   In these States of the Commonwealth of Australia, wheat is the chief product, but the yield is low on the average and is markedly variable. The vine is grown in both States, and wine is exported ; this is mainly done from South Australia, where cultivation is aided by water brought from the neighbouring " Highlands," but in the plateau region of Western Australia the limited amount of irrigation is dependent upon artesian wells.   There is also some cultivation of other fruits.   In general, the productivity of the " Mediterranean " regions of Australia is not great as compared with their area.

CHAPTER XV

MODES OF LIFE—AGRICULTURE (2)

Mid-latitude Plough Farming.—In mid-latitudes the plough is the typical agricultural implement, and its use is closely bound up with the distinguishing characteristics of the farming. Although the plough is employed to some extent in warmer latitudes, it is the essential basis of farming in the cooler parts of the world. Much of these areas was originally forested ; the ground had first to be cleared and the stumps of the trees removed, and it was then prepared for planting by the turning of the soil with ploughs which worked over comparatively large fields. Thus, as compared with the *intensive* hoe cultivation of the warmer regions, plough farming of the cooler regions is normally *extensive*, even though small areas of the ploughed lands may be further worked with the hoe and though specially valuable crops may be produced by intensive methods.

Mid-latitude plough farming has spread into regions of several different types of climate, but in all of them only one harvest a year is possible ; also, until recent scientific improvements, the yield of the crops in these cooler latitudes has generally been less than that of those which receive more heat in their growing period. Hence, as a given unit of land has not produced a large supply of food, the number of people it could support has been comparatively small, and an increase of population has stimulated movement of some of the people to unoccupied lands ; in this way wide areas have come under the plough.

Because the regions over which plough farming has spread differ widely from one another both in their natural conditions and in the traditions of their peoples, there are considerable differences in the methods and the results of farming of this kind.

In *Eastern Asia*, besides the " wet " ploughing of the warm rice lands with the aid of water-buffaloes, in the mid-latitude rainy-summer region of the Hwang Ho basin there has been from very early days " dry " ploughing with the aid of oxen and donkeys. Here wheat, millets, sorghum, soya and other beans are the chief food crops, and upon these a dense population is supported by intensive cultivation and thorough manuring of small-holdings, for similar methods and traditions dominate life here as in the warmer parts of China. Although the Hwang Ho lowlands are of unusual fertility, they are very liable both to disastrous floods and to droughts ; alternations of good harvests and famines are the lot of the farmers of North China.

Somewhat similar methods of farming as in China have spread to the lowland areas of Korea with the same type of climate, and immigrants from North China into Manchuria grow much the same crops as in their native land. In Manchuria there has been a notable development of the cultivation of the soya bean, which is of extraordinary nutritive value ; it takes the place of meat among many of the almost vegetarian people of the Far East, it is pressed for oil, it supplies food for animals, and it is now exported in great amount.

With varied forms of food production, mid-latitude plough farming has converted the plains of North China and Manchuria into a crop-land of a type quite distinct from that of the sub-tropical region to the south.

In south-eastern Siberia the climate is marked by its short summer, and is therefore less favourable to cultivation. Forest still predominates over most of the region and farming is limited to river valleys ; the hardier grains, vegetables and hay are obtained, and in general agriculture is much less productive than farther south. This type of farming is carried on also in the northernmost parts of Korea and Japan, and the general aspect of these three regions can be concisely expressed by the phrase : forests and farmlands.

Still farther to the north, in the sub-arctic climate region, the coniferous forest has given place to farming only in the valleys of the middle Lena river system. Apart from this area, agriculture is quite exceptional, being carried on in small and scattered spots and restricted to the hardiest forms. As a whole, the region may still be described in terms of the natural vegetation, viz. sub-arctic forest.

In *Europe*, the character of the agriculture was determined by the convergence of two streams of influence. (i) From the early civilizations of the Middle East came plough cultivation, especially of wheat and barley ; in Europe itself, however, was invented a heavy type of plough which, as contrasted with the simpler and more primitive form, enabled farmers to open the soil to a greater depth, to get bigger yields and to cultivate larger areas. (ii) From the pastoral peoples who migrated along the steppe-lands came increased knowledge of the rearing of flocks and herds and the use of their products. Thus developed the practice of " mixed farming," combining the growing of crops with the keeping of animals ; among its advantages are the use of animal manures to increase the yield of the crops and to maintain the fertility of the soil. Even so, only a relatively sparse population could be supported by agriculture until recent advances ; these include better rotation of crops, effective draining of wet soils and marshy areas, importation of natural manures and artificial production of fertilizers, and the scientific breeding of more useful varieties of plants and animals.

Meanwhile, the increase of population engaged in industry and commerce brought about an increased demand for food, especially in the form of cereals ; hence wheat, barley, oats and maize were increasingly grown where conditions were most favourable. Later, when supplies of grain were brought from overseas, the farmers in some parts of Europe, e.g. in Denmark and the Netherlands, turned to intensive dairy farming, keeping their herds largely upon imported cattle food. In some areas, too, there was great increase in the cultivation of " industrial crops " such as flax, sugar-beet and tobacco. In the warmer parts, fruits were increasingly produced and the making and export of wine became important in certain districts.

In the Soviet lands of eastern Europe and western Siberia, a markedly greater yield resulted from the formation of large-scale mechanized farms organized on a collective basis.

In Britain, the Second World War, with its need for reducing imports of food, brought about two important developments. The first was the ploughing up of much permanent pasture, to bring it into a rotation by which crops of grain or roots alternate with leys, i.e. areas of sown grasses or clover. This " ley farming " or " alternate husbandry " had been long practised in Britain on the borders of England and Scotland and had been recently developed by scientific research in certain parts of Wales ; it was now extended widely in the British Isles. The system has a double advantage : leys give a greater and better supply of fodder than permanent pastures, while the grass rotation helps to maintain the fertility and yield of grain-bearing land. The second change was due to increased attention given to the nutritional value of the food available in war-time. In particular, it was realized that the provision of essential vitamins in the diet of the people needed an increased production of milk and of vegetables. Hence the farming was organized so that an adequate amount of these dietetic necessities should be obtained in this country, even in post-war times when grain and other farming products could be again imported.

In western and central Europe, considered as a whole, the cool temperate climate with rain at all seasons encourages mid-latitude plough cultivation; yet within this region three varieties of farming may be noted, the differences being due in part to natural conditions of climate and relief, and in part to the traditions or policies of the peoples of the respective areas. (1) On the wetter Atlantic margins permanent pastures occupy much of the farmed area, while even the ploughed land may be devoted to a considerable degree to producing animal food; these pastoral regions are relatively scantily populated. (2) On the highlands and uplands only the valleys can be cultivated. The highlands are largely still wooded, and at a rather lower level the land is used as far as possible for summer pastures; hence transhumance is common, and in the upland huts cheese is made from cows' and goats' milk. In these regions, too, only a scanty population can get a living. (3) Over by far the largest part of Peninsular Europe, arable land is dominant, although almost everywhere the aim is mixed farming; the productivity of the work varies with the growing of particular crops, but on the whole there is a fairly dense rural population, and the general standard of living is higher than in most of the agricultural regions of the world. Cultivation occupies so much of the area that most of the region may be described as a crop-land.

In eastern Europe, including most of Scandinavia, four farming areas may be distinguished in succession from north to south. (i) In the north, adjoining the tundra, is the region with the sub-arctic type of climate where coniferous forests are dominant and agricultural clearings are still small. Plough and livestock farming has extended into this region, but it is not one of its main features. Recently, special methods of cultivation for this climate have been devised. There is, for instance, the process of " vernalization " : grain is stored in cellars during the winter, and when spring approaches it is there moistened and kept at certain temperatures until it begins to sprout ; then it is planted, and grows so quickly that it ripens in sub-arctic conditions.

(ii) To the south of this area in eastern Europe, the climate is of the mid-latitude, short-summer type ; the mixed forests have been more extensively cleared and farming is more productive. Rye and oats are the chief cereals, vegetables are grown, and the keeping of cattle and pigs is an important part of the work of the people. Yet a considerable proportion of the land is still wooded, and the region may be described as one of forests and farmlands.

(iii) Across most of the southern part of eastern Europe lies the better-watered part of the mid-latitude, light-rain climate region. In this belt, moderately high temperatures and sufficient rainfall during the summer allow a wide variety of crop production like that of the adjoining region of central Europe. Grain, including much maize and wheat, and root crops supply food for men and animals, industrial plants are grown, and vegetables and fruit of many kinds also contribute to the fairly high standard of living of a dense population. From the agricultural point of view this belt is a continuaton of the cropland of western and central Europe.

(iv) In the south-east, a scarcity of rain limits production; the drier part of the mid-latitude, light-rain climate region has only recently been farmed on modern lines, and mainly produces grain, especially drought-resistant varieties of wheat. Towards the more arid parts, cultivation gives place progressively to the grazing of animals on poor natural pastures. In its farming aspect, this region may be labelled a " grain- and grazing-land."

From European Russia, modern forms of cultivation have spread into *Western Asia*, and two farming regions extend from Europe for a considerable distance to the east. South of the almost unchanged sub-arctic forest is a relatively narrow belt of forest and farmland, and to the south again is a broader belt of grain- and grazing-land. These regions continue as far as the highlands of central Asia, but farther east farming is carried on only in specially suitable places along the line of the Trans-Siberian railway, until it reaches the eastern Asiatic regions.

In *North America*, mid-latitude plough cultivation has developed to the greatest extent in the mid-latitude, rainy-summer climate region. In the part of this region bordering the Atlantic early colonists grew much the same crops as those to which they were accustomed in western and central Europe, and here the agricultural production is now of very varied type with dairy farming playing a considerable part ; towards the south of this Atlantic area, winter wheat (i.e. wheat sown in the autumn) is an important crop and tobacco has been a valuable product from plantation days to the present time.

Across the Appalachians the wide, generally level expanses were opened to settlement before adequate labour was available and, to remedy the lack, mechanical power was applied to agriculture. First steam engines, and then internal-combustion engines using petrol, were employed to work huge fields, not only ploughing but also carrying out all the subsequent operations to the final reaping, storing and transport of the harvests. Thus the vast extent of this region was rapidly brought under cultivation ; moreover, the use of machinery in America was adopted in Europe and was a considerable factor in aiding the development of farming in that continent.

The use of machines on large farms with relatively few workers led in America to a different type of distribution of the agricultural population from that of Europe. In the Old World the most common arrangement is for the farmers to live in groups in villages surrounded by their lands—a heritage from the past when forests were gradually opened up from scattered clearings and when farm-houses were built closely together to resist attack. In the " Middle West " of America, the open prairies and peaceful conditions allowed wide-scattered homesteads to lie in the centre of their own holdings ; hence, until other means of livelihood were developed in the region, the farmers lived almost isolated lives.

In the central part of North America, north of the " cotton belt," maize, winter wheat, other grains and root crops, and in the east tobacco, are obtained ; much of the farm produce is used for the fattening of enormous numbers of cattle and hogs. North-west from this area is the " spring wheat belt," where the winters are too cold for the grain to be sown before the spring, while to the north-east is an area where hay is produced in large amount and dairying is important. Over much of the central areas of the United States the work, though " extensive," is productive and maintains a fairly dense farming population at a high standard of living. Broadly speaking, from the

Atlantic coast of the northern part of U.S.A. to about longitude 100° W. the country is of the crop-land type.

Farther west, both in the United States and in Canada, the growing of grain, especially wheat, together with sheep- and cattle-rearing, spread into the region of light rain, which became a grain- and grazing-land. Here, however, dangerous advances were made. At times of good or average rainfall settlement extended westward and a system of " dry farming " was adopted ; conservation of soil moisture was attempted by loosening the surface and so preventing the loss of water by capillary action. At times of drought, however, the pulverized soil was blown from this " dust bowl," farms became useless and were abandoned. This is one instance of the serious problem of soil erosion, discussed at the end of this chapter.

Farther north, the mid-latitude, short-summer climate region straddles the international boundary from the Atlantic westward till it swings northward in the Prairie Provinces of Canada. In this belt spring wheat and other grains are grown and in the eastern part dairy farming has become important locally ; yet large tracts of forest remain, the agricultural population is generally scanty, and the region is a forest and farmland.

On the west of the continent, parts of the dry interior plateaus of the Cordillera in British Columbia and the adjoining state of Washington are utilized for wheat production, and in some of the valleys fruit is grown with the aid of irrigation. The coast-lands of British Columbia and Washington, which have a climate comparable with that of western Europe, have but small areas of lowland in which agriculture is possible. Forests and farm-lands are therefore characteristic of the mid-latitude Pacific coastal region.

In *South America*, the only large area developed by cultivation under the plough is the Pampa around the Rio de la Plata and the lower Parana river ; this area lies mainly in mid-latitude, rainy-summer climate region where the dominant crops are maize and wheat, and alfalfa is grown to help with the feeding of large numbers of cattle, pigs and sheep. Near the lower courses of the rivers and by the estuary, the region has been transformed into a crop-land, and the export trade has determined much of the production in this part of South America. In particular, towards the end of the nineteenth century came the development of processes for freezing and chilling meat during its transport across the Tropics to Europe ; this allowed a great development of cattle-rearing and stimulated the growing of fodder.

Machinery is commonly used, especially on the many large farms. As in the " Mediterranean " climate region in Chile, so in this eastern part of South America the past acquisition of great estates by Spaniards has left its mark in the frequency of large holdings. The estancias, once extensive cattle ranges, are now often large farms under a single management.

In the areas of less rain, farther to the west and south, development came later. Here are wheat-growing districts, in which more of the farming is done on a smaller scale ; the land has been leased to Italians and other immigrants who either pay a definite rent or share the varying proceeds of the harvests with their landlords. The still drier areas are mainly given up to livestock ranching ; hence much of southern Argentina is a grain- and grazing-land. As droughts are of fairly frequent occurrence, agricultural prosperity is rather hazardous, especially when the droughts bring a scourge of locusts from the semi-arid region north-west of the Pampa.

On the west side of South America and in about the same latitudes, there is a small area of plough farming in the mid-latitude, rainy climate region in Chile. The cool, wet climate and the products broadly resemble those of the north-western coasts of Europe and North America, and the area is of the forest and farmland type.

In *South Africa*, plough cultivation by Europeans extended first over the interior plateaus with the mid-latitude, light-rain climate, and then northward to some parts of the tropical, rainy-summer region which because of their height have somewhat similar temperatures.

The area with most cultivation is in the Union of South Africa, where there has been most White settlement ; here the production of maize and wheat and the rearing of cattle and sheep are carried on partly to satisfy the local demand derived from the mining and other developments of the Union. Export is hampered by the interior situation and the general lack of facilities for communication. Farther north in Southern and Northern Rhodesia there are fewer White settlers, there is a smaller local market and export is even more difficult ; some maize and tobacco are grown and cattle are kept.

Although the area of South Africa over which plough cultivation has spread appears on a map to be large, the farms are often scattered, and especially in the north they are interspersed between lands worked by native hoe cultivation. Also, the yield of the crops is generally rather low and, as in South America, harvests may be ruined by drought and locusts.

In *Australia*, plough cultivation occupies the south-east of the continent, overlapping the mid-latitude, rainy climate region of the coasts and uplands of eastern Victoria, and in the interior the more extensive area of light rains.

The latter region is of the grain- and grazing-land type. The main crop is wheat, and the work is of a markedly extensive character, labour being scarce and machinery therefore necessary ; though the yield is by no means high there is a surplus for export. In the same area sheep are grazed on the natural pastures, and the production both of wool and wheat suffers considerable fluctuation due to occasional droughts.

In the better-watered coastal region the farming is much more varied ; besides the growing of cereals, cattle-rearing and dairying are carried on. In Tasmania the climate is of the same type, the growing of oats and hay, potatoes and apples being indicative of its relatively cool and wet climate. Both in south-eastern Victoria and in Tasmania, there is so much wooded upland that these areas fall into the category of forests and farmlands.

New Zealand has a similar climate, and with its large proportion of forest on uplands and highlands it, too, has the general character of forest and farmland. Economically, it is in the main a pastoral country, in so far as the object of farming is to obtain animal products—chiefly butter and cheese from cattle in North Island, and wool and mutton from sheep in South Island. Yet the basis of this production is plough farming, the animals being fed not on natural pastures but on cultivated lands sown with imported types of grass ; hence the high yield and the large exports of the pastoral industry. In addition a relatively small area is under wheat with a high yield.

SOIL LOSSES AND THEIR PREVENTION

Whenever man interferes with nature he runs a risk ; he upsets a balance which has been very gradually brought into a state of virtual stability, and his actions may comparatively quickly cause unforeseen and perhaps disastrous changes. These undesired consequences may threaten farmers of all types and in all regions when they substitute their crops for the natural soil cover of grass or forest, or when they introduce their animals to feed on areas which had not previously supported them. By such actions the age-long processes of soil formation, by which the growth of food-plants has been made possible, are altered ; also, other changes imperil the continued existence of fertile soil unless counter-measures are taken.

Dangers to the soil, which in many countries have already become acute, are of two main kinds. One is a gradual impoverishment by the removal of constituents which supply nourishment for plants ; this clearly occurs when crops are harvested and their products are sent away from the neighbourhood, or when animals are fed upon pastures and the beasts or their products are exported—unless by artificial manuring or other means the loss is made good. This impoverishment is relatively slow, and with fertile soils it may not become apparent for years, yet in the long run it is only by good management that productivity can be maintained.

The second peril, a far more urgent and practically worldwide problem, is soil erosion : the rapid removal of large masses by water or wind. Where trees or grasses form a more or less continuous cover, their roots or other underground parts bind and protect the soil ; but if the natural vegetation is destroyed for the sake of cultivation or by grazing animals, the run-off of rain and the effects of weather gain increased power. Deep gullies may be cut in the surfaces and soils may be washed or blown away so that large districts become barren wastes.

Soil Impoverishment.—The chief cause of the impoverishment of the soil is the removal of certain constituents, especially phosphates, nitrogen, lime and potash. Some plants use up more of one particular material than others do ; for instance, the grain of wheat contains a relatively high proportion of nitrogen and therefore is a valuable proteid food for mankind, but for that very reason the repeated cropping of wheat seriously reduces the nitrogen content of the soil. As another example of a special need it may be mentioned that sugar-beet makes heavy demands on potash. Considered in general, however, the mixed farming carried on in Britain requires much

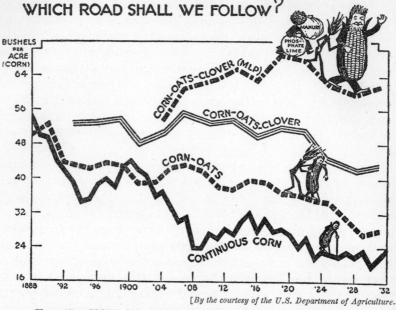

WHICH ROAD SHALL WE FOLLOW?

[By the courtesy of the U.S. Department of Agriculture.

FIG. 47.—HOW TO COMBAT SOIL IMPOVERISHMENT.

lime, while as regards an actual deficiency in the soil, low crop yields are frequently due to a lack of phosphorus.

A very ancient method of avoiding soil impoverishment is to give the land a rest and so to allow natural processes some opportunity of restoring the lost balance. This is done, for example, in shifting tillage ; again, for many centuries the plough farming of Europe gave to the fields in turn a period of fallow once in every two, three or four years.

Another old-established aid in maintaining fertility is the use of a rotation of crops which make varying demands upon the soil. The graph given above shows the reduction of yield by continuous cropping of corn, i.e. maize, on experimental field-plots in Illinois, U.S.A. Apart from seasonal variations due to weather conditions, over a period of about forty years the yield per acre decreased from about fifty bushels to less than twenty-four bushels. Where corn and oats were grown in rotation the reduction was not so great, and where clover was also taken into the scheme the yield diminished much less and even in the worst year was over forty bushels.

The introduction of clover into common farming practice

about the seventeenth century was important, for in addition to providing a valuable animal food it increased fertility (though the reason was not then known) by a positive addition to the supply of nitrogen to the soil. Clover, like beans, peas, vetches and alfalfa, belongs to the group of leguminous plants on the roots of which bacteria form nodules by utilizing nitrogen from the air; even if the above-ground parts of the plants are removed, the roots with nitrogenous nodules are ploughed into the soil and benefit subsequent crops. Mixed farming has a somewhat similar advantage in maintaining fertility, for the animal manure returns a certain amount of nitrogen and other elements to the soil, as well as some humus, while the spreading of cattle bedding on the fields has the additional value of improving the physical condition of the soil.

Returning to the diagram in Fig. 47 it is to be noted that the top part of the graph shows that not only can the yield of a farm be maintained ; it can even be increased if, in addition to a rotation of corn with oats and clover, animal manure and artificial fertilizers are applied to the soil. The letters " MLP " indicate manure and lime phosphate, and with this treatment the produce of the field plot was raised from about fifty to over sixty bushels per acre.

Other forms of good farm management have been evolved, and the practical problem of the present time is to induce, or to enable, farmers in general to follow the methods which are most suited to their requirements and their circumstances. But, taking a long view, it may be realized that other problems may arise. For example, in many parts of the world the soil constituents, after being utilized first by plants and then by man, are sent by modern methods of sanitation through sewers to the sea. In the sea-water a very small proportion may be utilized by marine plants and supply part of the needs of fish and thus may become of some use as human food, but the great proportion of the valuable soil material is lost to mankind.

Again, there may be a problem of continuance of the supply of some of the artificial fertilizers. In the rocks of the world as a whole there is an abundance of lime, and there is no difficulty about obtaining nitrogen. At the beginning of this century the greater part of the supply of nitrogenous fertilizer came from the enormous deposits of nitrates in the desert area of northern Chile, but although these are far from being exhausted they are now drawn upon to a comparatively small extent ; today the main sources are the by-products of the manufacture of gas, coke and other substances, and the synthetic production of nitrogen compounds from the air by electrical energy. Potash is chiefly obtained from minerals, beds of which are utilized in several countries where there are considerable reserves. Over wide areas potash salts, associated with which are sodium salts, are washed down by rivers, of course in small quantities in any particular case, and slowly accumulated in the ocean or in inland seas. It is possible that the salts may be extracted from sea-water on a large scale in the future, and already the brine of the Dead Sea is evaporated to obtain fertilizer material. Finally, phosphates, including the widely used superphosphates, are derived to a small extent from guano deposits, and to a larger degree from basic slag, a by-product of steel manufacture, but mainly from rocks of several kinds. Although phosphate reserves are great, they are not illimitable, and some scientists foresee a time when the constant requirements of phosphates can no longer be met.

Soil Erosion.—The United States' Department of Agriculture, in a publication addressed to farmers, thus begins its account of the problem : " Soil erosion is as old as agriculture. It began when the first heavy rain struck the first furrow turned by a crude implement of tillage in the hands of prehistoric man. It has been going on ever since, wherever man's culture of the earth has bared the soil to rain and wind."

To understand the situation in different regions of the world, one must distinguish between the action of running water and that of wind. Rain and streams bring about their greatest destruction in areas where there is considerable precipitation and the land surface has appreciable slopes. Where these factors are not very marked, there may be sheet erosion in which the top soil is so gradually and uniformly washed away over whole fields that the farmer may scarcely realize the cause of the gradual deterioration of the soil.

More common is gully erosion, where the rain collects in furrows and streamlets develop, progressively increasing their catchment-area ; after heavy rains they may visibly tear away their banks and beds, making great gashes in the fields. It is estimated by the Department of Agriculture that already in the United States, during the relatively short period of cultivation, fifty million acres of formerly good land have been ruined, three times as much has had its most productive soil washed away, and about the same expanse has been started upon a similar, literally downward, path.

Erosion by wind is most marked in regions of less rainfall and more level ground. For example, in the Great Plains of the west in the United States and Canada strong winds sweep up the lighter particles from the surface and produce great dust storms that travel across the continent, transport countless tons of soil and leave behind them barren wastes in place of farms and grazing-lands. A map of the United States showing the areas either moderately or severely affected by various types of erosion discloses only relatively small areas undamaged.

The other continents have been exposed to soil erosion in different degrees. South America, less exploited for cultivation, has suffered less than North America. The countries of central and north-western Europe have not experienced severe trouble, probably because gradual extension of farming has, in its slow development, adapted itself better to climatic conditions.

The lands around the Mediterranean Sea, however, with their typically hilly country descending steeply to the sea, and with alternate seasons of rain and drought, have by no means escaped. The cutting down of forests, and the eating of young shoots by goats, have increased the rapidity of the winter run-off and led to the removal of soil and even sub-soil. In fact, there has been not only loss to cultivation, but silting up of the lower courses of rivers and the formation of coastal swamps ; hence, too, have followed difficulties for navigation, together with an increase of breeding-places for malaria-carrying mosquitoes. Indeed, here are factors which have affected the history of the Mediterranean peoples, and even, it has been claimed, one cause of the weakening and final break-up of the Roman Empire.

In Asia, it appears that in southern and central China the careful use of the land has, as in western Europe, successfully fitted in with the relief and climatic conditions, but in the drier parts of northern China wind erosion has caused serious inroads upon once valuable areas of loess. Japan has suffered, on the other hand, from the attacks of heavy rain upon its mountainous surface. In different parts of India, with their contrasting types of climate, all forms of erosion have reduced the generally low productivity of the soil and thereby contributed to the low standard of living of the Indian people.

As might be expected from the arid or semi-arid conditions of the greater part of Australia, wind erosion is a menace in that continent. There, as in North America, pioneers advanced into the interior, ploughed up the soil and grazed animals much as they or their forefathers had done in better-watered regions, and as a consequence exposed their lands, animals and livelihood to the ravages which followed in the lean years of drought.

Africa is reported to have suffered, up to the present time, more than any other continent ; in several parts it has become increasingly difficult for the land to support its population. The most striking deterioration has occurred on the margins of the Sahara, where cultivable land has given place to scanty pasturage, and the semi-desert has in turn become almost completely devoid of vegetation. To what extent these changes are due to man's action in bringing about soil erosion or to natural changes in climate is a vexed question. A similar difficulty exists in determining the causes of depopulation observed in other desert regions.

If, then, the problem of soil erosion is so serious, what can be done about it ? Scientists, particularly those working for government agencies and advising farmers, point out that much harm has irretrievably been done but future trouble can be largely prevented.

The destruction of forests must obviously be stopped ; the cutting of timber must be so arranged that younger trees still remain to grow, while their litter on the surface and their roots below it protect the soil from water erosion.

In some semi-arid regions wind erosion may be checked by planting rows of trees as wind-breaks. Other dry areas would be better kept for grazing ; in this case, however, attention may be paid to the introduction of more suitable pasture plants, and also to the danger of over-stocking with its risk of the animals eating all the vegetation cover in times of scarcity.

In some districts the damage has gone beyond the power of farmers to deal with it, and local or State governments must act. One instance is where reafforestation is necessary, for this requires much capital and no return comes from the timber for many years ; another case is where large gullies have been formed and their further extension can be checked only by skilled and extensive engineering. In this connection may be mentioned the plight of those countries whose peoples lack adequate wisdom or wealth, and yet, for that very reason, are already faced with most serious problems of soil erosion.

Over much of Africa, help from outside seems to be essential if the peoples of this continent are to be relieved of the heritage of their past, and enabled both to improve their own standards of living and to contribute more to the food supply of the world as a whole.

CHAPTER XVI

MODES OF LIFE—
INDUSTRY AND COMMERCE

THE peoples hitherto considered are those occupied in obtaining animal and vegetable products ; together with miners, they form the group of primary producers. In order that their products may be used, much further work is in most cases necessary ; thus there has grown up a vast and complicated group of secondary occupations which are classified as industrial. Further, the products of both the primary and the secondary occupations must be interchanged at many stages of their preparation, and finally distributed to widely scattered consumers; hence, still another group of occupations is involved, and commerce is the work of a large proportion of the people of advanced communities.

Social Conditions.—In the early stages of development, and even at present when special skill or artistic feeling is essential, industry takes the form of handicraft and may be carried on in the homes of the workers. Such simple kinds of domestic industry, however, have now been almost superseded by work in factories; this is carried on with the aid of machinery driven by water-power, by steam from coal- or oil-fed boilers, by internal-combustion engines using petrol or heavy oil, or by electricity derived from one of these sources of power. Hence the increase of manufacturing has been closely bound up with the advance of physical science.

Moreover, by industrial development social conditions have been changed in many ways, of which a few may be mentioned.

(1) Nearly all forms of work have become divided into distinct processes carried on by individuals as their special jobs, and " division of labour " is a characteristic of our machine age. In some cases the work is simple, monotonous and ill-paid, while in other cases it is skilled and better paid. In addition there are managers and " captains of industry " who live apart from the wage-earners and have a higher standard of

comfort. There are also those who take little or no part in the actual work but, as a result of having supplied capital for the larger undertakings, obtain a monetary return which varies with the prosperity of the particular companies ; some " capitalists " are wealthy and influential persons, but very many more are small shareholders. In this way industrial communities are complex, composed of groups of people living very different kinds of life ; there are social strata, as it were, at different levels, sometimes sharply separated from one another.

(2) Another consequence of the application of science to industry is a great increase in total production and a corresponding rise in the general standard of living : yet the rise in the standard of living is very uneven. Hence, while the majority of the workers in the industrial and commercial regions live in ways which compare favourably with the less advanced modes of life common in many parts of the world, some may live in abject poverty while others have at their disposal an abundance of goods and can command products of workers in every part of the globe. These strongly contrasting conditions give rise to difficult social problems, and occasionally to sharp clashes between the groups, in the industrial and commercial regions.

(3) The increase in production has been accompanied by a great increase in the population, and as industry and commerce can be most efficiently carried on when the workers engaged in the many branches are in close touch with one another, the result has been the crowding of large numbers of people into towns and cities. In many cases, even hundreds of thousands live packed upon a few square miles, while in several parts of the world built-up districts so join one another that the countryside has disappeared. This unnatural state of affairs has brought to the people an artificial mode of life with both bad and good possibilities ; e.g. on the one hand, health can only be maintained by special hygienic and social services, and on the other, the close proximity of people allows them to enjoy medical, recreational and educational advantages almost unobtainable in small, isolated settlements.

An interesting comparison may be drawn between the industrial and commercial communities and those of the people who get their living by growing crops or by hunting or rearing animals. These primary producers are directly dependent upon nature, and are liable to extremes of bad or good fortune which cannot be foreseen and in many cases are beyond remedy. The industrial and commercial communities are removed from the direct vagaries of nature, and though bad harvests may limit their supplies of foodstuffs or raw materials from some particular sources, they are not as a rule entirely dependent upon these and their life may go on with less disturbance.

Yet they are subject to other troubles. There are occasional conflicts between employers and workpeople in the form of strikes and lock-outs. There are also dislocations of normal activity, on a far larger scale, which bring hardships to the workers and a loss of profit to employers ; these are the " slumps " in production and trade which have tended to occur every few years between periods of " boom," and they may affect, to a greater or less extent, many of the undertakings in all the main industrial and commercial regions. The causes of these trade depressions are complex and not fully understood, but they lie in the economic organization of society and in the actions of men rather than in the variability of nature. It is possible that the alternation of booms and slumps may be lessened or even prevented by the " planned economies " now being developed by some States, as will be described later.

Mining.—As mining is closely associated with manufacturing and is carried on to a considerable extent in the same regions, it is convenient to deal at this point with some of its character- istics, particularly those in which it differs from the modes of life considered in the three preceding chapters.

Few mineral deposits are due to present-day climatic con- ditions ; among the exceptions are the nitrates of Chile, which have been accumulated in the Atacama desert by slow deposit from surface evaporation of water. Past geological conditions have determined the existence of certain mineral resources in such present-day unattractive areas that there is a lack of other means of livelihood, e.g. gold in the Australian desert, silver and copper in the Andean Highlands, coal in Spitsbergen. Hence in a number of cases mining settlements are in un- propitious and remote districts and the miners experience isolation and perhaps hardships. Most of the mining, however, is carried on associated with other occupations, and may give rise to industries in the same locality if the particular ore or mineral fuel is of special importance in manufacturing processes.

In such cases, miners and other workers live much the same kind of life, except during the time spent at work ; even individual families may have members engaged in different occupations, the men and lads in mines and the young women perhaps in offices or factories. The maps on pp. 242 and 243, showing the distribution of certain important mineral workings, should be compared with the map of industrial regions on p. 246 in order to see, in a general way, to what extent mining is carried on in the same localities as other industries.

It must be remembered that all mineral enterprises have to be abandoned sooner or later, either because the deposits are exhausted or because their working no longer pays ; unlike agricultural and pastoral modes of life, mining of a particular type must therefore eventually disappear from any area, and is a transitory form of human occupation of a region.

Sources of Mechanical Power.—In addition to *coal* and *oil*, *water-power* is an important factor in industry ; the use of water-wheels in streams greatly helped early manufacturing enterprises, and in recent years an enormous extension has occurred through the application of electricity. At the present time, the main source of water-power is falling water which turns wheels or turbines attached to dynamos, and these produce electric current able to be transmitted by cable scores or hundreds of miles. The amount of power produced depends on two factors : the height from which the water falls, and the amount of water passing through the station in a given time.

Hence, mountain regions with heavy precipitation have great water-power resources which may be actually developed when the power can be economically utilized. Obviously they must be within reasonable distance of places where industry can be carried on, and also the flow of water must be reasonably constant. In this last connection, the régime of the streams is an important consideration ; e.g. where the precipitation is largely in winter, the subsequent melting of snow and ice in summer may allow the continuous production of power throughout the year. An artificial means of securing a constant flow is the damming of valleys and the consequent formation of lakes which store the water until it is required. From this point of view, glaciated areas are advantageous where they have natural lakes ; also, hanging valleys due to glaciation may provide falls of considerable height.

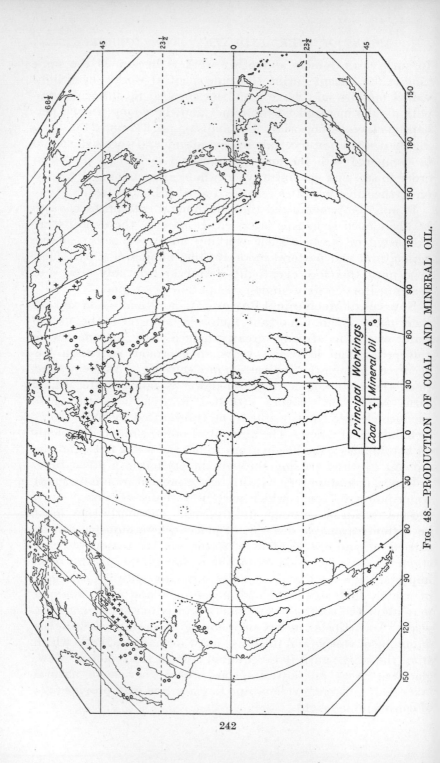

Principal Workings

Coal +   Mineral Oil °

Fig. 48.—PRODUCTION OF COAL AND MINERAL OIL.

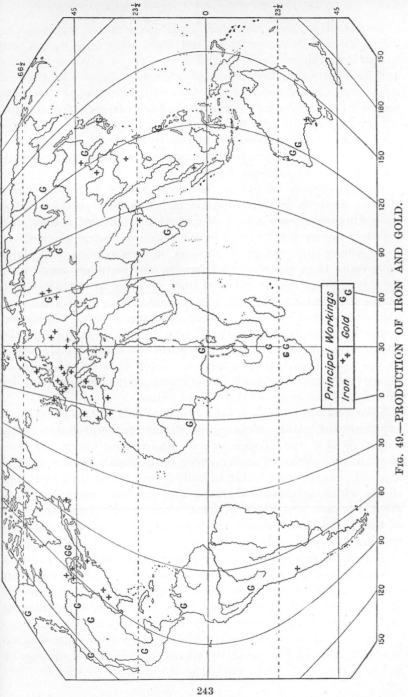

FIG. 49.—PRODUCTION OF IRON AND GOLD.

Principal Workings

Iron	Gold
+	G

In lowlands, too, glaciated areas give much water-power. Though the falls are generally not high, they may be situated in the lower courses and on the main streams of river systems, and this situation has three advantages : in the first place, there may be a considerable volume of water at the fall ; secondly, the water comes from a number of head-streams and, especially where it has traversed glacial lakes or swamps, the flow is relatively constant ; in the third place, the power is produced, not in a remote highland, but at a point favourable for industrial utilization.

Another source of power occurs at rapids and falls where streams have to cut across particularly resistant rock ; e.g. the river Dnieper crosses a belt of granite in southern Russia, and supplies the energy for an enormous hydro-electric station.

To secure uninterrupted working, power-stations sometimes have more than one source of power ; for instance, water may be the primary agent and coal may be used to operate steam plant when necessary. In some industrial regions there are extensive " grid systems " which draw on several widespread sources of supply, such as water, coal, lignite, peat, oil, and the waste gases of furnaces, and distribute the total electric power over a large area. It may here be noted that transmission of power by electricity may be cheaper than hauling coal by railway, or pumping oil through pipelines.

Solar heat has been used for more than half a century in small experimental plants situated in desert or semi-desert areas within or near the Tropics, where almost continuous sunshine is available. Various devices have been employed, the general method being to raise water to boiling-point, and thus to obtain steam which actuates a dynamo and produces electricity. A great advance was made in 1941 when in the Turkistan area of the U.S.S.R. improved types of such plants were devised first for the processing of products of the local milk supplies and then for the canning of fruit and vegetables from the irri-gated lands of the region. In this area the sun's heat has been employed also to obtain electricity which can then produce ice for commercial uses, while by other apparatus temperatures high enough to smelt metals have been obtained.

The *internal heat of the earth* has been used on a small scale in a few parts of the world by means of surface hot springs or by deep borings. *Tidal power*, as it exists in the Severn, has also been employed ; its use for industrial purposes on a more extended scale may be further developed as certain mechanical difficulties, which make working expensive, are overcome. The release of *atomic energy*, first utilized in the atomic bomb in 1945, offers immense possibilities ; how, when and where this energy may be employed is unpredictable, but existing power resources are likely to be supplemented and may even be largely superseded, and in that case the present geographical distribution of mechanical power and industrial development might be greatly modified. Indeed, science is constantly and in many ways devising fresh methods of using natural sources of energy and thus increasing the total amount of power at man's disposal, while there are consequent extensions of the regions of manufacturing and commercial activity.

Industrial Development.—Various forms of working up raw materials are employed to satisfy local needs ; these industries are on a relatively small scale and are widely spread over the world. Greater industrial enterprises are organized for a wider range of consumers and may send their products into far-distant regions. Such industries tend to congregate together in particular districts, for the workers and their families provide a " labour pool " on which other enterprises and even other industries may draw ; further, the population of such industrial areas offers a market which attracts still more industrial and commercial undertakings. Hence one might almost say in this connection that " nothing succeeds like success," and there is a strong tendency for the further growth of manufacturing and trading in those districts which already have a start. For this reason, a great proportion of the world's industry, and a very large number of industrial workers, are found in a few relatively small areas ; these are shown in Fig. 50, and one may note their small extent as compared with that of regions where other types of occupation are dominant.

Europe.—A band of intense industrial development stretches from Great Britain across the " Narrow Seas " into northern France, Belgium and Holland, and thence over central and south Germany into Czechoslovakia and Poland. The Industrial Revolution took place in Britain in the eighteenth and nineteenth centuries, when local water-power and coal were employed for the making of textiles, especially woollen and cotton goods, and local ore was used for the production of iron

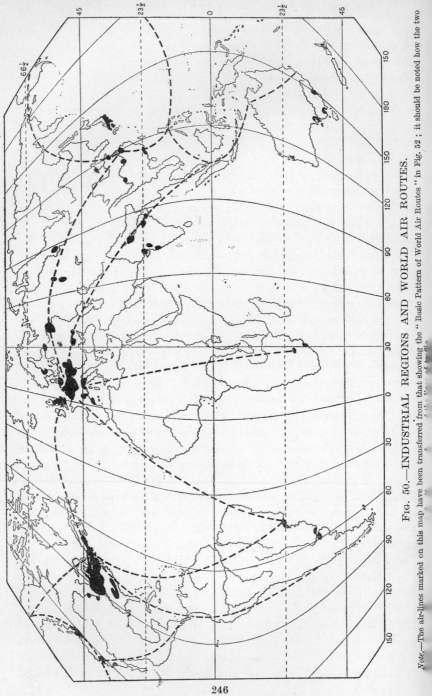

FIG. 50.—INDUSTRIAL REGIONS AND WORLD AIR ROUTES.

Note.—The air-lines marked on this map have been transferred from that showing the "Basic Pattern of World Air Routes" in Fig. 52 ; it should be noted how the two

and steel ; similar local resources were later utilized in the
adjoining countries of the continent. Other materials, such as
linen, silk, leather, wood and various ores, were also the bases of
manufacturing in the same and neighbouring districts.

In a number of cases, the original sources of supply of raw
materials or mechanical power became insufficient or were
exhausted, but frequently the start already made allowed the
industries to continue in the same places by " geographical
inertia " ; the materials were brought from a distance, or a new
source of power was utilized for the machines. In some
instances, the industries remained but were adapted to produce
rather different goods : e.g. the skill of the workers was applied
to one textile instead of another, such as jute instead of linen ;
new substitutes were found, such as rayon for silk ; finely
finished wares of metal or pottery took the place of coarser
products which were more cheaply made elsewhere. This
survival of industry by transference to another material or
product may be called " transferred inertia."

Thus in western and central Europe, the early start of
manufactures was followed by the influence of geographical
and transferred inertia ; with the aid of the great coal resources of the area and the existence of dense populations
which provide both abundant labour and also a great market,
this industrial region became the largest in the world and now
produces practically every type of commodity.

From this original area, large-scale industry spread later to
other parts of Europe where developments have been smaller.
Around the Alps and in some of the valleys, especially in
Switzerland, southern France and northern Italy, water-power
has been an important factor ; also water-power has aided
smaller industrial centres in northern Spain and in Scandinavia.
In eastern Europe, coal, water-power and ores are among the
bases of large-scale manufacturing in several districts reaching
as far east as the Urals, and the U.S.S.R. has encouraged
development where coal and ores are found in Siberia.

North America.—With the great industrial region of western
and central Europe may be compared that on the other side
of the North Atlantic, viz. the manufacturing area of the north-
east of the United States which extends also into the " Lake
Peninsula " of Ontario in Canada.

At the close of the eighteenth century the recently formed

United States introduced British-designed machinery into New England. Here, cotton was brought from the southern States to be manufactured with the aid first of local water-power and later with coal from the northern Appalachians ; here, in addition, other textiles, leather and metals were manufactured. Later, these industries spread southward and also westward to the central plains. Of great importance is the iron and steel industry based on the ore found at the western end of the Great Lakes and the coal of the northern Appalachians. A second large industrial region of the United States lies in and around the southern Appalachians where cotton manufacturing utilizes the raw material grown in the neighbouring States, and coal and water-power from the mountain valleys ; also, iron and steel manufacturing has grown up near iron-ore deposits at the southern end of the uplands. In other parts of " the South," a number of industries were established during the Second World War ; among them were the construction of ships and aircraft and the production of fertilizers and plastics.

Elsewhere in the United States centres of industry have grown up in locations particularly favourable for obtaining raw materials or exporting manufactured products, e.g. by the Mississippi and Missouri rivers and on the Pacific seaboard.

Asia.—Over most of Asia industry is still mainly of the domestic type supplying local needs. The first change came when the Industrial Revolution advanced into eastern Asia about a century after it had spread to North America. European and American capitalists promoted this extension in their own interests, while in Japan it was also fostered by the government as an aid to the support of a dense population which was outgrowing the agricultural resources. In the Monsoon Lands, as in several other parts of the world, the two world wars gave an impetus to industrial development when Europe was engaged in fighting and its shipping could not easily transport raw materials and manufactured products from and to distant lands.

In Japan, before the devastation of the latter part of the Second World War, an important belt of industrialized districts extended south-westward along the shores of Mainland (Honshu) to Kyushu ; here, greatly aided by water-power, there grew up manufactures of silk, cotton, iron and steel goods, etc.

Similar products were manufactured in China, but on a much smaller scale. The chief centres of silk and cotton working were set up at the larger ports, while iron and steel furnaces and factories were constructed at Hanyang and Hankow by the Yangtze river. When the Japanese invaded China and occupied these places in the war of 1937–45, the Chinese removed some of the plant and set up new industrial centres farther in the interior and even in the west of China.

In India, cotton manufacturing has developed mainly at Bombay and in the north-west of the Deccan, favoured by the neighbourhood of the raw material and the water-power of the Western Ghats ; jute is worked at and around Calcutta, near the area where the jute is grown and where coal from the north-eastern corner of the Deccan is easily obtained. In this area of the north-east of the Deccan, iron ore is also found and hence a large iron and steel industry has grown up.

The Southern Continents.—Except in India, industry has not arisen on a large scale in inter-tropical regions ; moreover, it has hitherto developed only to a limited extent in the sub-tropical and mid-latitudes of the southern hemisphere, for in these regions European settlements came later and are less populous than in similar latitudes of the New World in the northern hemisphere. In Australia, the main advance in industry was made at the time of the First World War, when the products of agricultural and pastoral work, especially wool, hides and sugar, were increasingly manufactured at home, and when iron and other ores became the basis of a metallurgical industry. This last development was markedly stimulated when aeroplanes and munitions of all kinds were made in the Second World War. The chief manufacturing centres are at and near the three capitals : Sydney, Adelaide and Melbourne.

New Zealand holds the promise of future development which will be encouraged by its great potential water-power, but its present small population does not offer a large market, and export is hampered by its remote situation.

In Africa, despite the varied mineral wealth, industrial growth has been slow. Only two centres have hitherto arisen : the seaport of Durban, and Johannesburg, an inland centre of communication near which are iron deposits and the most productive coalfield of the continent.

South America has been handicapped by a lack of coal and by the fact that the immense water-power of the Andes and other highlands are far from large centres of population.

The chief manufacturing area is in the neighbourhood of Rio de Janeiro and São Paulo, and its products of home-grown cotton and other textiles are worked with the aid of local water-power and are mainly consumed in Brazil. The only other noteworthy industrial growth has been in the Pampa region of Argentina and Uruguay, where meat-packing and flour-milling prepare the farming products for export.

Regional Factors in Commerce.—As with industry, so with commerce, there are two types, local and wide-range respectively. For trade other than local, man- and animal-power are utilized only when mechanical means of transport are out of the question, and in this connection railway and ocean traffic play the greatest part. The nature and amount of commerce are determined partly by the production in particular areas, partly by the ease or difficulty of transport between them, and partly by the economic, social and even political conditions of the peoples of these areas.

It is with the products of agricultural and industrial workers that the bulk of the world's commerce is concerned, for one large branch of international trade consists of the export of raw materials and foodstuffs from agricultural regions to industrial areas, while another branch deals with the compensating import, largely of manufactured goods, for the use of the agriculturists. There is no appreciable long-distance trade with the inter-tropical peoples who practise shifting or most of the fixed tillage, but plantation cultivation is the basis of a good deal of commerce between tropical and extra-tropical regions. Oasis cultivation and the production of Mediterranean fruits also give rise to some important branches of international trade. The greatest amount, however, is derived from field-crops of the sub-tropical type and those of mid-latitudes ; from the former, cotton, jute, rice and sugar enter the world's trade routes, while from the latter, wheat and maize, meat and meat preparations, dairy produce, wool and hides, tobacco and many other commodities are sent abroad.

A very large proportion of these agricultural products is exported by sea ; hence the map on pages 252 and 253, which shows the relative importance of the traffic along the ocean routes, may be compared with that of the cultivation regions in order to obtain some idea of the amount of the imports and exports based upon agricultural production.

The great part which industrial communities play in determining commercial interchanges is evident when one compares the map showing industrial regions with that of ocean routes. The most striking feature of this latter map is the great volume of the trans-Atlantic traffic between North America and Europe. This traffic includes commodities sent from primary producing regions through the industrial areas and thence across the Atlantic Ocean, but to a large extent it represents an exchange between these manufacturing areas themselves ; it is noteworthy to what a degree industrial regions trade with each other, even in the same or similar products.

The map also shows railway communications, and it must be noted that the important industrial regions have a much closer network than can be shown on a map of this scale. The closeness of the railway lines in these regions is an indication of the intensity of the trading and traffic within, as well as between, the manufacturing districts. The fact that in North America the area showing intensive railway development extends beyond the industrial regions is a reminder that in that continent railways came before roads as the first means of opening up the agricultural areas of the centre and west.

The Arteries of Commerce.—The routes utilized for long-distance transport by trains, ships and aircraft are sometimes referred to as the " arteries " of commerce, and the term is a useful one if it gives the idea that by these routes the interchange of commodities—the " life-blood of commerce "—flows from region to region, and thus maintains the economic life of the modern world.

Water-ways.—The main arteries of the world's commerce are ocean routes, for water transport is in general the cheapest form and the one most suitable for the conveyance of large amounts of traffic over long distances. The courses followed by sailing ships in linking region to region are affected by winds and currents, but the steamships which now carry the bulk of the traffic follow routes as short as are allowed both by the positions of the ports at which calls are made and also by the shapes of the continents.

As the most important of the industrial and commercial regions are in the northern hemisphere, viz. in Europe, Asia and North America, easy sea communication between them was hindered by the two southward-pointing continents of Africa

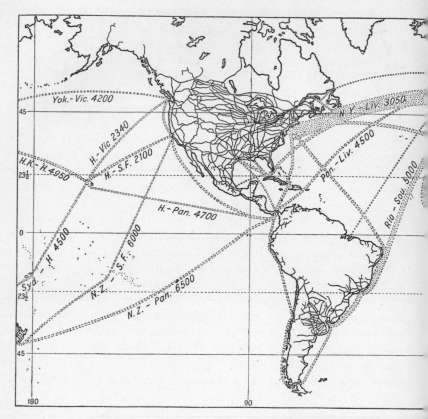

Yok.- Vic. 4200
N.Y.- Liv. 3050
H.- Vic 2340
H - S.F. 2100
H.K.- H. 4950
Pan.- Liv. 4500
Rio - Sou. 5000
H. - Pan. 4700
Syd. - H 4500
N.Z. - S.F. 6000
N.Z. - Pan. 6500

FIG. 51.—OCEAN ROUT[E]

Note.—(1) This map is drawn on Mercator's projection used for ocea[n]
Approximate distances of some of the ocean routes are given in nautic[al]
(2) The principal long-distance railways are shown, but in the areas of

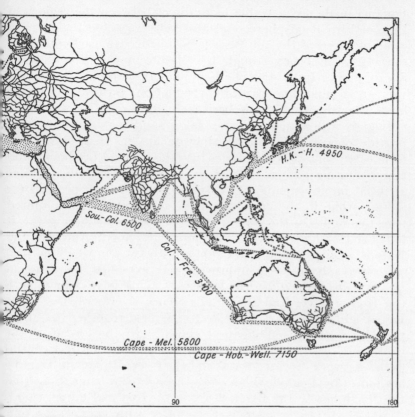

rates distances and areas progressively from lower to higher latitudes.
The width of the belts is proportional to the volume of the traffic.
ent many of the lines have had to be omitted.

and South America, each a great peninsula joined to the northern land-masses by a narrow isthmus. Consequently, the cutting of ship canals through the Isthmuses of Suez and Panama made ocean traffic more direct between the regions of the northern hemisphere, and also between these regions and some of those of the southern hemisphere. In particular, the route from Europe through the Mediterranean Sea and the Suez Canal to India, the Far East and Australia has become of very great importance, and the production and trade of all the lands near this route have been increased.

Inland water-ways—rivers, lakes and canals—not only provide opportunities for local trade but in many cases also form extensions of ocean routes into the heart of producing and manufacturing regions ; some rivers, either naturally or after artificial improvements, allow sea-going vessels to proceed far inland, while in the case of others trans-shipment is required near the mouth of the streams. The two continents of greatest industrial and commercial development, North America and Europe, offer outstanding examples of the way in which natural water-ways have been improved and extended by artificial means. In eastern North America, canals have joined both the Hudson river and the St. Lawrence river with the Great Lakes, and these lakes have been so linked together that they provide continuous navigation almost into the centre of the continent. In the case of Europe, there is in the west-central part a network of water-ways, and the rivers Rhine and Danube are joined by a canal which gives through communication from the North Sea to the Black Sea ; in the east of Europe, canals so link up the river systems that water-ways connect all four marginal seas—the White, Baltic, Black and Caspian Seas. In Asia, the Hwang Ho and the Yangtze Kiang are of great value for commerce.

Land-ways.—Trans-continental railways appear as striking features on a map showing communications, but as arteries of world traffic they are not to be compared with ocean routes. Because of their relative speed, trans-continental railways may carry passengers and mails across the whole width of a continent and also they may transport perishable goods for quite long distances, but their main function is to connect interior regions with those ports which provide the cheapest means of transport to the great markets. The railway systems which thus serve the seaports often have a fan-shaped plan, as is shown on the accompanying map by the railways converging upon Bombay and Buenos Aires ; even greater fan-shaped groups of lines are merged in the network of railways surrounding the great ports of Europe and North America.

The land-ways between ports and their hinterlands are obviously of vital importance where the rivers cannot be rendered navigable, unless at a cost which the traffic could not stand. For example, in South America the productive plantation region of the plateau behind Santos and Rio de Janeiro has no navigable rivers leading to the coast, and in consequence there is here one of the two areas of close railway network in the southern hemisphere ; the other is the hinterland of Buenos Aires where, except by the main streams of the Parana and Paraguay rivers, the Pampa is without water-ways. Again, over much of Africa the structure of the land causes falls or rapids near the mouths of the rivers, and overseas commerce is therefore largely dependent upon railways leading inland.

Africa, too, supplies examples of another type of land-way, viz. the motor road. In regions recently opened to international trade, motor vehicles may provide a cheap and efficient means of transport—at least, until the traffic can pay for the construction of railways ; thus, in the interior of what was until recently the " dark continent," motor roads are of considerable importance in exporting and importing commodities previously conveyed by human porterage. Another outstanding example of the importance of the motor road is the " Burma road " which links the railway system of that country to south-western China ; it was constructed across the almost impenetrable barrier of high mountain ranges and precipitous gorges when, in the Chinese-Japanese war, the Chinese government migrated to the west and was cut off from the Pacific Ocean by the Japanese occupation of the coast-lands and ports.

Air-ways.—The features which distinguish aircraft from other means of transport determine their special uses and the routes they follow. In the first place, aeroplanes have relatively great freedom in selecting their courses ; they are not hampered by the relief of the land to the same extent as are railway trains nor limited to sea areas or deep water-ways as are steamships. Secondly, aircraft need highly organized landing-places for refuelling and servicing as well as for taking up and setting down passengers and freight ; therefore they must work from air-port to airport, planned within certain limits of distance, when they are engaged in long-range flying. Thirdly, aeroplanes are capable of far greater speeds than any other mode of transport ; from this comes their suitability, and their importance, for conveying passengers, mails and urgently needed commodities. Fourthly, the cost of operating aircraft is great ; this makes charges high and reinforces their general limitation to carrying passengers and the lighter and less bulky kinds of freight.

Air routes are planned either to serve relatively small areas and in that case they form a criss-cross of intersecting lines, or to meet the needs of long-distance communications and therefore make a broad pattern stretching across continents. The lines in such a broad pattern join the areas from which most of the traffic originates, and they tend to follow great circles of the globe ; see the notes printed below the map of the " Basic Pattern of World Air Routes " opposite. This map shows that the greatest volume of long-distance air traffic (like that of ocean transport) crosses the North Atlantic between the world's most developed industrial and commercial regions, viz. that of north-western Europe and that which centres on New York. From each of these two primary areas, lines radiate outwards almost along great circle routes, while another series forms the circum-Pacific system which passes along the western side of the two Americas and crosses Bering Strait to skirt eastern Asia and thus to reach the Far East. Also, from the ports of the Pacific and Indian Oceans, lines go out to south-eastern Asia and to Australia. This map enables one to realize the primary pattern of world air transport, and to see how it serves the most important land areas while largely avoiding both the non-productive spaces of the oceans and also the bad-weather area of the Arctic region. This last consideration may become of less consequence to the extent that " stratosphere flying " allows planes to navigate at the very high altitudes where the atmosphere is almost motionless.

Another aspect of the same basic pattern is brought out in the map of " Industrial Regions and World Air Routes " on p. 246, on which the traffic lines have been transferred to a different projection. This allows one to see how the main routes fit to the distribution of the chief manufacturing areas ; e.g. it may be observed how the more northerly track from

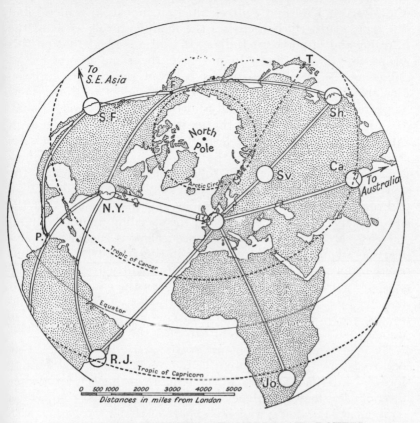

FIG. 52.—BASIC PATTERN OF WORLD AIR ROUTES.

Note.—1. This map is constructed on the Azimuthal Equidistant Projection, which allows distances to be measured according to the scale only along straight lines radiating from the centre, e.g. from London to Tokyo and from London to New York.   2. As all lines dividing the world into equal portions (such as the Equator) are " great circles," an indefinite number of these can be drawn upon a globe ; on this map parts of great circles are shown by lines radiating from the centre and also by the Equator, while the boundary of the map as a whole is itself a great circle.   3. The shortest distance between any two points on a globe is that along the great circle connecting them ; hence great circle routes are necessarily the most direct.   It may be seen that the air traffic routes shown on the map do not deviate markedly from great circles.   4. They show only the main directions of the flow of the traffic to and from the chief areas concerned with long-distance communications by air, the centres being indicated by initials : (Sv. = Sverdlovsk).   Note that Panama and Fairbanks (Alaska) are junctions, but not in productive areas where air traffic originates.

north-western Europe to eastern Asia passes through or near
the Moscow, Ural and central Siberian industrial centres, and
the more southerly line crosses the manufacturing areas of the
Ukraine and of northern India. It is also evident that on this
projection the air lines do not give the same impression of
following the shortest distances between the points ; in particular, the most direct route from London to New York
appears to " curve " markedly northward. Moreover, it may
be noted that whereas on the map of the " Basic Pattern of
Air Routes " the great circle route from London to Tokyo is
indicated by a dotted line, the map on p. 246 does not show
that a main route actually follows such a track across the
barrens of northern Eurasia.

From the foregoing considerations, one may deduce that the
special value of air transport is in the speeding-up of communications, particularly perhaps between persons engaged in commerce or in government, and in facilitating industrial operations
by the transport of small quantities of urgently needed material
or spare parts for repairs. This is indeed the case, but aircraft
may be used for carrying even fairly heavy or bulky commodities where other forms of transport are impossible or very
difficult, and where the freight can bear the high cost.

Two instances of such air traffic may be quoted. One
occurred when gold was found in the mountainous and densely
forested interior of New Guinea ; in this almost inaccessible
district development depended upon the aerial import of
equipment and stores, and the export of the ore, together with
the transport of the personnel. A second case was in the far
north of Canada where pitchblende, from which radium could
be extracted, was discovered near Great Bear Lake in 1930.
Three years later, air transport made possible the utilization of
the ore, and the virtual monopoly in the supply of radium
hitherto possessed by the Belgian Congo was broken ; almost
immediately the very high price of radium was about halved,
with the consequent extension of its use for medical treatment
and the great relief of human suffering.

Another valuable use of communication by air has been in
the overcoming of some of the difficulties of isolated communities. This is illustrated by the systematic provision of
medical and educational services to mining and pastoral settlements in the interior of Australia, and also by the assistance

given, when required, to the small and scattered groups of people living in the northern parts of Asia and North America. In these examples, as in many others, the " changing value of geographical conditions " has been very clearly illustrated by the development of air transport during recent years, in peacetime as well as in time of war.

Commercial Centres and Regions.—An answer may now be given, in general terms, to the question : What is the distribution of the people engaged in the various commercial occupations, including organizing, clerical work, and the conveyance and transfer of goods ? The answer is threefold : (1) Scattered traders and carriers form a minority of the population in primary producing, and consuming, areas and they are also found along routes of all kinds. (2) Large numbers of commercial workers live in close association with the manufacturing groups in industrial regions. (3) People employed in commerce form the nucleus of predominantly trading centres, some of these constituting the greatest cities of the world.

Commercial centres have grown up at nodal points on lines of communication, their importance and size depending upon the amount and nature of the traffic along the routes which converge upon them. The largest are the ports at the ends of the great ocean trade routes, e.g. New York in eastern North America; London, Hamburg, Liverpool, Rotterdam and Antwerp in north-western and central Europe ; Marseilles in the Mediterranean ; Bombay and Calcutta in India ; Hong Kong, Shanghai, Kobe and Yokohama in the Far East ; Buenos Aires and Rio de Janeiro in South America. Inland centres are frequently situated on rivers, though as a rule most of their trade is by road or rail ; they are very numerous, but individually the amount of their traffic is far less than that of seaports.

Other Occupations.—Closely associated with industry and commerce is a great variety of financial and legal business. Moreover, the administration of States and of smaller political divisions (e.g. counties and boroughs, urban and rural districts) requires the work of governing bodies and officials of various grades. Often, too, professional people such as doctors, teachers and engineers are employed in the public service, besides those who practise on their own account ; the writing and publication of newspapers, journals and books are also frequently carried on in political centres. Still other occupations associated with those already mentioned are too numerous to detail ; one must refer, however, to the services rendered to workers in their homes by members of their own families, for these services are essential to the life of the communities and the people thus employed form a noteworthy proportion of the total population.

CHAPTER XVII
COMMUNITIES AND STATES

Communities and their Influence.—The earliest and most widespread type of community is that based upon kinship, e.g. family and tribe ; yet in the modern world the more backward peoples whose organization is largely of this type are small in number, and almost all of them are dominated by others who are more advanced. Other communities have a basis not necessarily connected with any physical relationship between the members ; one such type of community of wide development is that of religious groups, while another comprises those with definitely economic aims, such as trade unions and employers' associations. Very important are political communities—those into which people are organized for carrying on the government of an area. They include, e.g. relatively small groups whose councils deal with local affairs, and much larger communities such as nations or even groups of nations organized into States. These States exercise the ultimate governing authority and determine the taxation and financial systems of the peoples concerned, and deal with foreign affairs, i.e. their relations with other States. It should be noted that commonly a single individual is a member of several types of community : he is a member of a family, he may belong to some religious organization, he may take an active part in a trade union or employers' federation, and he is a subject of a State to which he owes allegiance.

States may have great significance as geographical factors by their action in economic matters. While some States prefer to leave these matters to " free enterprise," others have systems of "planned economy " by which, to different degrees, they organize the various forms of production, industry and commerce within their territories. They may themselves undertake these activities, or they may ensure that subsidiary authorities, or even private organizations or individuals, carry on the work to the required extent, and perhaps at prescribed times and places. In any case the development and the economic geography of such States are different from those which would exist as a result of " natural " forces.

Sometimes governments may plan for a balanced economy and foster certain activities in order to produce a " round nation." In extreme cases, they may attempt to achieve self-sufficiency by obtaining within their territory all essential goods and services ; this policy is sometimes described as autarchy or autarky, and of course it produces geographical results unlike those which would follow a policy of unrestricted exchange between nations.

With the growth of national feelings and the formation of national States during recent times, there have been many such expressions of " economic nationalism." Instead of " free trade," " protection " has been applied and " Customs " tariffs have been drawn up, requiring duties to be levied on certain classes of goods entering the country ; the importers and consumers of such goods have, directly or indirectly, to pay the duties. Hence, if similar goods produced within the country are exempt from taxation the home products can be sold at a lower price and the home industry is thereby stimulated. Sometimes a similar effect to that of Customs duties is obtained by import " quotas," which limit the entry of particular goods to a definite amount within a given period.

Another method of aiding a special industry is to give it a direct subsidy or bounty, based either upon the whole of its production or upon that part of it which is designed for export and is therefore in competition with producers in foreign countries. There are many other ways in which a State may influence economic activities, e.g. by aiding research into improvements in agricultural, industrial or commercial methods, by lending capital for extensions of particular enterprises, or by giving assistance to representatives abroad.

Moreover, from the geographer's point of view it is important to realize that some forms of State help to internal development may have consequences in distant regions, for they may hinder increases, or perhaps cause decreases, in the production and trade of other countries, even though these may be better fitted by natural conditions for the activities concerned.

Two special cases of the influence of States may be emphasized. One is that in which the government assumes the ownership of economic enterprises. This action may be limited, as in Britain, to certain basic industries such as coal-mining, the production of gas and electricity, and large-scale means of transport by rail, canals, road-haulage and air traffic. On the other hand, ownership may extend to all types of production and trade, as it does in the communist system of the U.S.S.R. Public enterprises of this kind can be carried on for the benefit of the community as a whole, and so differ from those of a capitalist type, which must make a profit in order to survive; hence it is possible that State organizations may for special reasons be fostered in areas unlikely to be chosen by private managements, and the geographical distribution of industry within a territory may thus be affected.

A second case of the State's direction of economic activities is bound up with its duty of defence and, possibly, with a policy of offence. Either in preparation for warfare or when war is actually in progress, essential work such as the provision of food and munitions supersedes other forms of activity and is very likely to be greatly increased within the State boundaries wherever this is possible. On the other hand, during a war the normal export of goods may be checked, and other States may have an opportunity of developing their own production of the goods no longer exported. Moreover, changed conditions arising during war-time may be continued afterwards; thus during the First and Second World Wars " younger " industrial countries, including both overseas Dominions of the British Commonwealth and also other States, developed the manufacture of various kinds of goods they had hitherto purchased from the British Isles, and in some cases they entered the world market as exporting competitors of Britain in these branches of industry.

As the geographical influence exerted by present-day governments differs according to their special characters and extent, their structure must be considered in more detail.

Nations and Nationality.—First, however, it is well to examine some of the communities which may be comprised within States. It is sometimes said that the subjects of a State together form one nation, but this particular use of the word " nation " conflicts with other usages. For instance, before the political separation of the Irish Free State, now known as Eire, from the rest of the British Isles in 1921, the majority of the Irish people regarded themselves as a distinct nation although they formed part of the one State, the " United Kingdom of Great Britain and Ireland." In many other parts of the world there are still States which comprise people who are admittedly of more than one nationality. The terms "nation" and "nationality" may better be reserved for groups of people having common feelings and traditions which mark them off from other groups to such an extent that they wish not only to maintain their unity and their distinctive types of culture, but also to be free of any domination by another people. To this end, nations generally desire to form a State of their own—a Nation-State—though in fact their desire may be frustrated by a more powerful people, or they may accept some compromise such as " home rule " in their own affairs within the framework of a larger State.

Nations, in this sense of the word, have arisen and have formed Nation-States in Europe only in the past few hundred years, and in connection with the nations of the present time it is useful to ask what are the factors which bind people together so that they have a consciousness of distinct nationality.

To a certain extent, one element is kinship—the result of their intermarriage over a period of some generations. The nations of Europe may be regarded in some degree as the modern representatives of earlier tribal units or federations. Yet, as was emphasized in the chapter on Races and Migrations, account must be taken of immigrations of other peoples and the consequent mingling of stocks. The English, for instance, have evolved from many immigrant groups : to the British peoples of pre-Roman times have been added Angles, Saxons and Jutes, Danes and Norsemen, Norman invaders and Huguenot and other refugees, but the earlier differences due to these diverse origins are no longer thought of as reasons for denying the existence of one nation.

Among other influences which help to bring about the growth and the consciousness of nationality, two are specially powerful : one is close and friendly living together in a particular area ; the other, essentially combined with this association, is the use of a common language. If people can talk together without difficulty and can read the same newspapers and books and listen to the same broadcasts, they get similar information and views about events, and they tend to have similar ideas and ideals. Thus they acquire the communal feeling which lies at the basis of nationality; they evolve common customs, they inherit common traditions about the history of their nation, and they may develop a literature which links them closely to their past. In short, they may possess a characteristic culture. The English nation provides instances of these factors, for after initial conquests by invaders the various groups gradually settled down together into harmonious co-operation, while the growth of one language from their various forms of speech gave a wide basis for their further unification.

Yet the development and use of a common language are not essential to a feeling of union into one nationality; this is shown in the case of the Swiss people, for in their State there are four recognized " official " languages : German, French, Italian and Romansch. The Swiss nation had its beginning, nearly 600 years ago, in a defensive union of the people of three small Alpine districts, and to this union other neighbouring groups joined themselves on successive occasions until there is now a community numbering over four million people who, in spite of differences of origin, speech and religion, are conscious of a common nationality. They are associated in various ways, but the first reason for their union is still operative, for they still feel a need for common defence against the possibility of attack by powerful neighbours, and by now cherish a long tradition of independence due to their mutual support. This factor of common defence often shows itself in the development of a nationality ; it greatly contributed to the difficult task of the formation of the United States of America when the respective colonies asserted and won their independence from Great Britain.

Membership of one religious community is another factor which sometimes helps the growth of a nation ; conversely, religious differences may hinder the fusion of groups. The Roman Catholicism of the people of Eire makes a powerful contribution to their political unity, but as opposed to the Protestantism of Ulster it is one of the factors preventing the development of one undivided Irish nation and the establishment of a single State embracing the whole of Ireland. India supplies another example of the influence of religion upon the growth of nationality ; the conflict between the beliefs and practices of the Hindus and those of the Muslims is so sharp that it has proved a barrier to the growth of a unified Indian nation, in spite of their common demand to be free of British domination.

Plural Societies.—Historical events, especially migrations and conquests, have led to great complexity in the present geographical distribution of national groups ; for this reason, among others, there are not many cases of true " Nation-States " in which all the subjects are members of one nationality. Much more common is the existence within States of minorities who differ from the majority of the population in various ways, and resultant clashes between the rulers and ruled have been among the greatest causes of warfare in recent times.

Particularly serious have been the conditions over a broad belt overlapping the junction of Peninsular Europe and Trunk Europe, from the eastern part of the Baltic southward to the Adriatic Sea and the Balkans. For centuries past various peoples, largely Slavs, have pressed westward, and counter-movements have taken place by German-speaking soldiers and settlers in the northern and central parts of this debatable land and by Italian traders along the eastern Adriatic coast. As a result an inextricable mixture of peoples has characterized this area, and when dominant groups set up their governments or extended their boundaries, the States included considerable alien elements. The tides of conquest ebbed and flowed, and right up to the present this region has been " a belt of political change." Victors were often quite willing to include and exploit subject groups, and when after both World Wars some attempts were made to carry out the principle of self-determination, i.e. to allow the people of particular areas to have their own government, it was found to be practically impossible. Whatever changes were made, and however a frontier might be drawn, the States on both sides were bound to include majority and minority groups opposed to one another. This was the case, for example, where the boundary of Italian and Yugoslav territories ran northward from the Adriatic Sea in the neighbourhood of Trieste.

Such differences between groups, due mainly to national feelings, are one cause of the "plural societies " (sometimes called " plural communities ") of which some States are composed, but there are other causes of a wider character. Indeed, plural societies occur wherever a State comprises communities which differ in any respects, either racial or cultural, to such a degree that the groups do not share equally in citizenship or are strongly opposed in social, economic or political matters. In practically the whole of Africa south of the Sahara, the relatively recent penetration of the Negro population by Europeans engaged in trade, or in plantation or mining enterprises, or as government officials, has given rise to plural societies within the frontiers of the various Powers. In these cases the communities stand out from one another both by marked physical differences of racial origin and also by cultural contrasts. These latter commonly show themselves in a distinction between the more skilled and less skilled occupations of the White and Coloured peoples respectively and the related modes of life : the higher standards of education, health, nutrition and comfort among the Europeans ; their possession of much greater power in the destinies of the regions ; their assumption of superiority and an exclusive attitude in social relations.

In several of the countries bordering the Pacific and Indian Oceans, migrations of workers and traders from the crowded Monsoon Lands have caused numerous settlements of Chinese, Japanese and Indians who have not become assimilated into the local populations. Here again are obvious racial differences which become associated in peoples' minds with differences of habits and customs, of occupations, and of standards of living. Some of the people from the Monsoon Lands accept lower rates of pay or profit than those among whom they have settled, and therefore appear as dangerous competitors ; this is the case in the Pacific coast-lands of Canada and the United States of America. A great factor in the adoption of the policy of a " White Australia " was the prospect of an alien element in the Queensland plantations which could not be assimilated into the rest of the population of the continent. In some regions, the immigrants have displaced a considerable proportion of the earlier people by their success in work or trade, as the Chinese have done in parts of Indo-China, the East Indies and various Pacific Islands, the Tamil-speaking Indians in Ceylon, and both Chinese and Indians in the Malay Peninsula. It can easily be imagined that the resulting plural societies often constitute serious problems for the States as well as for individuals.

The settlements of Jews from Europe among the Muslim Arabs in Palestine have in recent years created a serious political problem with results spreading far across the world. Many other examples of plural societies could be given, but here it can only be said that as the circumstances vary greatly from region to region, the possible solutions of the problems are equally varied. The essence of the trouble is the difficulty of reconciling the groups and bringing about their harmonious association. Hence, where the cause lies mainly in differences of national feeling, a solution may be found by political rearrangements in the States concerned.

In Europe, two strongly contrasted attempts at dealing with minority problems were made after the Second World War. One was that of the " Sudeten Germans " who had long been settled in the west of the Czech lands and many of whom had been concerned in the German occupation of Czechoslovakia— one of the most important milestones on the road to the outbreak of the war. After the defeat of Germany, the Czech government decided that the future security and unity of their country required the removal of those people of alien origin and sympathy who would not accept whole-hearted citizenship of Czechoslovakia. In consequence, over two million German-speaking persons were expelled into Germany ; also, smaller numbers of Ruthenians went into the U.S.S.R., and Magyars into Hungary.

The other case was that of Austrians in Northern Italy. After the First World War the disputed territory of the South Tirol, south of the Brenner Pass, became part of Italy together with nearly a quarter of a million German-speaking Austrians, and the Italian government attempted to force these people to the use of the Italian language and to " Italianize " them in other ways. In 1939, after the Germans had annexed Austria, Hitler and Mussolini arranged to allow those Austrians who wished to leave Italian territory to enter the German Reich, and about a third migrated across the frontier. At the close of the Second World War, Italy retained the South Tirol despite Austrian protests, but the situation was relieved by a promise by Italy that the Austrians of the area should be granted the official use of their own language, should enjoy a large measure of autonomy in local government, and should have special customs arrangements providing for their wine and fruit to be exported easily and cheaply to Austria.

In other parts of the world, shifts of population have brought about the entanglement of racial groups possessing greater

differences in their physical and cultural characteristics. This
is markedly the case in South Africa where White settlers have
gone into Negro lands and in North America where Negro
slaves were taken into lands occupied by White people. Even
where disparities between the communities are great, these may
be so closely bound up with one another that the solution of
the present serious difficulties may be to achieve co-operation
between the communities by the gradual education and training
of the relatively backward group. This development may have
to cover almost all aspects of life—hygienic, intellectual, social,
economic and political; moreover, the more advanced community must be willing to accept the fundamental human
equality of their neighbours, to assist their development and to
give up their own privileges. In some areas, such an evolution
seems to the ruling groups so impossible, or so undesirable,
that they have adopted a policy of total exclusion, and elsewhere one of internal segregation and subjection, of the people
to whom they fear to give freedom of movement, economic
equality or the rights of citizenship.

Unitary, Federal and Multi-national States.—Some
States, and notably the Nation-States, have a fairly simple
structure; the small northern States of Europe supply instances,
for in each of them the government is carried on by one authority—a Parliament, at the head of which is either a President, as
in the Republic of Finland, or a Monarch who acts in conjunction
with the elected representatives of the people, as in the Kingdoms of Denmark, Norway and Sweden. In governments of
this type, the Parliament may have one or more Chambers, and
the Head of the State may have differing degrees of power, yet
there is only a single although composite authority; hence
these States may be described as "unitary" to distinguish
them from "federal" States in which there are a number of
governing bodies each having its own sphere of authority.

Switzerland is an example of a federal State. In 1291 the
men of the original three Alpine cantons entered into a defensive
league but otherwise independently organized their own lives
in their own valleys; when at later times other cantons joined
the league with the same common object, they retained much
of their government in their own hands. As a consequence,
in modern Switzerland the unified "Swiss Confederation"
must be distinguished from the twenty-two separate cantons.

The central authority of the Confederation resides in its Parliament and President, but its powers are restricted to foreign affairs, viz. those relating to war and to treaties with other States, together with matters affecting the Confederation as a whole, such as railways, certain economic regulations, monetary arrangements and the system of weights and measures. Yet the twenty-two Swiss cantons are still independent and sovereign in all matters except those handed over to the central authority ; they have full power of " home rule " based upon their respective popular assemblies or elected councils. This independence of the cantons in local government is doubtless one reason for the harmonious co-operation of the people of the Swiss nation differing markedly in speech as in religion. Other European examples of federal States are the Czechoslovak Republic with two constituent parts, and the " Federal Popular Republic of Yugoslavia " consisting of six South Slav Republics.

More extensive developments of this fairly common type of federal government are to be found in the New World. In South America there is the " United States of Brazil," covering an area nearly as large as that of Europe, and consisting of twenty States with their own law-making, administrative and judicial authorities for internal affairs.

In North America the " United States of America," with a rather smaller area but far greater population, also has a federal type of government. According to the Constitution drawn up in 1787 the original thirteen States were politically equal, and the present States are sovereign in all matters except those delegated to the Federal Government. The climatic and other physical differences between the various States, now forty-eight in number, are so great that the modes of life of their citizens show marked contrasts, often accentuated by the diverse national and even racial origins of their inhabitants ; hence the States tend to remain distinct and to retain jealously their rights and powers. Indeed, by the discrepancies between their policies and between the laws they have enacted within their territories, they have even increased some of the earlier distinctions between them, and have brought about marked differences in the cultural conditions in the regions comprised in the U.S.A.

Canada exhibits a somewhat similar type of federal government, for authority is shared between the Dominion Parliament and those of the respective Provinces. Again, the Commonwealth of Australia is a federation including five States on the mainland and the island State of Tasmania. The Union of South Africa, on the other hand, has a unitary form of government, for after the Boer War it was thought desirable to weld together its constituent provinces as firmly as possible. The constitution of the British Commonwealth as a whole, however, is so complex that a special account of it must be given in the next chapter.

By far the most extensive State (apart from the British Commonwealth which is an association of independent States) is that still sometimes referred to as Russia ; its correct title, " The Union of Soviet Socialist Republics " (U.S.S.R.), indicates its federal, and indeed multi-national, structure. The Russian dominion, in the thirteenth century consisting only of the small Principality of Moscow, gradually spread to much of eastern Europe, and at the end of the sixteenth century it pushed into Siberia ; by the beginning of the eighteenth century it had reached the Pacific Ocean, and in the nineteenth century the Caucasian region and central Asia were annexed. Now the total area of the Soviet State is about one-seventh of the land surface of the globe, and its subjects number about one-eleventh of the world's inhabitants. Moreover, the physical contrasts of the Soviet regions are extraordinarily great; correspondingly, the peoples of the U.S.S.R. show great diversity in race, speech, religion and modes of life.

Before the revolution of 1917, the Asiatic territories formed a great Colonial Empire built upon conquest, the economic exploitation of the regions and the suppression of the peoples. In many ways the Empire of Russia resembled the Empires belonging to west Europe, which were established overseas and are referred to in the next chapter. After 1917, however, the Soviet government initiated a change of policy of which the keynotes were the extension of equal rights of citizenship to all peoples within the borders of the U.S.S.R., and the free development of their national cultures.

The State is now formed of sixteen Union Republics, by far the largest being Russia Proper—the Russian Soviet Federative Socialist Republic—which includes both the greater part of European Russia and Siberian territories extending to the

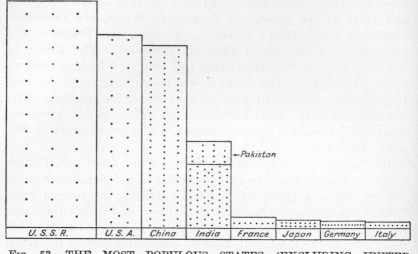

FIG. 53.—THE MOST POPULOUS STATES (EXCLUDING UNITED KINGDOM)—AREAS AND POPULATIONS AFTER SECOND WORLD WAR.

Note.—(1) Areas of States are proportional to size of rectangles ; (2) each dot represents approximately 5 million people ; (3) closeness of dots shows average density of population.

Pacific Ocean. There are also the Ukrainian, White Russian, Estonian, Latvian, Lithuanian, Karelo-Finnish and Moldavian Republics in Europe ; those of Georgia, Armenia and Azerbaijan in the Trans-Caucasian region ; the Turkmen, Uzbek, Tadzhik, Kazakh and Kirghiz Republics in central Asia. Further, these sixteen constituent Union Republics are themselves composed of subordinate areas, including " Autonomous Republics," " Autonomous Regions " and " National Areas."

The system of government is based upon a series of soviets, i.e. councils, which represent the people of all the administrative areas, beginning in the villages, going upwards to those of the sixteen Union Republics and culminating in that of the U.S.S.R. as a whole. The final authority of the " Supreme Soviet " has two Chambers : one is the " Soviet of the Union," consisting of members each chosen to represent a constituency containing a certain numerical proportion of the population ; the other Chamber is the " Soviet of Nationalities," with twenty-five deputies from each Union Republic irrespective of its size, and chosen to include representatives from its " Autonomous Republics," " Autonomous Regions " and " National Areas."

It is an essential part of the constitution of the U.S.S.R. that its peoples should maintain their national groupings, languages and traditions, and at the same time share their allegiance to the Union with its characteristic form of communistic social and economic organization. Hence this State claims to have a distinctive multi-national character.

The federal character of the U.S.S.R. is shown in the fact that the sixteen Union Republics have a certain degree of independence ; indeed, in theory they have the right of secession. In foreign affairs White Russia and the Ukraine may deal directly with other Powers, although there is, in addition, a common foreign ministry of the U.S.S.R., which treats of matters affecting the Union as a whole. Similarly the sixteen Republics have some powers relating to defence, but there is also the common defence force assembled from the Republics and organized as a unity under the central authority. In general, the Union Republics manage purely internal affairs, such as education and social services, and some of their economic concerns ; but because certain matters, e.g. transport and the working of the " heavy " industries, extend over the political boundaries, the wider aspects of economic organization are centralized under the Supreme Soviet in Moscow.

Political Changes.—While nature changes the physical geography of regions slowly and generally imperceptibly, their human geography may be much more quickly altered by man's action ; economic conditions may be transformed within a life-time, and political upheavals may occur almost in a day.

States may have their constitutions frequently modified or even recast, and as one consequence of such variations no hard-and-fast lines can be drawn between types of government. Wars may bring kaleidoscopic changes in political boundaries, and occasionally States may entirely vanish ; small ones may be swallowed up by their larger neighbours, and great ones may be split into a number of smaller ones.

The political map of a considerable part of Europe, for example, was redrawn as a result of the First World War. The Empires of Germany and Russia were replaced by Republics, their territories were shorn of substantial areas hitherto in-habited by alien minorities, and the dual Monarchy of Austro-Hungary was completely broken up. Related to these changes, across the whole of Europe from the Arctic to the Mediterranean

Sea appeared a belt of new or transformed States : Finland, Estonia, Latvia, Lithuania, Czechoslovakia, a truncated Austria, a similarly contracted Hungary, Yugoslavia, Albania ; also, the territories of Rumania and Greece were enlarged, partly at the expense of Bulgaria.

Another epoch of change followed the Second World War. The Soviet Union incorporated the States of Estonia, Latvia and Lithuania, and parts of Finland, Czechoslovakia, Rumania and Poland. Poland, losing some of its territory in the east, gained other land from Germany by moving the frontier westward to the River Oder. Other territorial changes affected Austria, Hungary, Yugoslavia, Italy, Rumania and Greece. Not only areas were involved : in some cases their populations became either willing or unwilling subjects of their new States ; in other cases there were large migrations of people, either those who wanted to go to the territories still retained by their compatriots or those who were forced out of their homes by the newcomers.

The economic effects of the political alterations were great. Over large areas the land changed ownership, in some countries by the break-up of large estates and its occupation either by the State or by small-holding peasants. The natural resources passed to the disposal of new governments, industries were dislocated at least for the time, and trade was often diverted into different channels. Many years will be required for the secure establishment and the smooth working of the new régimes.

Drastic changes accompanied the occupation of Germany by the Allied forces ; some of its industries were cut down to prevent further aggression, and its economic and political systems were transformed. In the Far East, similar results followed the occupation of Japan.

In western Europe, attempts were made to increase production and to improve commerce by the formation of " Customs Unions." Within such groups of States trade would be free and therefore production could be better organized ; at the same time, common tariffs of Customs duties on external trade would be instituted. The first of these Customs Unions was known as " Benelux," the name being formed from the first letters of the constituent States : Belgium, the Netherlands and Luxembourg.

CHAPTER XVIII
COLONIES AND COMMONWEALTH

Colonial Dependencies.—While Russia expanded eastward across the Eurasian land-mass, the States of western Europe stretched out across the newly opened ocean-ways to all parts of the globe and founded overseas empires. These were in many cases begun as colonies in the original sense of the term, for there were numerous settlements of colonists from the mother countries. From Britain, France and Holland, for instance, men set out with their families to seek freedom or better conditions of living in lands with somewhat similar climates to their own. Colonists went across the seas also from Spain and Portugal, but from these countries the early adventurers were more commonly actuated by desire to obtain treasure or to extend the dominions of their monarchs, and sometimes also by the desire to save the souls of the Natives by bringing them into the Catholic faith. Some of the settlements of Europeans were later conquered by other Powers, but eventually all obtained their independence ; in middle latitudes there are now the self-governing Dominions of the British Commonwealth, and almost all the western hemisphere has passed from European rule.

In lands unsuited by climate for permanent settlement by peoples of mid-latitudes, however, the " colonies " had a different history. Native lands became " possessions " or " dependencies " ; other dependent areas had a somewhat different status as " protectorates " or " trust territories." In the first centuries of European expansion some of the colonial possessions were regarded simply as sources of wealth in the form of precious metals, jewels or slaves to be carried off by the newcomers ; elsewhere the lands were utilized for plantations or mining enterprises worked by the Natives, or were thought of as giving opportunities for barter or trade. In general their attraction for White men lay mainly in the exploitation of their natural resources by means of the labour of their inhabitants.

Early in the history of European penetration, companies

were formed to trade with or develop the overseas regions, and some of these companies obtained rule over large areas. Subsequently the European States from which the companies originated took over the government of the areas concerned and annexed them as political possessions ; such States assumed imperial powers, whether or not they were called Empires or their monarchs adopted the title of Emperors. Thus, the English East India Company was founded at the end of the sixteenth century to compete with Dutch merchants, and gradually acquired large territories especially on the mainland of India ; in 1858 the administration was taken over by the British government, and later the Queen of England became the Empress of India. The Dutch East India Company was formed a few years after its English counterpart ; it developed its trade and made its acquisitions in the island areas off south-eastern Asia. The company was dissolved at the end of the eighteenth century when the " Netherlands Indies " came under the government of the mother country.

In the latter part of the nineteenth century the States of western and central Europe adopted a definite policy of imperialism, largely as a consequence of their competing industrial developments for which they needed access both to raw materials and to markets. By acquiring colonial dependencies or by establishing " protectorates " or " spheres of influence " over territories nominally under native rulers, they hoped to obtain either a monopoly of trade or at least unrestricted commerce in these areas. Political rivalries between the great Powers were an additional factor in the drive towards colonial expansion. In some instances, too, missionary enterprise and humanitarian feelings urged that European rule should put an end to slavery or native warfare.

Hence, except in a few cases where native States such as Thailand (Siam) were able to resist penetration, practically all south-eastern Asia and the Pacific Islands passed under the power of Britain, Holland, France or Germany ; also, for a time the United States governed the Philippines which it had acquired from Spain, and Japan followed the precedents set by the European Powers and seized Formosa after defeating China. Meanwhile, in the eighties of last century, occurred the similar " scramble for Africa " which completed the partition of nearly all that continent among Britain, France, Portugal, Spain,

Belgium and Germany, and later Italy took her share of the spoil. The effects of this foreign control and its influence upon the lives of the native peoples took different forms in different regions and in some were revolutionary or even catastrophic.

For example, in East and South Africa the Natives' ways of life have been greatly affected, or actually transformed, by the settlement of the Europeans. These have acquired large areas of land, often the most productive, and have introduced farming on European methods for which they require Native workers ; also, the Natives have had to yield up their lands and supply labour to mining companies owned and managed by Europeans. Where the newcomers have settled in large numbers, the old ways of life have entirely disappeared and the old tribal organizations have been broken up. Elsewhere the Natives' lives have been modified in various degrees ; e.g. the demand for labour on farms or in mines has given employment to the young men, who in the old days would have been warriors, while their withdrawal from the villages has upset the social balance and the traditional customs of the tribes. Also the Natives have to pay the taxes which are necessary for the government of the colonies, and most of them want to buy European clothes and other articles ; for these purposes they must have money and therefore they must sell either their produce or their labour to Europeans. Hence they have had to change their old self-sufficing economic systems. Because of all these upheavals, age-long codes of conduct and modes of thought gave way, and were replaced with difficulty by an understanding of the strange ideas and the new systems of law brought by the foreigners.

If the preceding paragraphs appear like an indictment of the colonizing Powers and the actions of the White people, one must not judge men of past times according to present standards ; in many respects the general ideas of earlier generations were different from those of today. Moreover, if the conditions of many of the inhabitants of the dependencies must indeed be deplored, yet one must bear in mind that the state of the Native peoples before the entry of the Europeans was very seldom better than at present and was often worse. Want and disease were in some parts constant features of the Natives' lives, while elsewhere they were the frequently recurring effects of climatic variations or of the invasions of disease-carrying insects or smaller organisms. Also, in earlier times these evils prevailed without the preventive or alleviating measures now known to science and increasingly applied by European and Native administrations. Moreover, slavery was common before it was extended by White traders, and wave after wave of conquest and despoilment preceded the intrusion of the Europeans ; indeed, the abolition of slavery and the enforcement of peace have been among the benefits of the new régime. Education, as the term is generally understood, may at present be regrettably limited, but earlier it scarcely existed.

In many colonial areas, as indeed in many other tropical regions, there is still a vicious circle in human life—a circle of poverty, disease and ignorance, each factor reinforcing the others ; to break this circle is essential to progress, although it is very difficult.

It may be fairly said that if the advent of the White men was marked by exploitation and occasionally even by savagery, nevertheless on the whole there has been the gradual growth of a humane attitude : a revulsion against oppression and unfair treatment ; a desire to improve the economic and social conditions of the Natives ; attempts to provide them with opportunities for education. Connected with these changes, there has been in recent years a growing acknowledgment of the innate capacities of the hitherto backward peoples and a willingness to give them at least some political responsibility ; in many colonies, internal affairs are largely in the hands of the local administration in which the people themselves take a part. Of course, these changes have been brought about at different rates in the many colonial territories, and in some, opposition to reform is still too plainly observable. Also, the general policies of governments have to be carried out by individuals, whose personal characteristics may cause either unusually good or unusually bad conditions in actual practice.

Many of the educated people of the dependencies think that measures of economic and social betterment are inadequate and that political independence is being granted by unnecessarily slow steps. They especially resent the " colour bar " which has been particularly rigid in parts of the British Empire and Commonwealth, and in certain areas still marks off the Native from the White people as socially and economically inferior.

The reactions of the native communities to foreign dominion have been of all kinds, from submission to revolt. In recent years, at least among the more advanced groups, there has been a two-fold tendency : on the one hand, an acceptance of economic changes now realized to be inescapable and perhaps thought of as advantageous ; on the other hand, a demand for political independence. This two-fold attitude has long been powerful in India, Burma and Ceylon, where it has attained its objects ; it became strong in the Indo-Chinese Peninsula, Malaya and the East Indies Archipelago, while its growth is now to be seen in Africa and in the colonies of the Caribbean area. Such feelings of the inhabitants of colonial territories were greatly intensified by the Second World War, particularly in south-east Asia and the East Indies. The overrunning of large areas by the Japanese, with their slogan " Asia for the Asiatics," and the breakdown of European authority gave both incentive and opportunity to revolt and to the actual attainment of autonomy in British, French and Dutch dependencies.

In other parts of the world, after both World Wars, there were transfers of colonial power from the defeated States to the victors. This was notably the case in Africa where colonies were taken from Germany after 1918, and from Italy after 1945 ; it occurred also in the Pacific region where Japan lost all her overseas acquisitions after her defeat in 1945. In 1919, Peace Treaties gave the administration of the German possessions to Great Britain and the Dominions of the British Commonwealth, to France, to Belgium and to Japan, to be held under Mandates from the League of Nations. In 1945, the Charter of the United Nations established a somewhat similar system of Trusteeships.

A further account of the International Trusteeship system of the United Nations Organization is given in the last chapter of this book, but the following quotation from the " Declaration regarding Non-Self-Governing Territories " shows the view of colonial government now accepted by the Powers : " Members of the United Nations which have responsibilities for the administration of territories whose peoples have not yet attained a full measure of self-government recognize that the interests of the inhabitants of these territories are paramount, and accept as a sacred trust the obligation to promote to the utmost . . . the well-being of the inhabitants of these territories, and, to this end : (a) To assure, with due respect for the culture of the peoples concerned, their political, economic, social and educational advancement, their just treatment, and their protection against abuses ; (b) To develop self-government, to take due account of the political aspirations of the peoples, and to assist them in the progressive development of their free political institutions, according to the particular circumstances of each territory and its peoples and their varying stages of advancement. . . ."

When one considers the numerous trustee and other colonial dependencies one sees a great diversity in the methods by which they are ruled ; in general, however, there is an irrevocable tendency towards the disappearance of " empires " in the past sense of the term and their replacement by self-governing communities.

The British Commonwealth and Empire.—This unique combination of States and their dependencies requires a double-barrelled name, for no shorter label indicates its twofold structure. There is, on the one hand, the Commonwealth itself—the voluntary association of " The United Kingdom of Great Britain and Northern Ireland " with its partners, the self-governing Dominions of Canada, Australia, New Zealand, the Union of South Africa, Eire, Newfoundland, India, Pakistan, Ceylon and Southern Rhodesia. These States occupy over 9 million square miles, i.e. about one-sixth of the habitable land of the globe, and their populations total nearly 500 millions, i.e. nearly one in four of the world's inhabitants.[1]

On the other hand, there is the Colonial Empire—the territories of all sizes, of different stages of economic and social development, and with forms of government ranging from almost complete British rule to virtual self-government in internal affairs. Most of these colonial dependencies are controlled by the United Kingdom ; a few, however, are under the sole or conjoint administration of Australia, New Zealand and the Union of South Africa. The total area of the dependent territories amounts to over $2\frac{1}{2}$ million square miles, and their populations number about 60 million persons.

The British Commonwealth.—After the American War of Independence, the British government accepted a policy of granting a limited degree of independence to settlements of British, or partly British, origin ; in course of time a number

[1] Note these statistics, at the beginning of 1948, include India and Pakistan, which together occupy about $1\frac{1}{2}$ million square miles and have about 400 million inhabitants.

of local administrations and parliamentary systems were set up and their powers were gradually extended. The slowness of the process was in some cases resented, even with bitterness, and it is true that one factor was the reluctance of the mother country to give up her earlier rights and privileges and to accord complete freedom to her offspring. Yet, to continue the metaphor, the younger generation needed time for development and the attainment of political maturity.

The formation of the present great Dominions began under the British North America Act of 1867 by the establishment of what was later termed the Dominion of Canada, although not all the present Provinces were at first included. Similarly, in 1901 the six separate colonies of Australia and Tasmania became the States of the Commonwealth of Australia. New Zealand, which is more than 1,200 miles distant from Australia and had a distinct political evolution, obtained Dominion status in 1907. In South Africa, after a complicated and troubled history, the colonies of the Cape of Good Hope, Natal, the Transvaal and the Orange River Colony (henceforward known as the Orange Free State) were in 1910 formed into the Union of South Africa.

During the First World War, an insurrection against British rule led to the separation of 26 counties in southern Ireland, which then proclaimed itself a republic ; in 1921, it signed a treaty with Great Britain accepting Dominion status for the time being, and later took the ancient name of Eire. The north-eastern part of Ireland, comprising six counties of the province of Ulster, remained in the " United Kingdom of Great Britain and Northern Ireland," with its representatives in the House of Commons at Westminster, and also with its own parliament for local affairs.

The constitutional history of Newfoundland, with its mainland territory of Labrador, has been very chequered. It was granted representative government as early as 1832, but with its poor natural resources its population has remained small and its economic and political development has been slow ; in consequence, its constitution has more than once been suspended. In 1934 the administration was placed in the hands of a Commission, composed of three Newfoundlanders and three British officials, responsible to the Government of the United Kingdom, but after the Second World War it was decided that proposals for the future political status were to be submitted to the people of Newfoundland by means of a referendum.

The question of what " Dominion status " actually means is difficult to answer for several reasons : first, there is no written constitution exactly defining the relations between the United Kingdom and the other members of the Commonwealth ; secondly, there are differences in the practice of the various governments in this connection, e.g. Eire objects to use a title which may suggest subordination and elects its " President," while in the other Dominions the Crown, which is the link between them, is represented by a Governor-General ; finally, the association of the members of the Commonwealth is purely voluntary and its form is subject to change as the wishes of the Dominions vary or as their external circumstances alter.

Yet there are certain principles broadly underlying the structure and working of the British Commonwealth. A fundamental one is that its peoples are regarded as distinct nations organized into independent States. Their political relationship was set forth in an agreed declaration drawn up after an Imperial Conference in 1926 and given legal form in the Statute of Westminster in 1931 ; by this, the Dominions and the United Kingdom were defined as " Autonomous communities within the British Empire, equal in status, in no way subordinate to one another in any aspect of their domestic or external affairs, though united by a common allegiance to the Crown, and freely associated as members of the British Commonwealth of Nations."

In actual practice there is complete independence in home affairs, and their relationship in external affairs may be illustrated by the fact that the overseas Dominions have their own representatives in foreign States wherever they so desire, although they may also avail themselves of the services or reports of the ambassadors or consular officials of the United Kingdom.

A cardinal principle is the right of every member of the Commonwealth to decide upon its own policy of peace or war ; in 1939, the governments of all the Dominions decided upon war with Germany, with the exception of Eire which remained neutral.

The reference in the agreed definition to a " common allegiance to the Crown " needs further explanation. Within the United Kingdom, the King (who has been described as " the tenant of the Imperial Crown for the time being ") acts in conformity with the wishes of the people as expressed by their elected representatives, for he must follow the advice of Ministers who have the confidence of Parliament. In each of the Dominions the representative of the Crown is styled (except in Eire) the Governor-General, and is appointed by the King on the advice of the government of the Dominion concerned. The Governor-General is not the representative of the government of the United Kingdom, but functions as the Head of his particular State in the same way as the King does in Great Britain, i.e. acting solely on the advice of Ministers responsible to the Parliament of his Dominion. Although the King of Great Britain is still, at the beginning of 1948, recognized as a link by all the Dominions, Eire has proclaimed itself a Republic, and so does India in its draft constitution.

As a Prime Minister of Australia has said : " The Crown is no longer a symbol of subordination, but in very truth a symbol of equality."

Yet the common allegiance to the Crown is but a symbol ; the bond which unites the Commonwealth consists to some extent in feelings of loyalty, but essentially in the willingness of the Dominions to act together for their mutual benefit. In their outlook upon world problems they have similarities which are partly due to community in origin, speech and methods of government, and they realize the advantages of their past association in war and in peace. A valuable institution has been the series of Imperial Conferences—meetings which until the outbreak of the Second World War were attended by the Prime Ministers to discuss common problems and policies. The United Kingdom and the Dominions have also formed joint councils and committees on subjects as diverse as trade-tariffs, shipping, agriculture and health, in order to advise their respective governments or to carry out common measures. The defence of the Commonwealth, on land and sea and in the air, is co-ordinated by various methods including conferences, exchanges of officers, and standardization of training and equipment.

In addition to these special contacts, there is a system of continuous consultation and negotiation by means of High Commissioners. The United Kingdom maintains a High Commissioner in the capital of each Dominion, and the

Dominions have their High Commissioners in London. In London they meet together daily or at frequent intervals, and also transmit to the British government the views of their particular States ; in economic affairs they are assisted by Trade Commissioners.

Agreement between the members of the Commonwealth, both in ideas and in actions, is strongest where their peoples have in largest degree shared a common descent, and where the mother country has most willingly granted freedom as the overseas settlements developed. The bonds are less strong in the cases where the people in the Dominions have had different origins and where independence has been demanded with bitterness or yielded with reluctance.

The ideas and ideals of the members of the Commonwealth vary, too, according to their geographical conditions and their relation to other Powers ; hence each Dominion has its special problems to face. For instance, the map opposite shows that Australia and New Zealand have an outlook towards the Pacific Ocean as contrasted with the situation of Britain on the margin of the Atlantic Ocean. Thus, these two Dominions were seriously affected by the growth of Japanese influence, and during the Japanese conquests they were protected by the naval forces of the U.S.A. Also, trade between them and the States around the Pacific Ocean is, from the point of view of distance and cost of carriage, easier than that between them and Britain. It is significant that, although at the close of the Second World War consultations regarding the issues which then arose took place between the governments of the United Kingdom and the Dominions, yet at a Peace Conference in Paris the representative of Australia took lines on some matters quite different from those followed by the United Kingdom. Nevertheless, at the same period the two States initiated practical measures for their common defence, should this be required.

Finally, it must be noted that as time goes on, each of the Dominions, already having its special characteristics, must evolve in its own way and therefore differences between them must become more marked. Hence the continuance of their association will depend upon increasing mutual understanding and assistance.

The British Dependencies.—These number some forty

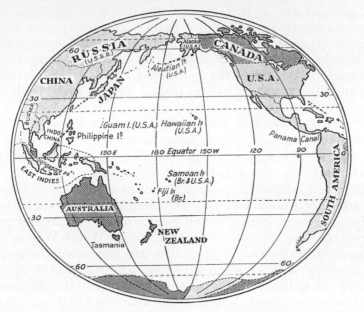

FIG. 54.—POLITICAL DIVISIONS OF THE PACIFIC MARGINS.

colonies, protectorates or territories ; both in the manner of their acquisition and also in their present political and economic conditions, they exhibit as great a variety and lack of system as a patchwork quilt. A study of an atlas map of the world shows that most of them are situated within or near the Tropics, and that they fall into several geographical groups.

In the western hemisphere are the islands of the British West Indies, Bermuda and Trinidad, and on the mainland are British Guiana and British Honduras. Generally speaking, these dependencies were early accessions to the Empire, being either original acquisitions following the discovery of the New World or taken from other European Powers on later occasions during the seventeenth and eighteenth centuries.

The most extensive dependencies are those of tropical Africa. Some are the result of the occupation of various places along the coasts, especially in West Africa from Gambia to Lagos, in the first three-quarters of the nineteenth century, but the greater areas were acquired during the scramble for Africa in the last quarter of that century.

The third large group consists of those of south-eastern Asia,

Malaya and the East Indies ; although some of these were acquired by traders at earlier dates, the greater part of the present dependencies or protectorates came under the control of Britain during the nineteenth century. Still farther eastward are the islands of the south-west Pacific Ocean, in which responsibility is shared by the United Kingdom, Australia and New Zealand.

Within this tropical zone of British Possessions, relatively small naval, military and air bases have been acquired to safeguard lines of communication. Trading bases have also been established, e.g. Hong Kong and Singapore.

In middle latitudes, too, acquisitions have been made in order to secure communications. The Mediterranean route from Britain to India, Australia and New Zealand has been of great importance, as was shown in the Second World War by the defence of Malta and Egypt. The strategic consideration of bases along lines of communication was responsible for the capture of Gibraltar in 1704, the treaty with the Maltese in 1814, and the annexation of Cyprus in 1914 ; it was also a factor in the establishment of British control at Aden and in Somaliland at the southern end of the Red Sea. In the South Atlantic Ocean are some small island territories, from Ascension Island and St. Helena to the Falklands and S. Georgia in the far south.

At the time of their acquisition most of the tropical territories were inhabited by peoples at a relatively backward stage and their internal conditions were often complicated by the existence of strongly contrasted plural societies. Consequently, as compared with European settlements in mid-latitudes, the tropical dependencies needed greater developments to adapt them to the economic conditions of the modern world and to fit them for even local self-government.

The attitude of the British government to the dependent peoples has gradually been changed, and the trend was indicated in the phrase " dual mandate," introduced in the early part of the present century. It expressed a double obligation : (*a*) that the government of a colony should put the interests of the Native inhabitants before those of the rulers ; (*b*) that the resources of the region should not be allowed to remain neglected or inadequately utilized by the Native peoples, but should be developed for the use of mankind in general.

As the result of the acknowledgment of an obligation to the dependent peoples, the government of Britain has had to accept financial liabilities, for as a rule the dependencies have not at present the means of paying for their economic and social advances. The British Parliament therefore, at the end of the Second World War, passed the Colonial Development and Welfare Act by which it expends sums amounting to several millions a year to aid the Colonies in starting approved undertakings ; these must be of such a nature that in course of time they will pay their way and enable the respective territories to utilize their resources and improve the conditions of their inhabitants.

The changed policy of the British government may be illustrated by the following examples. Economic innovations which were at first mainly for the benefit of the foreigners were later made with a more direct aim of improving the conditions of the colonial peoples. This was the case in improving means of communication and also in aiding agriculture ; irrigation, for instance, provided products for export, but it has also yielded more abundant food supplies for home needs.

Private enterprises by foreign companies and individuals have been increasingly controlled by the various administrations in the interests of the Native populations. For example, the occupation or purchase of land has been restricted, and the conditions under which Coloured people may work for Whites made subject to government regulations. Even trade unions among the Native labourers have been encouraged and aided by some governments.

British administrations followed, often after a considerable lapse of time, the work of missionaries in the provision of medical services. Yet when Europeans, both official and unofficial, introduced new ideas and methods in the treatment of disease and the adoption of hygienic ways of living, these could not have much effect until the Natives had been taught to understand them and to co-operate actively in their adoption. This change of attitude has been slow, for the peoples naturally trusted their age-long remedies and habits, sometimes bound up with religious beliefs and observances, and they viewed with suspicion or hostility the substitutes offered by the White rulers.

Education, too, has waited upon changes in the attitudes both of governors and governed. As in other branches of the social services, the work was led by missionaries, and taking the dependencies as a whole, more than half the children who get any education are in schools begun or maintained by missions. On the part of the British administrations, in the earlier stages very little was done, and first came the provision of training for the children of chiefs and the relatively well-to-do classes. There was often a long lag before the beginning of a system of free education for the masses, one great difficulty being the lack of funds in the exchequers of the respective territories. On the part of the Natives, in addition to a common reluctance due to their initial ignorance, there were added practical difficulties due to their poverty and the need for children's labour in the struggle to get a living.

As to the kind of education, there had to be a gradual realization that the " bookish " type common in Britain was even more unsuitable in the dependencies ; practical training in gardening and agriculture, in handicrafts and domestic work, were not at first seen to be essentials. Still later developments came in the establishment of secondary schools and colleges where, together with the humanities and arts, science was studied and applied to the needs of the communities in such matters as hygiene, farming and the use of machinery. Even when these advances had been made, at about the time of the outbreak of the Second World War, it remained true that fewer than one-quarter of the children attended schools, and of these the great majority left before they had learnt to read and write.

Political progress has sometimes had to wait upon improvements in the fundamental matters of feeding, health and education. It needs also a feeling of community among the peoples, and this varies greatly in the respective dependencies. Among the population of Nigeria, for instance, there are strong contrasts in cultural conditions and a marked lack of unity or even close association. In the Niger delta are " naked pagans " living in huts built above the swamps ; in the modern port of Lagos, educated Negroes manage the businesses and banks, edit newspapers, take their share in the city government and serve their fellows as doctors and Christian clergymen ; inland, some tribes still practise shifting cultivation in traditional manner and commonly suffer from malnutrition if not actual hunger ; other farmers have been brought into the web of international commerce and grow palm oil, ground nuts and cacao for export ; in the north of the Protectorate are tribes upon whom Muslim influence has been brought and emirs rule people of mixed descent, some living as pastoralists or cultivators in villages, others carrying on crafts or commerce in large cities whose walls are overtopped by the minarets of mosques.

In some colonies there has been so little organization among the Natives that only " direct rule " by the British is even yet possible. In other territories, and especially where in tropical Africa there are well-organized tribal communities or even kingdoms, " indirect rule " or " Native administration " has been instituted. In such relatively advanced areas the general policy and the legal system are determined by the Colonial Office in Britain, and it is the business of local White officials to arrange for the administration of the law through the local rulers ; these may be kings, emirs or chiefs, and they act in consultation with their assemblies, councils or elders. The system is not one of complete self-government even in internal affairs, for the actions of the local rulers are supervised by a British resident or district officer ; thus authority resides finally in the Parliament, and therefore in the electors, of the United Kingdom. Nor is the system of indirect rule always democratic, for the local rulers may owe their position to an autocratic tradition. Other territories are known as " protectorates," e.g. Zanzibar, where laws are issued by the Sultan when countersigned by the British resident, but there is often little practical difference between protectorates and those dependencies which are under indirect rule.

Conditions during the Second World War led to a grouping of neighbouring territories and the establishment of joint councils to allow co-operation between them in war services and in postwar reconstruction ; thus in Africa there were a West African Council, an East African Council and a Central African Council.

From the international point of view, the most interesting example of this kind of association was the Caribbean Commission set up by the governments of Britain, the United States, France and the Netherlands, to promote the social and economic well-being of the peoples under their jurisdiction in the West Indian Islands and on the mainland shores of the Caribbean Sea. A series of conferences was arranged between representatives of the various territories, the delegations being led by Native members of the local legislative councils, with officials attached as expert advisers. The main subjects discussed were food, health, employment and industrial development ; the conclusions were reported as recommendations, for the conferences could not dictate to the ruling authorities of the respective Powers. A further advance was suggested by the fact that a discussion on the important subject of land tenure was attended also by representatives from three independent Caribbean Republics.

A number of the colonial dependencies have already a considerable measure of self-government, exercised through some kind of parliamentary institution. This may, for example, take the form of a legislative council elected by the inhabitants, and thus to a certain extent corresponding to the House of Commons in the United Kingdom, together with an executive council consisting of Ministers, either elected by the people or nominated by the Governor, who are in charge of the various departments of the administration. Home affairs would normally be in the power of the local government, but the Governor would have an emergency right of final decision, and as the Governor is appointed and instructed by the Colonial Office in London, the ultimate authority is thus retained by the Parliament of the United Kingdom. In several cases, such a modified form of self-government was established as a definite and acknowledged step towards Dominion status.

Malaya has had difficult conditions for a reform in government, as Chinese and Indian immigrants together outnumber the Malays. Also, among the Malays themselves there are local groups with feelings of loyalty to their particular Native rulers, some inheriting treaty rights which prevented a unified government. Yet a " Federation of Malaya " has now been formed by new treaties between the Native rulers and Great Britain, and with agreements ensuring more representative government within the States.

Southern Rhodesia has achieved Dominion status, but there are two exceptional conditions. (1) As the right to vote does not extend beyond the British, and the total European population is fewer than 100,000 while the Natives number about 1,500,000, the Government of Great Britain has been reluctant to give a small minority complete power over the majority of the inhabitants. (2) Relations with other States are still controlled by the United Kingdom.

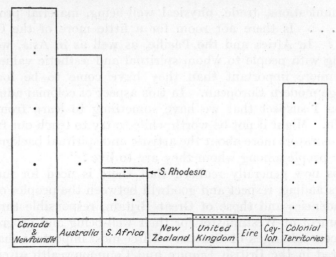

FIG. 55.—BRITISH COMMONWEALTH AND EMPIRE—AREAS
AND POPULATIONS AFTER SECOND WORLD WAR.

Note.—(1) Scale of areas is the same as in Fig. 53 ; (2) each dot represents approximately
5 millions, or less than 5 millions ; (3) with South Africa is included S.W. Africa ; (4) the
Anglo-Egyptian Sudan and Antarctic areas are not included ; (5) India and Pakistan are
shown in Fig. 53.

While several colonial territories desire independence, Cyprus
is a notable exception in the fact that many of its people feel
themselves part of another nation. Because of its strategic
position, this island has been occupied by several Powers in turn,
yet four-fifths of the inhabitants are Greek-speaking and most
" politically conscious " Cypriots demand union with Greece.

A significant advance in the government of tropical British
dependencies was proposed in an official report, published after
the Second World War, upon the selection and training of colonial
officers. The main intention was to have a large share in the
administration of their respective territories taken by educated
Natives who would be trained with their White colleagues, and
in this way to secure a closer understanding and co-operation
between the British and Native peoples. A new spirit, it was
urged, should actuate colonial governments, and the report
included the following suggestion of the Director of Recruitment
and Training :

" Possibly one weakness in British colonial administration
has been that we have too closely followed the Roman model.
Have we too much concerned ourselves with material things :

communications, trade, physical well-being, material prosperity ? . . . Is there not room for a little more of the Greek spirit ? In Africa and the Pacific, as well as in Asia, we are dealing with people to whom spiritual and æsthetic values are often more important than they have come to be for the average modern European. In this aspect of colonial administration I suspect that we have something to learn from the French. Might it not be worth while to try to teach our future administrators more about the artistic and spiritual background of the people among whom they are to live ? "

It is now generally realized that there is need for mutual understanding, respect and goodwill between the peoples of the dependencies and those of Great Britain, responsible through Parliament at Westminster for their well-being and progress.

Recent Changes of Status.—Three most important changes occurred in the British Empire and Commonwealth after the Second World War.

Self-government in *Ceylon* had been delayed by dissensions between the Sinhalese and the minorities of Tamils, Muslims and others, but this difficulty was adjusted when at the beginning of 1948 Ceylon obtained " fully responsible status within the British Commonwealth of Nations." In view of the strategic position of Ceylon on the Commonwealth lines of communication, the new Dominion agreed to the United Kingdom retaining naval and air bases, and in the matter of external affairs it declared its willingness to follow resolutions of past Imperial Conferences.

At the same time, *Burma* achieved independence. Here was a rather similar problem of a plural society, including many Indian and Chinese immigrants and less-advanced hill-tribes, but the new Burmese government was willing to give some amount of freedom or representation to most groups. Burma had not the strategic situation of Ceylon, and although a temporary defence agreement was made, the British Government acceded to the demand that Burma should become a sovereign and independent Republic outside the Commonwealth.

The greatest problems have arisen in connexion with the *Indian Independence Act*, which came into operation in August 1947. During the twentieth century desire in India for self-government and for freedom from British domination became strong, and at the end of the Second World War Britain was willing to give up its power ; yet two problems had to be solved : the existence of " Princes' India " in which several hundreds of Native Princes ruled under treaties of long standing, and bitter conflict between the Hindu majority and the Muslim minority in " British India."

The latter knot was cut by the partition of British India into two separate Dominions of the Commonwealth—one mainly Hindu and known as India, the other mainly Muslim and known as Pakistan. The partition was based generally upon the religion dominant in each province, but in two cases a division within provinces was made, viz. in the Punjab between the Hindu East and the Muslim West, and in Bengal between the Hindu West and the Muslim East. In the Punjab, however, about 4 million Sikhs lived in a belt which ran across the line dividing the East from the West ; hence, the Sikhs revolted against the splitting of their community and the subjection of one part to a Muslim government. At the same time armed riots broke out between Muslims and Hindus, and there resulted disastrous mass-migrations of Sikhs and Hindus from West to East and of Muslims from East to West.

The problem of the Princes' States was dealt with by giving to each the choice of which Dominion to join ; most chose India. The system, as a whole, was made workable by the union of many of the smaller States and by adopting more democratic forms of government within them.

The broad result of partition has been that the Dominon of India occupies about three-quarters of the sub-continent and has about 320 millions or more people, while Pakistan has one-quarter of the total area and a population of somewhere about 70 millions. Pakistan, moreover, has two geographical disadvantages : East Pakistan is an " island " in the Dominion of India 800 miles from West Pakistan, and West Pakistan contains the North-West Frontier region through which many invasions have come in the past and which is still inhabited by tribesmen with a tradition of warfare and of raiding the cultivated plains of the Indus.

Although the Indian Independence Act created two new Dominions, it is implicit that either may exercise its right of secession, and that only its desire or its interests will determine whether it remains within the Commonwealth.

CHAPTER XIX

POPULATION:
DISTRIBUTION, TRENDS AND PROBLEMS

Introduction.—Quite a number of population problems face the nations of different parts of the world ; some of these problems, which are among the most serious of those of today, are closely related to geographical conditions and cannot be omitted from a study of the earth as the home of men.

Four sets of questions arise in this connection. (1) Are there at present too many, or too few, inhabitants in certain regions of the world ? There is, for example, the contrast between the densely populated Asiatic Monsoon Lands and the empty spaces of Australia. (2) Are the populations increasing or decreasing in particular countries ? For instance, is Great Britain to expect a continuation of the increase, or a decline, in the number of its inhabitants ? (3) What are the geographical factors affecting the desire of some nations to have outlets for their peoples in other lands ? Conversely, do the natural resources of certain States justify their willingness, or their refusal, to admit immigrants ? (4) Is the earth as a whole capable of being a good " home of man " for its present, or an even larger, population ?

To help towards answering these and similar questions, four groups of facts are needed : (1) the present distribution, i.e. the comparative density, of population over the lands ; (2) changes which have occurred in recent times ; (3) the trends now to be observed towards increases or decreases of population in certain States ; (4) the present standards of living, and the conditions affecting over-population or under-population.

Present Distribution.—Most people have to live where nature, together with the organization of their communities, gives them opportunity for carrying on their special kind of work ; hence the distribution of the various occupations described in preceding chapters gives the key to the distribution of population. A convenient way of studying the world

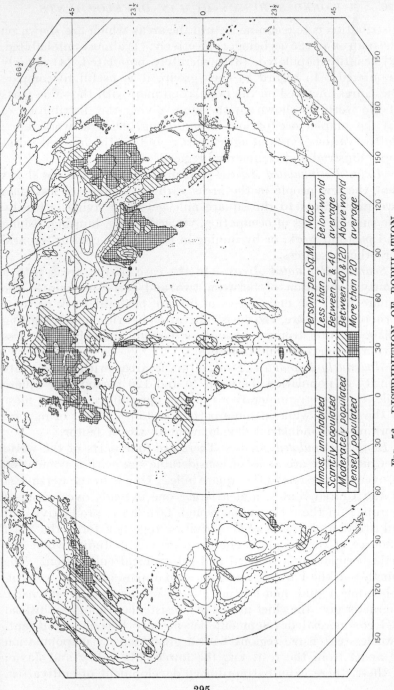

FIG. 56.—DISTRIBUTION OF POPULATION.

Persons per Sq.M.		Note
Almost uninhabited		
Scantily populated	Less than 2	Below world average
Moderately populated	Between 2 & 40	average
Densely populated	Between 40 & 120	Above world
	More than 120	average

distribution is to examine in turn the areas which are shown on the map on p. 295 as being, respectively, (1) almost uninhabited, (2) scantily populated, (3) moderately populated, (4) densely populated.   In regard to each group, it is useful to compare these areas marked on the population map with the same parts of the world as shown on the maps giving the distribution of (*a*) the simpler occupations of gathering, pastoral work, etc. ; (*b*) the various types of agriculture ; and (*c*) the mineral-working, industrial and commercial regions.

Almost Uninhabited Areas.—A comparison of the maps shows that the few people in the areas with an average of less than two inhabitants to the square mile get their living either by the simpler types of occupation, viz. gathering, hunting, fishing and pastoral work, or by mining in regions too cold or too arid for other resources.

Scantily Populated Areas.—In the case of the areas with a scanty population of between two and forty persons to the square mile, the main bases of life are pastoral work or some form of agriculture, viz. oasis cultivation in arid regions, shifting tillage in inter-tropical regions, or plough farming in the less favoured parts of mid-latitudes.

Moderately Populated Areas.—In the areas with a moderate density of population, between 40 and 120 persons per square mile, the more remunerative types of agriculture support most of the people, while in some parts a certain amount of mineral working and industrial development is also a factor.

Densely Populated Areas.—There are four parts of the world in which there are areas of considerable size with a population of over 120 persons to the square mile.   One is in the north-east of the United States, and a larger one extends over much of Europe ; in these two areas plough farming is productive, but industrial and commercial activities together form the chief resource of the people.   The third area is in India, where the main occupation is tropical and sub-tropical cultivation.   The fourth is in the Far East, in China and Japan, and here tropical, sub-tropical and mid-latitude kinds of farming of intensive character give the chief means of subsistence, though industrial and commercial development has already become significant. Two less extensive regions with a great density of population lie apart from the rest, viz. the lower Nile valley and Java ; in these, there is an extraordinary development of cultivation, based upon the irrigation of unusually fertile soil and undertaken for the requirements of distant manufacturing countries as well as for home needs.

Cities and Conurbations.—Within all these densely populated areas, and also scattered more sparsely over other lands, are small districts in which live large numbers of people. Where important lines of communication come together there is a strong tendency to an agglomeration of people engaged in industry and commerce. Mineral deposits, too, may form the basis of town or city development.

Moreover, the government of States is in many cases carried on at great cities which have arisen at focal points ; e.g. London and Paris are the political capitals, as well as very important centres of manufacturing and commerce, in their respective countries. In some States which have been formed in recent times by the federation of smaller political units, it has been thought wise to avoid jealousies and not to put the new seat of government at any one of the chief towns of the constituent units ; hence capitals have been created upon new sites selected for this special purpose, e.g. Washington, Ottawa and Canberra.

For various reasons, the development of an agglomeration of people may be so great that neighbouring settlements originally under separate administrations may coalesce into one continuous built-up area, called by geographers a conurbation. For instance, the conurbation of London extends beyond the City of London and even beyond the encircling County of London to include urban districts controlled by adjoining local authorities. Paris and Berlin are nuclei of other large conurbations, as also are many commercial cities such as New York and Hamburg. Unless special care is taken, such huge and densely populated conurbations without unified organization may result in undesirable social conditions.

The number of great local concentrations of people is increasing ; at the present time there are in the world over fifty " millionaire cities," about a dozen of which have populations of 5 millions or more, while each of the conurbations of London and New York has about 10 million inhabitants.

Population Contrasts.—From the preceding sections it is seen that there is a most striking contrast between the almost uninhabited or very scantily populated condition of most of the land surface of the earth and the grouping of large masses of people into a few relatively small regions. The total population of the world in 1940 has been estimated at about 2,000 millions ; as the land surface (excluding the Arctic and Antarctic ice caps) is about 50 million square miles it follows that, if the population could be spread uniformly over that area, there would be about 40 persons to the square mile. In point of fact, only a small part of the world had a density of population near this figure. A comparison between the continents shows marked contrasts ; e.g. Australia, with Tasmania, had a population of 7 millions on an area of about 3 million square miles, i.e. an average of a little over 2 per square mile, while in Europe there were about 500 million people living on $3\frac{3}{4}$ million square miles, an average of over 130 persons to the square mile.

Special attention may be drawn to the following figures of the total numbers of inhabitants of the four most populous parts of the world :

ESTIMATED POPULATIONS (in round numbers) IN 1940	MILLIONS
The Far East (China and Japan)	About 500
India and Ceylon	,, 400
Europe	,, 500
Eastern North America (east and centre of U.S.A. and adjoining parts of Canada)	,, 120
These four main populated areas	,, 1,520
The whole world	,, 2,000

The very important fact emerges that three-quarters of the world's population are crowded on about one-eighth of the land surface, in four distinct regions.

One of the two greatest aggregations is that of the Far East, almost cut off by mountains from the less numerous group in India and Ceylon. These two population groups of the Monsoon Lands, apart from smaller ones in Indo-China, together include about 45 per cent. of the inhabitants of the world ; they are in the main communities which have developed from old civilizations. At the opposite end of the Old World is the

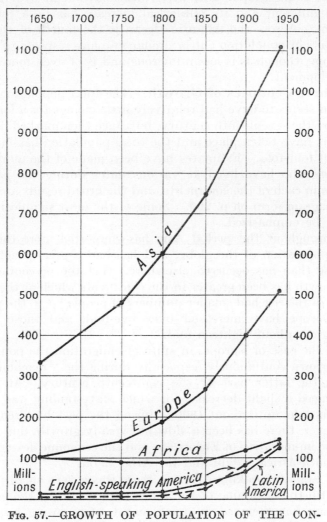

FIG. 57.—GROWTH OF POPULATION OF THE CON-
TINENTS.

Note.—(1) The broken line near the bottom of the diagram refers to English-speaking America. (2) The populations of Australia and New Zealand cannot be shown on the scale of this diagram. (3) The positions of the dots show the numerical increase of the populations, but the steepness of the slope of the lines joining the dots does not indicate the comparative *rate* of increase at different levels on the diagram.

European group, about as numerous as that of the Far East ; it also is based upon ancient civilizations, but its evolution has been different and its numerical increase has been relatively recent.   Across the Atlantic Ocean is the fourth of the great clusters of population ; it is similar in many respects to that of Europe, though it is less numerous and is of even more recent development.

Three Centuries of Growth.—The total population of the world seems to have had relatively little change for a long time before the seventeenth century, but since then marked developments have taken place and the total population has increased about four-fold.   Estimates have been made of the numbers of people who have lived at various dates during the past 300 years in each of the continents, and the broad results are shown in diagram form on p. 299.   Some of the most significant facts may be emphasized.

Throughout the period Asia has supported more than half the population of the globe, and has had a greater actual increase than has occurred elsewhere.   Yet the percentage rate of growth has been greater in the continents which at the beginning of the rise had smaller numbers of people ; e.g. the peoples of Europe have increased over five-fold, and those of the Americas about eighteen-fold.

In the case of Europe, in spite of emigration the population has grown continuously, especially during the " machine age " from the latter part of the eighteenth century.   Africa experienced a slight decrease, for which slave-raiding was largely responsible, until about 1800 ; during the past hundred years, however, there has been a slow but steady growth, due mainly to the immigration of Europeans and the economic development of South Africa, Egypt and the Atlas Lands.

In English-speaking America there was a very small population till the beginning of the nineteenth century ; the greatest increase has occurred in quite recent times owing largely to immigration and to the growth of manufacturing and commerce. Latin America had a larger population than English-speaking America until the industrial revolution in the northern continent ; during the twentieth century there has been a very considerable advance in the cooler regions of South America and in Mexico.   The settlement of Australia did not begin till about the opening of the nineteenth century nor that of New Zealand till nearly fifty years later ; until recently, pastoral work formed a considerable part of the economy of these most distant lands and it could not support a great population.

The continents, however are not good units for a careful survey of the growth of population during recent times. From the geographical point of view, the most important matter is to see in what types of environment the increases have occurred. There are the " new " lands of what has been called " Europe overseas," i.e. much of North America and those parts of the southern continents which have been settled by Europeans ; yet with the one exception of eastern North America the numbers of their populations are still very small in comparison with those of the Old World. Moreover, the settlements of any considerable number of people, i.e. enough to constitute " moderately populated " areas as shown on the map, have been restricted in the new lands mainly to a few regions with favourable climates, while beyond these limited areas only scanty populations have been able to subsist. Indeed, there has been a retreat from drier areas, such as the " dust-bowl " of U.S.A., where farming settlements attempted more than nature permitted.

Another group of regions with a marked increase of population consists of comparatively small areas of the Old World—either relatively hot ones transformed by irrigation (especially in Egypt, Java and the north-west of India), or cooler areas previously known but little developed (notably parts of the U.S.S.R. and Manchuria) which have now been brought into touch with modern developments.

The greatest growth of population in recent times, however, has been in the long-occupied regions of Europe and the Monsoon Lands. Moreover, within these regions it has been their more densely populated parts which have received the greatest additions, often at the expense of the areas with less people ; a great increase in the number and size of the conurbations has gone on side by side with rural depopulation.

Broadly speaking, therefore, the result of the modern growth of population together with large-scale and small-scale migrations has not been to spread the inhabitants of the world more evenly over the surface. On the contrary, the effect of recent developments has been (a) to add eastern North America to the three earlier dense aggregations of people, and (b) to strengthen the contrasts between the small crowded areas and the " vast open spaces " of the world.

The chief cause of the general increase of population was the lowered death-rate due to several factors which affected one another. (1) Until the recent World Wars there was a general, though of course not universal, improvement in the maintenance of order and security within the various countries, and this allowed peaceful development in man's productivity and general advancement. (2) Improvements in agriculture gave greater, more reliable, and more varied and nutritive supplies of food. (3) The Industrial Revolution brought about improvements in manufacture and transport which enabled very large numbers of people to find employment in supplying other necessities of life. (4) Medical knowledge co-operated with better diet, housing and sanitation to bring about a great reduction in mortality from a number of diseases, e.g. smallpox, bubonic plague (the " Black Death "), and malaria (" ague "), in many regions, including the British Isles. (5) As one result of these combined advances, the large proportion of the children who in each generation had died young was lessened, and more grew to maturity and had children of their own ; by this means, in many countries the number of births was raised while the number of deaths was lowered.

It must be added that considerable setbacks to the growth of population resulted from the World Wars ; the second specially affected the two most populous regions, Europe and the Far East, where many millions of people died—both combatants and non-combatants, men, women and children.

Present Trends.—The third set of basic facts about population comprises those relating to present-day trends in particular countries, either towards continued growth or towards a decline in the numbers of people.

It might appear from the graph on p. 299 that the population of the world is everywhere increasing and that the increase will continue, but such deductions would be misleading.   In several parts of the world there is now a marked trend towards a slackening in the rate of increase, or even towards a positive decrease.

Apart from immigration or emigration, an increase or decrease in the population of a country depends on the number of births compared with the number of deaths ; yet a simple comparison of the total birth-rate per 1,000 of the population compared with the total death-rate per 1,000 does not tell the whole of the story. The essential facts are (1) the average size of families, and (2) the number of children who live to the age at which they themselves can have children.

How the size of families has decreased in England and Wales may be inferred from the figures giving for certain years the number of births per 1,000 women between the ages of 15 and 45.

1861	1871	1881	1891	1901	1911	1921	1931
152	159	149	130	114	100	90	65

The facts and some of their consequences are commented upon in the following quotations from a statement, issued in September 1945, by the Royal Commission on Population appointed in the preceding year. " The main fact is the fall in the average size of family, which began in the 1870's. Until then, married women, on the average, had more than five children before the end of their childbearing period. Many had ten or more. By the 1930's, at the rates at which married women were then having children, the number was down to about two. . . . An average family of five children made ample allowance for the people who did not marry and for the children who died, and still left a new generation half as big again as the one before ; the population therefore grew rapidly. An average family of two children makes no allowance for children who die young and for those who do not marry. If people go on having families no larger than this, each generation will be succeeded by a generation smaller in numbers.

" The full effect of the fall in the average size of family on the growth of population was slow in manifesting itself. For many years after it began, the total number of children born each year went on growing because the number of young people coming to the ages at which they marry and have children was still growing. Not until the early years of the present century did the annual number of births stop increasing and begin to decline. . . . In 1919, Great Britain had approximately 16 million persons under 20 years of age ; in 1939 there were only 14 millions."

Another factor in preventing an immediate decrease in the total population has been the lowering of the death-rate during the period considered. Moreover, as the mortality among children was markedly reduced, a larger proportion of the smaller families survived to become potential parents of the next generation. Yet the total population of Great Britain has already slackened in its rate of growth, and under the present conditions it will suffer a positive decline in the course of a few years.[1]

The situation is, therefore, that what is called the " net reproduction rate " of the people of Great Britain is below " replacement level." If this latter level is expressed as 1·0, the net reproduction rate in 1937 was just below 0·8, or in other words, the next generation would be about four-fifths that of 1937. It is clear that without an increase in the size of families the population of Great Britain must soon shrink and, indeed, in course of time it would become extinct. Even to stabilize the number of people the net reproduction rate must rise from 0·8 to the replacement level of 1·0.

In addition to the decrease of population, there are other consequences of the present trend which have important geographical bearings. If the number of births is less than that in the past, a few years later the number of people of working age will also be lowered, and unless compensating improvements in methods of working are introduced, the economic production of the country will be reduced. One social problem which will then arise may be indicated. The older people in the population, representing those who were formerly in early or middle life, will be relatively numerous, and as they pass from the ranks of the workers their increasing numbers must be supported by the decreasing body of active people ; in addition, with healthier conditions in general the average length of life is increased. From the economic point of view, therefore, the nation will become more and more " top-heavy."

The question suggests itself : What has happened, and is happening, in other countries ? As far as available statistics go, it appears that the birth-rate (but not, of course, the total population) began to decline in France, and also among the white population in the United States, as early as the beginning of the nineteenth century. In the sixties of that century

---

[1] During and immediately following the war years from 1942 to 1945, the birth-rate rose, but this may have been due to a temporary increase in the number of marriages and first births ; unless the size of families changes, the trend towards the reduction in numbers of the people of Great Britain will continue.

Sweden had a definite lowering of the birth-rate, and was soon followed by Great Britain and by north-western Europe in general. Later the decline extended to south-western Europe and, in the present century, to the central and more easterly parts of the continent with the exception of Russia. Meanwhile, the same change occurred among peoples of European descent overseas, notably in Australia and New Zealand, and later in Canada and South Africa.

In estimating the effects upon the countries concerned it must be remembered that a lowering of the birth-rate might be off-set for a time by a reduction in the death-rate, and also by considerable immigration in the case of some European countries and the overseas lands. Moreover, a fall in the birth-rate did not necessarily mean that the net reproduction rate was lowered so far that it fell below replacement level, with the consequent tendency to a diminution of the population.

Precise knowledge of what is now happening is not available for all countries, but the following statistics illustrate the trend in some States in the years before the outbreak of war in 1939. They are arranged in descending order of their net reproduction rates, showing in the first column those countries where the rates were still above replacement level, and in the second column those with rates below that level and therefore either with a trend towards an eventual decline in numbers or with an actual decrease of the native-born population :

COUNTRY	N.R. RATE	COUNTRY	N.R. RATE
Japan	1·44	U.S.A. (Whites) . .	0·99
South Africa (Whites) .	1·30	Australia . . .	0·98
Bulgaria	1·19	Germany . . .	0·98
Ireland	1·16	Scotland . . .	0·91
Italy	1·13	France . . .	0·88
Netherlands . . .	1·12	Norway . . .	0·83
Poland	1·11	England and Wales .	0·78
Canada	1·09	Sweden . . .	0·76
New Zealand . . .	1·07		

Similar statistics have been obtained for earlier dates and from all these, together with less definite estimates, the following conclusions can be drawn. (1) During the present century, in most countries for which information is available, the net reproduction rate has shown a decline. Nevertheless, until

1920 it was still above 1·0 (i.e. there was a trend towards increase) everywhere except in France and Germany which had a rate below unity. After 1920, the reproduction rate fell below 1·0 in a number of countries.

(2) In Europe (excluding the U.S.S.R.) the situation just before the Second World War was that the rate had already fallen below replacement level in the northern, western and central parts of the continent, with the small exceptions of Ireland and the Netherlands. Over this region as a whole the trend presaged a decrease in population ; this could be averted only by a reversal of the decline in the net reproduction rate. In the southern and eastern countries, however, the decline had not proceeded so far ; even here, however, the net reproduction rate was less than it had been, and if the decline continued there must ultimately be a trend towards decrease in the total population.

(3) For the U.S.S.R., complete statistics giving the rate at different times are lacking. By far the greatest number of the people of the U.S.S.R. live in the European area, and of these it can be only said that shortly before the Second World War the rate was very high—possibly more than 1·5. For the Ukraine figures for different years exist, however, and a comparison of these shows a fall in the rate although this is still above the replacement level. In Moscow, as in the great cities of the other States of Europe, the net reproduction rate has dropped below unity ; it has long been a general rule that in large cities an increase of numbers is brought about by an influx from rural areas.

(4) In overseas settlements of European origin there had been a decline before 1939 in the reproduction rate, but it had not in general proceeded as far as in the countries from which the settlers came. In Australia and among the White population of U.S.A. the rate had dropped just below the replacement level, but in New Zealand and Canada it was still above unity, while among the White minority of South Africa it was still remarkably high. In Latin America the total population is increasing and probably the present rate is above unity, but definite knowledge about the trend, either among the people of European descent or among those of mixed origin, is very scanty.

(5) In regard to the Negro population of Africa a similar lack

of information exists ; in general, there is an increase in numbers rather greater than that among the European settlers.

(6) Of the trends in the Monsoon Lands there were statistics only for Japan ; in that country the net reproduction rate had shown a decline during the pre-war period, but it was still exceptionally high. About the situation in China there is an almost complete lack of information and even the total number of inhabitants is uncertain. Yet in some of the more fertile areas the dense population is probably still increasing. Considering China as a whole, it seems likely that while at some periods there occur great losses due to famines, wars and the consequent upheavals in economic and social conditions, at other times there is a recovery or even an increase in the number of the Chinese people. Both in China and in Japan, the strong feeling of the importance of the family and of its maintenance works against the almost world-wide tendency towards a smaller birth-rate. In India the population certainly increased considerably during the twenty years before the census of 1941, and further increase seems probable unless prevented by the occurrence of major calamities.

The Monsoon Lands taken as a whole, and in this connection the East Indies may be included with them, appear to have had a trend towards an increase in the numbers of their peoples during the period between the World Wars, and to stand out from much of the world in this respect.

The long-range results of the war of 1939–45 upon the populations of the areas directly involved cannot yet be estimated. There were great displacements of people connected with the alterations of State boundaries, and there must also have been some effect upon net reproduction rates and therefore upon trends as distinct from actual numbers. The mortality rates were raised both at the time of warfare and later as the consequence of privation and disease, e.g. even in the Paris area, which was not fought over, the infant mortality doubled during the six years following the outbreak of war ; these high death-rates considerably reduced the numbers of surviving children and must therefore entail a reduction of the next generation. Hence the future populations of Europe and the Far East have been seriously affected. Where, as over much of Europe, the reproduction rate had already fallen below unity, the fall must have been accentuated ; where, as at least in parts of the Far East, it was still above replacement level there must have been some decline although its extent cannot be measured.

Apart from catastrophes the causes of changes in birth-rates are complicated and vary from country to country. A rise may occur when a nation increases its capacity to support a larger population. In the case of an agricultural community, however, more and better food means a lowering of the mortality for a time, but soon the resulting larger numbers put a greater pressure on the land and they tend to overtake the greater production : thus improvement in conditions is, as it were, automatically checked unless other factors come into play. If, on the other hand, an increase in capacity to support a larger population is due to some form of " industrial revolution," there is not an automatic check ; indeed, one advance leads to another, and a higher birth-rate is at least a possibility.

Yet even in this case a reaction may occur, though for quite a different reason. If people collect in towns or large cities, their ways of living alter, and their standards of values change : they may rate more highly such matters as the enjoyment of various comforts and amenities for themselves, or improved health conditions and better education for their children. Under these circumstances, there is a tendency to voluntary limitation of families, and it is probably largely due to this fact that the present trend to lower reproduction rates has become most marked in those parts of the world in which industrial developments have gone farthest and standards of living have risen.

Comparative Standards of Living.—This matter is of such importance that a more precise consideration is desirable. Among the elements which make up people's standards of living are the goods they can acquire, such as food, clothing, housing and furniture, and the services they can obtain, such as education, medical aid and transportation. No complete and balanced comparison can be drawn between standards of living of different peoples, but estimates have been made [1] of the " real earnings " per worker in the various States of the world.

Simple " money earnings " may be misleading, even when the different currencies are reduced to one system, because the prices which workers must pay for similar goods and services vary from country to country. Hence a common measure of real purchasing power must be found, and in the book quoted

---

[1] By Colin Clark, in *The Conditions of Economic Progress.*

this is devised and expressed as " international units," viz. the amount of goods and services which could be purchased for $1 in the United States. In other countries the same amount of goods and services could be obtained for certain sums reckoned in their currencies, and by a simple calculation the money wages in each country can be turned into these units of purchasing power ; thus a comparison between the " real earnings " in each country can be made. For example, during the decade 1925–34, the average worker in the U.S.A. could purchase 1,381 units of goods and services, while in Great Britain the average worker could purchase 1,069 of the same units, in Norway 539, in Italy 343, and in China the average worker could purchase only 110 units.

To make the map printed on p. 310, the States have been arranged in five grades ; e.g. those where the workers obtained an annual average of over 1,000 international units are classed as having a " high " standard of living, and so on in descending order to the States where the workers obtained fewer than 200 units and the standard is graded as " very low."

The statistics treat each State as an entity, but of course there are great differences within them. Hence those States which include areas of contrasting types, although shown uniformly on the map, actually comprise different parts which should (if information were available) be represented by different numbers of units and possibly even by different grades. For instance, the " medium " grade shown for Brazil should doubtless be raised for commercial areas near the coast and lowered for remote districts of the interior. Also, to avoid misconception, in making the map the large areas of the world which are almost uninhabited, i.e. those which have less than two persons per square mile, have been left blank. There is the further point that the statistics relate to earnings, and there is generally a small number of people whose incomes are not reckoned in this class ; in some States these individuals are relatively numerous and may be very wealthy.

The statistics employed in the estimates here used were averages for the decade 1925–34 ; as this period saw an almost world-wide depression, the statistics show lower standards than those which obtained in other inter-war years, but they may not be very different from those of many countries in the post-war period. Although the exact number of units doubtless need

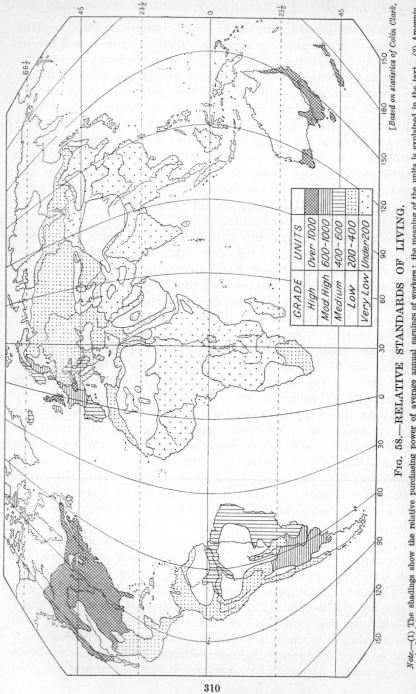

FIG. 58.—RELATIVE STANDARDS OF LIVING.

[*Based on statistics of Colin Clark.*]

GRADE	UNITS
High	Over 1000
Mod. High	600–1000
Medium	400–600
Low	200–400
Very Low	Under 200

Note.—(1) The shadings show the relative purchasing power of average annual earnings of workers ; the meaning of the units is explained in the text. (2) Amounts are calculated for each state as an entity. (3) Areas which, on the population map, are shown as almost uninhabited are left blank.

alteration, few States are likely to have had their standards of living so changed from those of 1925–34 that they should be put into a different grade. In making the map, only two countries have had their grade altered : Germany, following the results of war destruction and of the post-war policy of the Allies to limit its industries, has been reduced from a previous " moderately high " grade to the " low " grade common in the countries of eastern Europe ; for similar reasons Japan has been lowered from the " low " to the " very low " grade which dominates in southern and eastern Asia.

It must be realized that the names of the grades are merely relative. Thus the standard of living in Great Britain is labelled " high " and indeed it is so when compared with that of most other countries, yet an authority on dietetics [1] made a scientific survey from which he concluded that in Great Britain 50 per cent. of the people had not an income sufficient to provide the food necessary for well-being.

From the point of view of relative standards of living it may be pointed out that the workers in the " medium " grade have only about half the purchasing power of those of Great Britain, that the great majority of mankind comes into the " low " or " very low " grades, and that the average standard of living of the hundreds of millions of Chinese is about one-tenth of that of the British people. Indeed, the economist upon whose work the map is based summarized his results in the statement : " The world is a wretchedly poor place."

The map should be examined to find correlations between standards of living and other geographical conditions ; a few of these may here be briefly indicated. One is that the peoples in the medium or higher grades are Europeans or those of mainly European descent who live in mid-latitudes or in sub-tropical latitudes. This generalization is broadly true when allowance is made for States being treated as entities, and in this connection it may be pointed out that in South Africa the white minority has a much higher standard than that of the " black " or " coloured " inhabitants. An exception to the generalization appears in the case of the U.S.S.R. where for historical as well as geographical reasons even the European members of the State have a " low " standard, though this may remain low only for a limited period.

A second deduction is that in the western hemisphere there is a

[1] Sir John Boyd Orr, in *Food, Health and Income.* 1936.

generally higher standard than in the eastern hemisphere, with the exception of parts of Europe and Australia.

A third and important conclusion is that in the Monsoon Lands a very dense population has a very low standard of living, and this state of affairs strengthens the view that this part of the world is indeed over-crowded.

Over-population and Under-population.—Questions of whether given areas are over- or under-populated cannot be answered till it is clear what these terms really mean ; and there is often misunderstanding on this matter. First, it must be realized that a densely populated region is not necessarily over-populated, nor is one with a scanty population necessarily under-populated. This is shown by facts given above : e.g. in the Old World, industrial and commercial regions already densely populated have successfully attracted people from areas with relatively few inhabitants ; again, in scantily populated parts of the new lands immigrant farmers have found by bitter experience that these districts cannot absorb a greater number of people than they already have.

Over-population truly exists wherever a reduction in the number of people would enable a smaller population to earn a better living. An acute state is evident when natural causes force a decrease in the number of occupants of an area by actual starvation or by migration in search of subsistence in other regions. These generalizations may be illustrated by certain cases of over-population, although available facts do not permit a definite answer as to whether every country is or is not over-populated.

For some parts of India, statistics of births and deaths have been kept for a few decades, and it appears that while in most years births are more numerous than deaths, yet when the monsoon rains are delayed or poor, the harvests fail in certain parts, starvation and illness result, and the deaths exceed the births. Hence it may be concluded that the population has become so great that, at least in the less favourable years, it has more than overtaken the present means of support. Moreover, even in normal years the standard of living of most of the people is very low, and this in turn is largely responsible for the very short average length of life of the natives of India, viz. twenty-seven years. Together, these facts indicate that India is indeed over-populated.

Here it may be noted that although the average length of life in a region is affected by a number of factors, malnutrition is one of the most important, and from this point of view it is worth comparing the " expectation of life at birth " in certain countries ; while in India it is twenty-seven years, in Japan it is forty-eight years, in Italy fifty-five years, in England and Wales sixty years, among the whites of U.S.A. sixty-one years, and in the exceptional case of New Zealand it is as high as sixty-seven years.

Returning to the question of over-population, we may see a close parallel to India in the case of China. Although births and deaths have not been notified, there is no doubt about the general state of affairs. In the fertile parts of the country the pressure of population upon the land is such that at the present time the average size of the farms is very small for the support of the commonly numerous family or even family-group ; hence on the meagre holdings constant toil can gain but a scanty living. Moreover, the periods of bad fortune which occur fairly frequently in the north and centre and occasionally in the south, and are due especially to drought or flood, bring a terrible death-roll and cause many people to leave their ancestral lands to seek food elsewhere.

Japan presents in some ways a more complicated situation. After it was opened to Western influences its population greatly increased ; yet it did not at once become over-populated if one may argue from the fact that the standard of living rose. For a time, these two developments were able to go on side by side because of two other advances. In the first place, there were improvements in agriculture ; e.g. rice, which is grown on more than half the cultivated land and forms the main food supply, now has a higher yield than in almost any other land. In the second place, industries were introduced on a large scale, and Japan entered the ranks of the manufacturing countries which can support a dense population by exchanging the results of their labour for food and other requirements. Yet it became apparent that such developments were approaching their limits while the population was still mounting. This state of affairs was one of the reasons adduced by the governing classes of the Japanese to justify a long policy of forcible annexation of territories in eastern Asia which might furnish food for the people, raw materials and markets for manufacturers, and possible reception areas for emigrants. With the defeat of Japan in 1945, the failure of its policy of expansion, and the reductions which war brought to its previous industrial and commercial activities, the country appears to be faced in the future by a more acute problem of over-population—unless the reproduction rate is greatly reduced.

The extraordinary increase in the numbers of the people in Egypt and Java since the early part of the nineteenth century has menaced these lands with over-population ; in the West Indies, too, there are evidences of over-population.

In Europe, before the war of 1939–45 there were indications of over-population in those countries which had a high net reproduction rate but had not established large industries. In Poland and Italy, and probably in Bulgaria, Rumania and Yugoslavia, the population had outgrown its means of maintenance, with the consequence that when emigration had not been possible the standard of life had been forced down.

Under-population, on the contrary, exists where the inhabitants of a region are so few that an increase in their numbers would enable them to utilize the natural resources more effectively and so to better the conditions of life. It was to be seen during the eighteenth and nineteenth centuries when people from the old countries were attracted to the relatively empty new lands overseas. In these latter areas the settlers were at first able to get a living only with difficulty and sometimes with positive hardships. Yet as they won from the soil the necessities of life, other immigrants came and helped, mutual aid was afforded in agriculture and pastoral work, roads were made, trade was developed, social services were instituted. While this period lasted, a condition of under-population showed itself by the fact that an increase of numbers was accompanied by a rising standard of life. During the present century, however, immigration has slowed down in most of the overseas lands. For a time, some States which desired more members made attempts to attract or assist newcomers but found their schemes costly or ineffective, until even the relatively scantily populated overseas States as a rule not only ceased to invite newcomers but restricted immigration. For the time, at least, under-population had disappeared.

This statement does not mean that these new lands, and perhaps also some of the old lands, are incapable of supporting more people as methods of utilizing the natural resources are developed. For example, industries may be established to make better use of primary products, and other forms of manufacturing may be introduced or extended and also may involve increased commercial activities. Thus during the Second World War the British Dominions undertook the production and export of certain kinds of " processed " food, as well as cars, lorries, ships and aeroplanes, besides vast quantities of munitions ; the impetus thus given made an appreciable change in the economic structure of the Dominions and made possible a post-war demand for suitable labour from Britain and elsewhere. To take one example, it was estimated by some economists that Australia might eventually be able to increase its population of about 7 millions to about 20 millions.

In South America, too, war-time developments led to post-war plans for immigration : in particular, Argentina, Brazil and Venezuela have begun to arrange for the entry of suitable settlers—especially from among Catholics and Jews who have been forced from their homes in Central Europe.

In somewhat similar ways an increase in the population of other regions may be achieved, allowing immigration from other parts of the world, without a fall in the standard of living. Hence, present conditions of over- or under-population relate only to the present stage of economic development in the countries concerned.

But the questions may still be asked : If there are more people in industrialized countries, whence will they be fed and supplied with raw materials ? Will either they, or other peoples to whom they export goods, be able to meet their needs ?

The Future.—These questions raise the broad issue of the world's capacity to support a larger number of inhabitants without an even lower standard of living than that of the present time. This is one of the fundamental problems of " the earth as the home of man," and it appears that for a long time to come the answer lies with man himself.

Already science has made it possible to produce far more of practically every material required. Measures can be taken to remedy or prevent soil exhaustion and soil erosion ; irrigation systems can give additional areas of cultivation ; new varieties of plants and improved breeds of animals, together with more efficient practices, can yield greater returns to farming and forestry ; valuable substitutes for many vegetable and mineral products have become available ; new ways of obtaining and making use of mechanical power have been devised ; more nutritious diets and methods of combating diseases can give man improved health and can increase his efficiency.

Yet over much of the world these scientific achievements still await practical application, for this needs two other developments in human thought and organization. The first lies within the spheres of the respective States, and relates particularly to the people directly engaged in production, e.g. the farmers, the workers and organizers in industry, and the " common men " in various occupations. They must have both the knowledge to avail themselves of the advances now possible and the willingness to adapt themselves as well as their work to new ways ; often this may mean that they have to be freed from age-long and deep-rooted prejudices. Indeed, if one reviews what has already been pointed out, it may be realized that those parts of the world (notably many tropical and inter-tropical areas) in which man's necessities are most lacking are the parts in which the requisite changes in the lives and modes of thought of the people present the greatest difficulties. It follows that in many cases the governments must undertake, or at least aid, the spread of technical knowledge together with a wider education of their peoples. Further, there may have to be changes in their laws and economic systems.

Another and parallel line of advance lies in the necessary co-operation between States. They may give mutual assistance in many ways ; to take one example, international organization is essential in combating insect pests which extend or migrate over large areas regardless of political frontiers. Moreover, States determine policies of international trade, which may either help or hinder the exchange of food and other goods between producers and consumers, and thus increase or diminish the total at man's disposal. To bring about such co-operation between States on the widest possible scale the Food and Agricultural Organization of the United Nations was established ; its methods are described in the last chapter of this book.

CHAPTER XX

CULTURAL REGIONS (1)

In the preceding chapters the main cultural aspects of mankind have been considered separately, viz. language, religion and forms of government ; occupations and the associated ways of life ; distribution of population and standards of living. But it must be emphasized that in every group of men these elements exist together in the most intimate relationship. Hence, after the preliminary *analysis* there is required a *synthesis* which indicates as far as possible the outstanding combinations of cultural characteristics. A useful method is to think of mankind as being composed of large groups of people, each group living in its own particular region and showing a certain combination of cultural conditions ; for example, the people of western and central Europe would form one such group different in all the above aspects from those of the Far East. If mankind is divided in this way into characteristic groups, the corresponding " cultural regions " may be marked out on a map of the world, as is done in Fig. 59 on p. 318 ; of course, in a broad survey only the major cultural regions can be considered.

The following survey of the peoples in each of the regions must involve some repetition of what has been stated in the earlier chapters, but now the facts relating to each group will be brought together in their natural relationship. Certain further facts will also be introduced, particularly some connected with developments in the past which have had a marked effect upon the peoples of the present time and have given rise to the problems with which they are now faced.

The photographs of characteristic architecture of each region, or of dwellings where construction has not reached the stage of architecture, have been selected to bring out some of the features of the culture—e.g. in the buildings themselves, or in the special purposes for which they have been designed, or in some other indication of the typical modes of thought and action of the peoples of the respective regions.

1. Peninsular Europe.—The peoples of Peninsular Europe

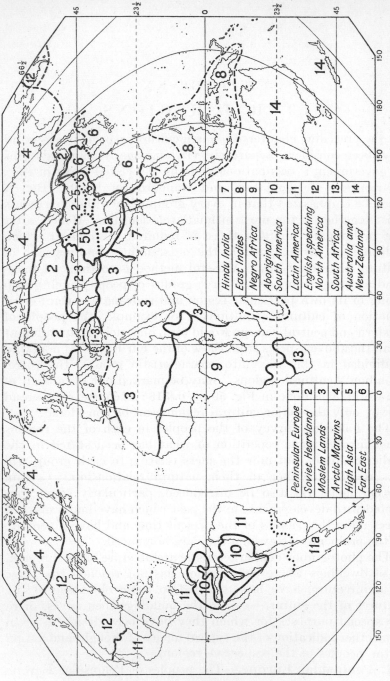

FIG. 59.—MAJOR CULTURAL REGIONS.

Note.—The Peninsula of Indo-China is shown as a major cultural region intermediate in characteristics between 6 and 7.

Peninsular Europe	1	Hindu India	7
Soviet Heartland	2	East Indies	8
Moslem Lands	3	Negro Africa	9
Arctic Margins	4	Aboriginal South America	10
High Asia	5	Latin America	11
Far East	6	English-speaking North America	12
		South Africa	13
		Australia and New Zealand	14

are among the lighter-skinned sections of the wavy-haired division of mankind, being descended from the Nordic, Alpine-Dinaric and Mediterranean ethnic groups. Because of the migrations of these groups, almost all the people of this region speak somewhat similar languages belonging to the Indo-European family.

The typically " European " culture has gradually developed from the very early civilizations which grew up in the eastern Mediterranean area, especially in Egypt and Crete, and the later ones of ancient Greece and Rome in the south of Europe. From the Roman Empire is due the common dominance of either the Roman Catholic form of Christianity (see illustration opposite p. 324) or the Protestantism which arose from it.

During recent centuries the central and north-western parts of the continent have taken a large share in all branches of man's cultural advance. This advance has shown itself in literary, artistic, political and scientific achievements ; it has shown itself also in the application of science to practical affairs in medicine, industry, agriculture and commerce, and indeed these technical developments are especially characteristic of the European type of culture.

The great majority of the people of Peninsular Europe are educated at least to the stage of being able to read and write their mother tongue, and in general the level of culture is high compared with that in the world as a whole. Social organizations have developed greatly, and in many parts of the region there are marked social strata among the people, and the ways of living show considerable contrasts.

Moreover, feelings of nationality are strongly held and a large number of separate States has been formed in a relatively small area. In a number of cases States have competed with one another in economic affairs, and this competition, together with the intense feelings of nationality, has contributed to armed conflicts. During the past 150 years there have been repeated wars in which almost all parts of the continent have been involved ; as a result, the States have been so altered that the political map of Europe has changed almost like the patterns in a kaleidoscope.

Physical and mental energy are characteristic of many of the inhabitants of this cultural region, especially in the more northerly areas ; these qualities are favoured by the temperate climatic conditions, and especially by the stimulating effects of the moderate changes of temperature and the strong winds which accompany the frequent cyclonic depressions.

Because of the enterprise of the people in utilizing the geographical possibilities, industry and commerce have become the characteristic forms of economic activity over a large part of this region. Agricultural production of the plough-farming type has been widely improved by scientific methods, though the far north and the north-western margins are handicapped by climatic conditions ; in the south the Mediterranean type of agriculture is less remunerative than that in much of western and central Europe. Consequent upon the economic developments, much of the region is densely or very densely populated, save on the uplands and in the extreme north. The standard of living, judged by the criteria adopted in Fig. 58, is about or above the average level ; Great Britain and Switzerland are exceptional as being distinctly " high," while on the other hand considerable areas in the east and the south come into the categories of the countries with a " low " standard of living.

Apart from the effects of wars, industrial developments in recent years have led to marked increases both in the urbanization and in the standards of living of the people, particularly in the central and north-western parts, and these increases have been associated with a marked trend towards smaller populations ; indeed, it appears likely that Peninsular Europe may now be at its peak period so far as the number of its people is concerned.

The intellectual and economic advances made in this region since the Middle Ages have made it pre-eminent in its influence upon the rest of the world. The migration of its peoples and the spread of its knowledge have been decisive factors in the growth of somewhat similar cultural regions overseas ; also, military power enabled some of its States to obtain colonial possessions in other regions, and its commerce has spread into every part of the globe.

2. The Soviet Heartland.—This region may be labelled the " Soviet Heartland " because (*a*) it is the " heart " of the widespread Soviet Union and (*b*) it almost corresponds with the Soviet portion of the " Heartland " of Eurasia as explained in Chapter I. Belief in communism as a general theory of social and economic organization, and its eventual application in all parts of the world, may be taken as the main criteria of the Soviet mode of thought and way of life. The " Heartland " in which these Soviet characteristics are shown in their entirety is mainly a belt, broad in eastern Europe but narrowing as it follows the course of the Trans-Siberian railway across Asia till it reaches the Pacific Ocean at Vladivostok at the mouth of the River Amur.

While the Russian people display the physical characters of the wavy-haired ethnic groups most clearly where they adjoin Peninsular Europe, the peoples of the Soviet Union are increasingly more Asiatic in type towards the east. Over most of the U.S.S.R. Slavonic tongues are spoken, though in all the marginal areas the more recently incorporated peoples retain their own languages. As regards religious beliefs, until the revolution the Russians were devoted adherents of the Orthodox Christian Church, but the Soviet government disestablished this Church though as individuals people may still belong to it. In the Asiatic territories there are Muslims in the south, while primitive forms of religion still exist in the north and east.

The feature which most distinguishes the Soviet cultural region is the motive behind all branches of its organization, viz. the welfare of the common man. To ensure as good a life as possible for the mass of the people was the aim of those who shaped the policies of the U.S.S.R., whatever harshness towards individuals and groups resulted from its application. The fulfilment of this aim appeared to the planners to need three revolutions at the same time : political, agrarian and industrial. Elsewhere, e.g. in Britain, these three revolutions were spread out over centuries, but in the U.S.S.R. they had to be carried out simultaneously. Hence they involved upheaval in practically all spheres of life, and thus rapid change became another characteristic of the Soviet region.

The constitution of the State embodies the system of soviets which ensures the active co-operation of citizens at all levels. This is of special importance in the U.S.S.R. because political issues determine every aspect of the work and life of every man and woman. Hence practically all citizens share in both detailed and general discussions, and political education has therefore proceeded far in a short time.

The driving force behind the political machine is the " Communist Party," a relatively small body of men and women

imbued with the missionary spirit and specially trained in communist doctrine.   They are leaders or workers in industry and
agriculture and representatives in the various soviets ; it is
their special function to set examples to the others, to stimulate
their efforts, to explain the policies behind the measures, and
to enforce obedience to decrees.   The Party, small as it is, holds
the higher positions in the system, and has effective power in
shaping major decisions.

The agrarian revolution was accomplished by the break-up
of the large estates and by the grouping of these and the small-
holdings of the peasants into communal farms, either State-
owned or " collectives."   With scientific aid and the use of
mechanization, agriculture was able, after a period of struggle
and setback, to enlarge the range and the amount of its production, and to support both the families of the farmers and
the rapidly growing populations engaged in mining, manufacture and other branches of work.

The industrial revolution had a similar double aim, viz. to
obtain those commodities which the State determined as its
first necessities, and to give better conditions to the workers.
Among other methods of achieving the aims were : (i) the use
of factory councils to suggest improvements in production
methods ; (ii) the institution of very considerable differences
of payment and the granting of special privileges and honours,
both to induce greater efforts by the ordinary workers, and
also to stimulate the most able ones to study technical matters
and to become managers and organizers.

The planners of the new society early realized the need to
raise cultural standards.   Within a few years, compulsory and
free education of children, with voluntary classes and schools
for adults, had practically eliminated the illiteracy which was
common under Tsarist rule ; the rapid progress of education
was perhaps most remarkable among the hitherto backward
tribes of the Asiatic parts of this multi-national State.   The
higher forms of culture, too, have spread widely : they include
the scientific and technical training and research which have
had notable results in their application to economic production,
and they embrace also the appreciation and the practice of art
in all its forms.

Under the old régime, the average standard of living was very
low in comparison with much of Peninsular Europe, and after

the revolution, improvements were by no means rapid. Communist practices had to be established during a state of chaos, when the normal working of the political and economic systems had broken down. Civil war and armed foreign intervention occurred ; the new leaders were unprepared for organizing a huge and complicated machinery of government and production ; false starts were made and fresh expedients devised ; discontent and obstruction arose and were suppressed. Moreover, the leaders decided that as soon as possible they must make the State secure, and to that end the army had to be formed and equipped. Then came the German invasion of 1941, involving enormous destruction of the means of livelihood, besides terrible loss of human life itself. Now goods are being produced in greater amount, and the standard of living is distinctly higher than in the past.

The future of the U.S.S.R. among the Great Powers of the world must be affected by two outstanding facts : one is that the enormous natural resources are only in the first stages of development ; the other is that the population has as yet shown little sign of the trend towards decrease apparent in most of the Western Democracies.

Beyond the western boundary of the U.S.S.R. is a wide belt of Peninsular Europe, extending from the southern Baltic to the Adriatic, which may now be regarded as transitional to the Soviet Heartland. Over much of this area Slav languages are spoken, and since the Second World War the States, to varying degrees, have become politically associated with the Soviet Union and adopted communist methods in economic matters.

On the map of cultural regions, the semi-arid Caspian and Turkistan Lowland is marked " 2–3 " to indicate a transition between the Soviet Heartland and the Muslim Lands. Although this area is part of the U.S.S.R., Islam remains the religion of many of the people ; also the occupations have much in common with those which characterize the regions to the south, for agriculture is mainly dependent on irrigation, and over large parts pastoral work is the chief resource, though transhumance or ranching has taken the place of the older form of nomadism. Yet even in this region Soviet political doctrines have become dominant if not universally approved. Another transitional region is Outer Mongolia, marked " 2–5 " on the map ; it is dealt with in a later section.

3. The Muslim (or Moslem) Lands.—This region consists in general of the belt of arid and semi-arid land extending across northern Africa and south-west Asia to north-western India and central Asia, together with the more fertile southern and eastern Mediterranean coast-lands and the eastern coasts of Africa at least as far south as Zanzibar. It is the area over which the faith of Islam was effectively spread and in which, with small exceptions, there is still a common feeling of kinship based upon that religion.

Over most of the region, the major part of the population consists of the brown or darkish-white groups of the wavy-haired racial division of mankind, viz. the Oriental and Hamitic, Armenian-Iranian and Indo-Afghan groups. On the southern margins of the Sahara, however, peoples of Negro or partially Negro descent have been sufficiently imbued with Muslim traditions to be included in this cultural region, while in central Asia some of the straight-haired groups form part of the population. Because of the imposition of the Muslim religion and culture upon a number of peoples, the Semitic, Hamitic, Indo-European and Ural-Altaic language families are all represented in the region. In Africa, European Powers have assumed either complete or partial control of all the Muslim Lands except Egypt ; in Asia, on the contrary, the region consists almost entirely of independent Muslim States as far as the frontiers of U.S.S.R., Tibet and Hindu India. Yet it must be made clear that the boundaries of the cultural region are drawn to include the main areas in which the Muslim faith is predominant and do not necessarily coincide with political frontiers.

The physical geography comprises three types, which give rise to a threefold cultural structure. (i) Excluding the un-inhabitable deserts, the most extensive areas are the semi-deserts where pastoral work is the main source of livelihood and where, in consequence, the population is scanty ; the family and tribal organization of the people still persists ; external influences have little effect ; the stage of culture has remained at a relatively low level, and the standard of living is definitely low.

(ii) Sharply contrasted are the areas of oasis cultivation, especially in the river systems of the Nile, the Euphrates and Tigris, and the Indus ; their extent is very small in comparison with that of the pastoral areas, but they support a large part

[*Dorien Leigh*

PENINSULAR EUROPE

This view of Florence shows the characteristic architecture of mediæval Italy, one of the centres in which originated European culture. On the left is the Cathedral, representing the Roman Church which, directly and indirectly, much influenced the thought of this region. On the right is the Old Palace, the early seat of the Princes of the City-State; then, as now, relatively small political divisions were characteristic of Peninsular Europe.

[*J. Allen Cash*

THE SOVIET HEARTLAND

The administrative offices of Kharkov, the capital of the Ukraine, illustrate a modern aspect of the Soviet region. Erected on the outskirts of the old city, the building exhibits simplicity in design and is of the functional type, its aim being technical efficiency. The architecture may thus suggest some typical characteristics of the Soviet mode of thought.

[*Courtauld Institute of Art*

THE MUSLIM LANDS

This shrine in Persia exhibits several features of the art of the Muslim Lands. The curves of the arches are common in the architecture, and the coloured glazed tiles make patterns used also for other materials, e.g. in the leather work of North Africa and the carpets of South-west Asia. The main building has the flat roof suited to semi-arid climates, and upon it has been constructed the dome with the characteristic curve.

[*British Arctic Air Route Expedition*

THE ARCTIC MARGINS

An Eskimo tent set up by the women for the brief summer. The scene is the Greenland coast far south of the "Polar Eskimo" described in Chapter XXIV. The tent is constructed of poles strapped together and covered with about eight sealskins weighted down with big stones. Note the restricted space for the family, and the imported articles : the clothing, the metal pail and possibly the tent poles.

of the people. Their early rise to civilization and their later
development with the aid of outside States have brought about
a much more complicated social system, in which some strata
of the population have attained a higher standard of culture
and of comfort.

(iii) The third type of country consists of the marginal districts which have a greater rainfall and therefore a moderate
amount of agricultural production and a moderate density of
population. In the Mediterranean climate region the people of
these areas were long ago pioneers of cultural advance, though
others took their place as leaders when civilization extended
northward. Now, in several respects they are being brought
into line with those of more developed regions, and their levels
of production, of living and of general culture are rising.

In addition there are two peninsular regions where north-
western Africa and Asia Minor are thrust into the Mediterranean
region, and are separated from Europe only by the narrow
Straits of Gibraltar and the Dardanelles respectively. Here,
in the Atlas Lands and in Asia Minor, the changes in recent
years have been so great that from the human aspect these
regions are now transitional between Peninsular Europe and
the Muslim Belt ; these regions are therefore marked " 1–3 "
on the map on p. 318. In the Atlas Lands, European governments and colonists, particularly the French, have made great
alterations in the political and economic spheres ; in Asia
Minor, the Turkish State has been reconstituted on the European
model, and although Islam is no longer officially recognized as
the State religion, the majority of the Turkish people remain
Muslims.

A striking characteristic of the areas which at present constitute the Muslim Lands is that over the greatest span of human
history they have included the centres from which the world
of man received most important streams of influence. In the
great river valleys the first civilizations had their origin, and
later, from the lands now in the Muslim Belt, teachers and
prophets gave rise to great religions—Judaism, Christianity
and Islam. For many centuries, peoples from this area advanced into surrounding lands, diffusing widely their languages,
religions and other elements of their cultures. How the Muslim
influence affected other cultural regions may be illustrated by
many notable instances, from among which one may refer to

irrigation in Spain, architecture in various lands no longer under Islamic power (e.g. the Taj Mahal at Agra in Hindu India), and to many contributions to world-wide science—in effect kept alive by the Arabs during the " Dark Ages."

In modern times the tide turned, and European States sent streams of influence into the Muslim Lands, affecting their forms of government, their economic developments and the ways of life of their peoples. In several parts the process involved opposition between the interests of Europeans and those of the Muslim peoples, and this opposition showed itself very clearly where the land and water routes between the eastern Mediterranean Sea and the Indian Ocean crossed the Muslim Lands. On either side of this route-way Arabic-speaking peoples constituted a group of Arab States, and in 1945, seven of these States formed themselves into the " Arab League." The aim was partly to assist co-operation between themselves and partly to show a united front against external interference ; the formation of the League, moreover, was an indication of a growing feeling of kinship between the Arab peoples.

About the same time there was increasing tension between Arabs and Jews in respect of Palestine. Islam and Judaism had their origins in the same belt of relatively fertile areas on the western side of the Arabian-Syrian desert, and this geographical fact, among others, lies at the root of the present-day problem—the clash of feelings between the Muslim inhabitants of the region and the immigrant Jews who have sought a " National Home," and in many cases a refuge from persecution, in the tiny land of Palestine.

4. The Arctic Margins.—In the tundra lands adjoining the Arctic Sea, and in those parts of the sub-arctic forests where climatic conditions are most severe, dwell the peoples of the Arctic Margins of the world of man. Plough farming is almost impossible here, and the White men have been represented only by relatively few people, some isolated and some in small groups, occupied in mining, hunting and trapping, lumbering or trading. Nevertheless, foreign Powers have extended their dominions northward to cover between them the whole of the region : the U.S.S.R. over the Asiatic portion, Norway over Spitsbergen, the British Commonwealth and the United States over the mainland of America, and Denmark over Greenland.

Nearly all the native population belongs to the Palæo-Arctic, Tungus or Amerind racial groups, and therefore to the straight-haired division of mankind, although there are elements which show the influence of wavy-haired peoples. In America, the Eskimo language has spread through the tundra lands, and Amerind tongues are spoken by the Indians of the sub-arctic forests. In Eurasia, languages of the Ural-Altaic family include the speech of the Lapps, Samoyeds, Yakuts, Tungus and other groups. The religious ideas of the native peoples have been little developed from the animistic stage, except where Christianity has made converts.

The simple social organizations of the people are bound up with their occupations : hunting and fishing, which are the main resource in the tundra of North America and are carried on in the sub-arctic forests of both continents, can best be followed by single families or by a loose association of small groups of families, while the reindeer herders of the Old World are for the most part organized into small clans and tribes.

A nomadic or semi-nomadic way of life has been imposed upon most of the dwellers in the Arctic Margins by the migratory habits of the animals upon which they depend, the migrations being due to the great seasonal changes of climate. The lack of permanent habitations and the very scanty natural resources have been hindrances to cultural advance. Yet it may be pointed out that the Eskimo and Lapps, for example, show a high degree of adaptation to their environment, and the limitation in their development has probably been due to the restricted sphere of physical work and mental activity which nature has allowed them.

Apart from the European immigration, in this region only an extremely scanty population can exist and the standard of living is low ; the largest settlements and the greatest degree of comfort, if the word may be used, are found where the Arctic waters bring the most abundant life, directly or indirectly, from warmer latitudes to the coast-lands, and where the people have best learnt to utilize the limited resources.

The isolated situation of the Arctic Margins and the fact that immigrants must adapt themselves in a very special manner to the environment have combined to restrict intercourse with the rest of the world. In recent years, however, aircraft and coastal shipping have enabled people from the south to bring an increasing number of changes, and in some parts to impose new ways of life upon the dwellers in the Far North. The effects of the contacts have varied. For example, in the North American area, many of the Indians and Eskimo suffered from the depletion of the herds of animals which they had hunted, and attempts have been made to introduce the keeping of reindeer; on the whole, the numbers of these peoples have tended to diminish. In the Asiatic area the adaptation, especially among the relatively numerous Yakuts, to the developments brought by the Soviet government has been more successful; the means of gaining a livelihood have been extended and education has made considerable progress.

5. High Asia.—This is the central upraised core of the continent. Because it is far inland and ringed by mountain ranges, it is arid or semi-arid; because of its drought and cold it has little vegetation, except in valleys where water, brought by rivers, can be spread by irrigation. Most of High Asia therefore supports small numbers of nomadic pastoralists scattered over large areas, who lead hard lives and have remained at a low stage of cultural development. Yet the fertile spots connected by trade routes give a better living and their inhabitants are at a higher cultural level. As a whole, this region is one from which raiders and permanent emigrants have descended into adjoining regions, but along the river valleys and the lines of oases other peoples have entered bringing racial and cultural influences. Taking into account both the human conditions and the physical environments which have affected them, High Asia may be divided into four sub-regions : (*a*) Tibet, marked " 5a " on the map ; (*b*) Eastern Turkistan, marked " 5b " ; (*c*) Outer Mongolia, marked " 2–5 " ; (*d*) Inner Mongolia, marked " 5–6."

Tibet is a very high plateau largely bounded by still higher ranges ; it can be entered with least difficulty by the river valleys on its eastern margin. Hence its people belong racially largely to the Southern Mongoloid group ; they speak a language allied to Chinese and their religion is that form of Buddhism sometimes known as Lamaism. Pasturage can support but a fraction of the people, while the rest of the small population depends upon agriculture, carried on in some of the valleys and based on irrigation. Social conditions are also unfavourable ; dominated by a small number of land-owners and by the

Buddhist lamas, the bulk of the people are serfs, working the land inefficiently and living in miserable conditions. Moreover, the region is so shut off from the outer world, both by mountains and by the policy of exclusion adopted by its rulers, that it can receive little invigorating influence from other lands ; the Tibetan Highland forms a human backwater.

Eastern Turkistan, a basin region including fertile oases and belts of pasture between its central desert and the surrounding mountains, has attracted settlers and invaders from both east and west. The main stock of the present population seems to be derived from the Turanian or Turki group of the wavy-haired division of mankind, much influenced physically by Mongolian elements. Turkish conquests imposed Islam, but this has not been so strongly rooted that there is here much feeling of kinship with other Muslim peoples. Political dominance of the basin region shifted in the course of history between Turk and Tibetan, Mongol and Chinese Powers. In the latter part of the nineteenth century, however, Chinese suzerainty and influence were re-established over the greater part of eastern Turkistan, and this area became known as Sinkiang ; the relatively small area of the Pamirs and part of the Tian Shan now form part of the Soviet Union.

In *Mongolia* the inhabitants belong in the main to the northern branch of the straight-haired division of mankind and show in a very marked form the physical characters of the " Yellow " peoples ; they speak dialects of the Ural-Altaic languages. The lama-dominated variety of Buddhism has spread over most of the area. Both Russia from the one side and China from the other have brought political and cultural influences into the region.

Everywhere in Mongolia nomadic pastoralism has been dominant ; a minor occupation is the conducting of caravans along the natural routes which connect the " East " and the " West " of the Old World, and lie north of the great highland barrier of Central Asia. No great number of people can get a living from the poor pasture, and periods of decreased rainfall have forced the Mongols along the great routes westward towards Europe and south-western Asia and eastward into China ; the south-eastern boundary of the Mongolian region approximately coincides with the Great Wall of China built to the north and west of Peiping (Pekin) as a protection against the nomads.

Apart from these excursions, Mongolia over long periods remained largely apart from other cultural regions of Asia ; for this reason and because of the almost changeless nature of nomadic pastoralism, the culture of the Mongol people for long kept at a comparatively low level.

Chinese influence, however, affected Mongolia, particularly the south-eastern strip known as Inner Mongolia. This is marked as a transitional region, " 5–6," for while the nomads are Mongolian, the townsmen and farmers are now of Chinese origin, and the area is under Chinese sovereignty.

The northern and greater part of Mongolia, known as Outer Mongolia, has recently come under Soviet influence. In 1924, a revolution established the " Mongolian People's Republic," and in 1945 a " treaty of amity and mutual aid " was signed with U.S.S.R. There had already been settlers from Siberia, and the effect of the later developments is to extend Soviet ideas and organization ; Outer Mongolia is therefore indicated as another transitional region, and marked " 2–5."

6. The Far East.—Eastern Asia, south of the Soviet Union, has close human relationships and a distinctive type of culture which is most clearly expressed in China, its geographical centre and its main place of origin. China in particular, but also the Far East as a whole, has been protected by mountain barriers (except in Mongolia) from attack by other peoples of the landmass of Eurasia ; on the other side, the Pacific Ocean has formed an effective defence during the greater part of man's history. In the Chinese and Japanese areas, climatic conditions are neither too hot nor too cold to limit man's activity for any appreciable length of time during the year, and the return for strenuous labour is sufficient for the maintenance of a large population.

China, despite certain differences between North and South, possesses a unity in cultural characteristics of which the most marked may be summed up thus : a civilization persisting for over 4,000 years in spite of internal political weaknesses and external attacks ; an economic system based on an exceptionally thorough cultivation of the soil with the aid of irrigation ; a social system in which the family has been the essential unit, fortified by the veneration of ancestors and by carefully preserved traditions and customs ; habits of frugality and industry ; a common, and tolerant, religion in which Buddhism has played a large part ; a common language over most of the country ; a common system of government, though often exercising little local control and subject in the past to upheaval at the centre ; a deep feeling for beauty and fitness as expressed in art, litera- ture and polite conduct ; a high degree of intellectual achieve- ment among the educated classes, although until recently with- out the developments of scientific method which have made possible many advances in Western civilization.

The Chinese are mainly of the Sinic branch of straight-haired peoples, though from one side Mongolian and Manchu incur- sions and from the other side South Mongoloid migrations have complicated their racial make-up and their cultural tradi- tions. The Chinese tongue is typical of the monosyllabic family of languages, and in the matter of language, as in other ways, Chinese influence has spread to the other parts of the Far East.

In the nineteenth century, the West (including under this term the United States) forced open the doors of the East to trade, and thereby to economic, social and cultural changes ; in China, external commerce increased under both Chinese and Western management, and large-scale industries began with the aid of Western capital and organization. In the early twentieth century came the downfall of the alien Manchu dynasty and the establishment of a republic. Still more recently, and partly as a result of the Japanese war which ended in 1945, great develop- ments occurred, including an increase in nationalism, the raising of the status of China among the States of the world, an extension of education, the introduction of new ideas in economic affairs, and conflict between the conservative and almost feudal South and the North, where communist ideas have been adapted to suit Chinese conditions. China is now in a state of transition, and grafting of Western practices upon the ancient civilization of the East may bear fruit in a new type of culture.

The people of *Japan* are of more mixed racial origin than the Chinese, and the insular position of the country has allowed the entry both of immigrants and also of cultural influences from several directions. The Japanese were relatively late in emerging from a " stone age," but when they perceived the advantages of the Chinese ways of life, they willingly adopted and adapted new ideas and worked diligently to improve their own material conditions. Nor did they neglect cultural devel- opment : their appreciation of the beauty of their landscapes was expressed in poetry and painting, while the good taste of their dress and their household equipment became a characteristic of the Japanese people.

After the entry of Western travellers, missionaries and traders into the Far East, the rulers of Japan decided on a policy of seclusion which lasted from about the middle of the seventeenth century for nearly 200 years. Then this policy was reversed, and from the middle of the nineteenth century Japan has reacted towards the West in a very different way from that of China.

Unified by its political organization and aided by the religion of Shinto, Japan set itself to learn from its Western disturbers ; it adopted their military, economic and scientific methods, and became an industrial and commercial as well as an agricultural country. Internal change was more rapid and far-reaching than in China, and Japanese ways tended more towards those of Europe and America. The density of population was high, but improvements in agriculture and the addition of manufacturing as a means of livelihood allowed still further increase in the number of the people. As an industrial State, however, Japan needed to import raw materials and to find markets for its exports. Partly for this reason, after a victorious war with China in 1894, it extended its Empire first over Formosa and later over Korea, and finally occupied Manchuria, while Japanese industrialists and merchants acquired control over some of the natural resources of China itself.

Within a few decades Japan became one of the Great Powers of the world. In 1937 it invaded China, and soon after hostilities had broken out in Europe, Japan engaged in a war involving much of the Pacific region. It attacked the U.S.A. fleet at a naval base in the Hawaiian Islands, and attempted to carry out a plan for the military, political and economic domination of all south-eastern Asia. The attempt failed, and the defeat of Japan involved, besides great immediate destruction in that country, demilitarization and an enforced reduction of those industries which might be used for future wars. The loss of all the territories seized during Japan's rise to power, together with changes in the internal political structure of the State, was also imposed from without. Moreover, a constitution including a limited monarchy has been adopted, and a number of other institutions and ideas of the Japanese people are now in the melting-pot. Hence, it is difficult to assess the present characteristics of Japan as a cultural region.

Similar difficulties are found in attempting to estimate either the current situation or the tendencies among the peoples of other cultural regions of Asia, Malaya and the East Indies, partly because of the effects of Japanese occupation and the subsequent changes.

In the case of *Korea*, this mountainous peninsula was for centuries a buffer State between China and Japan. Weaker than its neighbours it was raided by both in turn, and also served to some extent as a cultural bridge. From China it received most of its modes of life and thought, until the Japanese intrusion in 1905. This enforced great changes in the economic organization : while agriculture remained the main occupation, mines were opened up, industries (chiefly of textiles and chemical products) were established, and trade developed, especially with Japan. When the Japanese withdrew, complications came from the occupation of North Korea by the Russians, who fostered communist methods, and of South Korea by the Americans, who favoured free enterprise ; this clash further hindered the growth of a characteristic Korean culture and form of government.

Manchuria has had, and still has, different conditions from those of Korea because of its different geographical situation. The great grassy lowland of Manchuria gives access from the " Heartland " of Eurasia to North China, skirting the highlands and deserts of Mongolia. By this route nomadic tribes invaded China, and the Manchu Emperors ruled in that country for nearly three centuries until the revolution of 1911.

By that time, however, Chinese immigrants had for long sought refuge from famines by moving northward, and the population of Manchuria had become overwhelmingly Chinese. The immigrants retained their language and religious beliefs, but the type of agriculture was necessarily different in the colder country and the newcomers modified their traditional methods of work and some of the associated ways of life.

Meanwhile the Russian power had extended to the Pacific, and by the beginning of the nineteenth century the Chinese and Russian Empires had agreed to a short cut for the Trans-Siberian railway across Manchuria to the Pacific Ocean. At the same period Japan had begun its policy of expansion, and after defeat of the Russian navy in 1905, Manchuria was divided into a Japanese " sphere of influence " in the south with a

Russian " sphere of influence " in the north, though relatively few Russians or Japanese settled in the areas.

In 1931, Japanese military forces were sent into Manchuria, and it came under Japanese control.   Railway extensions were pushed on ; ports on the Yellow Sea were constructed ; agriculture, forestry, industries and trade with Japan were developed.   The labour supply was, however, mainly obtained by increased immigration from northern China, the climate being too severe for Japanese immigrants.

After the Soviet revolution, Russian influence penetrated Manchuria in another way, viz. by the spread among the peasantry of northern China of communist ideas ; also, Chinese communists played an active part in resisting the Japanese invasion of China.   Thus, when in 1945 Japan was defeated, a new situation arose.   By the terms of a treaty, the U.S.S.R. recognized Chinese sovereignty over Manchuria, but obtained the right of operating all the Manchurian railways, together with joint use of a free port and of a naval base on the Yellow Sea— where ice-free access to the Pacific offers great attractions to the Soviet Union.   In point of fact, however, the Chinese government was powerless, and Russian influence prevails at the beginning of 1948.

Thus Manchuria is a meeting-place between Chinese and Soviet methods of economic organization, and it may become another of the regions in which two types are blended into a new form of culture.

7. Hindu India.—The fundamental character of the culture of the greater part of India is religious ; hence this cultural region is limited to that area which is predominantly, though not exclusively, Hindu ; it may be named Hindu India.   It should be noted that the boundary shown on the map has not been drawn to represent a political frontier.

The situation of the region has led to the entry of a number of racial groups and therefore to great diversity in the characteristics of the people, and in this respect India shows a marked contrast to China.   In India there are striking physical differences between the peoples classed under the general terms Pre-Dravidian, Dravidian and Indo-Afghan.   The diversity of the many languages of India has already been remarked upon, and also the variety and complexity of the religious beliefs of the people commonly grouped as Hindus.   Other differences between the inhabitants of Hindu India are due to the facts that they entered the region at various stages of cultural advance, they now live in very diverse environments, and they have adopted different modes of life. As examples of such contrasts, one may cite the tribes of the interior of the Deccan, primitive yet jungle-wise, small and shy yet tough and brave ; the Madrasis of the fertile south-east, agricultural villagers and trading city-folk ; the Bengalis of the Ganges valley, of subtle mind and with a heritage of literary and artistic achievement ; the Rajputs of the semi-arid north-west, finely built men proud of a tradition of fighting and ruling.

It may therefore be asked : What is there in common between the inhabitants of this area to justify the view that it does constitute a definite Hindu cultural region ? To find a satisfactory answer one must leave in the background, as it were, the large number of people who live at the lower levels, and consider rather the modes of life and thought of those who have developed to a higher level and have the greater influence.

The past expressions of Hindu culture, in the narrower sense of the word, include the classical Sanskrit literature and the painting, sculpture and architecture ; the achievements of the present time are even wider in scope, and it may be pointed out that some of the poetry and prose writings are expressed in Indian tongues and some in English—these latter thereby enriching the literature of Western civilization.

Despite differences among the Hindus there are certain beliefs and customs common to them all. There is a universal reverence for the Brahmans, and Hindu shrines are visited by large numbers of pilgrims who thus bring into touch the inhabitants of widely separated parts of India. The caste system is an important characteristic of the overwhelming majority of the people, and its social and economic consequences described in a previous chapter operate everywhere. In this connection, however, the existence of Sikh, as well as Muslim, communities within this cultural region must not be overlooked.

Another feature common in Indian life is the more or less autonomous village organization which the Aryan-speaking peoples adopted from the Dravidians ; the existence of this social characteristic is important because India is still a country of relatively few large towns or cities but of hundreds of thousands of villages. On the other hand, the Aryans contributed the important, though smaller, social unit of the family-group, which is under the headship of the oldest man, is supervised by a family council and may co-operate in owning and cultivating the land-holdings.

With so much communal life organized in the village and the family-group, it is not surprising that until recently there was but small development of a feeling of a common nationality, especially as there are so many differences between the peoples in different parts of the region and such great distances between one part and another. The growth of nationalism was partly a result of the British occupation, for internal warfare was checked and the whole of India was brought under one rule, while roads, railways and postal services helped the various parts to get into touch with one another, and the English language became a *lingua franca* for many Indians of different mother tongues. Moreover, the British aided education both in a general sense and also in political matters ; the ideas and practice of representative government were gradually introduced, and the administration of the country was increasingly carried on by Indian officials.

A somewhat similar process of change occurred in the shares taken by the British and Indian peoples in economic activities. Although these were begun mainly by British capital and organization, in recent years Indian skilled labour became a great factor, and Indian capitalists and planners became the leaders in developments. At the same time the proportion of imported manufactured commodities decreased. Yet factory production within India, like the preceding import of foreign goods, has caused a decline in the skilled domestic crafts-manship which was a feature of Indian culture, e.g. in the arts of the weaver, the potter and the metal-worker. The rise of mass-production in India has also been accompanied by a movement from village to town life, often with a consequent modification of traditional customs, and a change, if not a loss, in social values.

A considerable increase of total production has followed the various economic changes of recent decades, particularly the improvements in agriculture, still the main resource of India. This increase in production has not raised the very low standard of living, for it has been offset by the great increase of population. The growth has become most marked during the last hundred years, owing to a number of causes among which are the prevention of invasion and of the civil wars which earlier had been recurrent, and the partial relief of famines. The food requirements of the enlarged and new urban centres engaged in industry and commerce cannot be met by the relatively small surpluses from the rural areas ; hence the extension of such surpluses as well as an increased importation of food is essential. Also, it is now widely recognized in India that further applications of scientific methods for developing all the natural resources are urgently necessary.

Besides this general economic problem are others of a political or social character arising from the diversity of the population : e.g. the " communal " differences due to religious beliefs and practices ; the marked discrepancies between the standards of living of the few very rich people as opposed to the great numbers of miserably poor ; the contrasts between the stages of cultural advance among the successive immigrant groups. Further, there is the immense scale of administration to be taken into account—the huge numbers of the population and the enormous extent of the " sub-continent." All these difficulties face the Indian government which should express the will, and must determine the destinies, of a people who until recently have had little general education and little political experience.

Ceylon is scarcely to be regarded as a cultural unit, although it is geographically an island and politically a single Dominion. While the majority of the population are Sinhalese and occupy the greater part of the island, the northern portion has been largely settled by Tamils and other people from southern India ; hence the north of Ceylon may perhaps be thought of as an extension of Hindu India.

Even over the rest of Ceylon, the population has varied cultural characteristics ; most of the cultivators are Buddhist Sinhalese, many traders and fishermen are Muslims, and in addition there are Christians of either European or partially European descent. From the economic point of view, Ceylon is noteworthy for the development of plantation agriculture ; this has involved for the people of Ceylon past dependence upon European capital and organization, and their good or ill fortune is largely settled by the state of world markets. In the economic as well as the political sphere, however, Ceylon has already gone a considerable way towards independence.

6–7. Indo-China.—This term is here used in a wide sense to denote all the south-eastern peninsula of Asia beyond Hindu India and China, except that comprised in the Malayan tip. Indo-China as thus understood is transitional in its cultural relationships between the Far East and Hindu India, and therefore marked " 6–7 " on the map.

In its physical characters the population of Indo-China shows that it is largely derived from South Mongoloid peoples who were pushed into this region by the expansion of the Chinese ; in many individuals, too, the effect of recent Chinese immigration is to be seen. In some groups, the Nesiot racial element is noticeable, bearing witness to the eastward advance of the wavy-haired peoples through India into Indo-China.

Common cultural elements which indicate similarities with those of the Far East are the monosyllabic languages and the prevalence of the Buddhist religion over most of the region. Moreover, along the coastal districts of the South China Sea the effects of Chinese immigration are clearly seen in the cult of ancestor worship among the people, the forms of their art, and the type of irrigation they employ.

On the other hand, influences of Indian civilization were brought by Hindu merchants and adventurers who formed a ruling, though small, class among the people of a large part of the fertile river valleys, particularly in the western part of the peninsula ; to these aliens are due, for example, the storage ponds which recall the irrigation tanks of the Deccan, and the wonderful temple of Angkor which has been disinterred from the jungles of the lower Mekong valley. As a result of these influences upon their natural endowments, the Burmese people, in addition to a purer form of Buddhism than is now generally found, have acquired an appreciation of art, music and drama, and to many observers they have given the impression of unusual charm of character and manners.

Although along the coasts and by the rivers migrants from both sides have introduced developments, in the high and rugged mountains and on the broad plateaus which separate the valleys live relatively isolated tribes of varied origin ; many of these still retain their primitive modes of thought and ways of life.

The fertility of the deltaic soils and the abundant heat and moisture in the south of Indo-China have made it so easy for the people of that part to get a living that they have little need, and perhaps little capacity, for showing energy, especially as there is no reinvigorating cool period during the year. Certainly they have been overrun by the hardier mountain folk from the north of Indo-China who, in the relatively densely populated south, established kingdoms which struggled for supremacy with one another. Then Europeans came by sea, the French dominating the Pacific side of the peninsula and the British extending their rule from India over Burma ; only the Kingdom of Thailand (Siam) retained its independence.

Economic changes, of course, resulted from the coming of the Europeans. The varied mineral resources and the valuable timbers of the forests were exploited ; plantations were made ; the paddy-fields of the deltas and flood-plains of the rivers were extended, and the rice, besides furnishing the staple food of the region itself, is now exported in great amounts, notably from Burma, to supplement the deficient food of India.

British and French enterprises were directly responsible for much of the developments in their respective colonial spheres ; into the same two areas entered also many Asiatic industrial organizers and traders, money-lenders, and workers of various kinds. They came from India on the one side and from China on the other, in some respects to the disadvantage of the native peoples. Thailand was affected less directly by European influence, but Chinese immigrants were numerous and became an important minority controlling much of the production and commerce in this State.

The Japanese occupation, besides bringing about a temporary reduction in productivity and trade over large parts of the region, had a lasting effect upon the political status of the British and French colonies by stimulating nationalist feelings. Both in Burma and in French Indo-China insistent demands for political independence resulted in the loosening from control by foreign Powers. In the former French territory was formed an almost completely independent Federation of French Indo-China. This Federation is linked with other French overseas territories and with France itself to constitute the French Union which to some extent resembles the British Commonwealth.

The nationalist movements, however, had a wider significance, for they included resentment against the other Asiatics who had migrated into the peninsula ; hence, not only in the former British and French areas, but also in Thailand, there were popular agitations against all forms of alien economic intrusion. Thus the politically conscious groups among the peoples of Indo-China have three main aims, which interlock and in some particulars may be opposed to one another : (i) freedom from domination or influence by foreign Powers ; (ii) subordination to themselves of the alien, and enterprising, communities within their frontiers ; (iii) the continuing development of the natural resources of their lands, and the improvement of the physical and cultural conditions of the people.

8. East Indies.—This region, including on the one side the Malayan Peninsula and on the other New Guinea, has been a crossing-place at which have mingled racial and cultural streams to an unusual extent. Hence there is diversity, rather than unity, in several important respects, though the Malay people are the most numerous and their culture is the most outstanding, and most of the languages belong to the Malay family.

Even the Malays are of mixed racial origin ; the Southern Mongoloid branch of the straight-haired races is the most important element in their make-up, but wavy-haired Nesiot characters are also present. Moreover, the woolly-haired division of mankind is represented by the Papuans of New Guinea, and also by small groups of very early inhabitants who are widely distributed through most of the region, especially on interior highlands where they have been driven by later comers who have occupied the coastal lowlands.

The Malay peoples predominate over most of the region, except in the interior of those islands where descendants of earlier comers live under more primitive conditions. For many centuries the Malays have been in the main largely a maritime people ; in earlier times they were pirates on the high seas and conquerors of coast-lands throughout the region, but their seafaring descendants are now peaceable fishers and traders. Many of the Malay folk are keen-minded, with capabilities in many directions, and among them are skilful and artistic workers in textiles, wood and metals. On Java the Malays, who form the great majority of the Javanese, are also the cultivators : most of them are peasant farmers producing the greater part of the rice needed for the food requirements of the very dense population, and others work for the export trade on the plantations which are owned and managed by Europeans or by Javanese. The Malays of the less developed islands,

HIGH ASIA

[*The Mount Everest Committee*

This Tibetan monastery is one of a very large number, for lamas form nearly one-quarter of the population. The religious settlements occupy commanding positions and are built in a simple, and almost primitive, way of rough-hewn stone plastered with mud. They comprise a hall of worship (the highest building in this view), small chapels, living-quarters, granaries, etc. Near the left margin is a memorial " stupa " containing holy relics.

THE FAR EAST

[*Courtauld Institute of Art*

A hall in the ancient Chinese Imperial University at Peiping, where princes received their tutors' instruction. It exemplifies both the age-long respect for learning and also the simple yet dignified form of Chinese architecture in a gracious setting. Upturned roofs are characteristic, and those of the Imperial palaces had glazed yellow tiles which, in the sunlight, appeared from afar to be of gold.

Left: HINDU INDIA

A Hindu temple in South India. It comprises a great enclosure with several huge, bulky towers such as that shown, smaller buildings, and tanks of holy water. On the towers is an accumulation of ornament consisting mainly of close-packed statues of gods, goddesses and mythological figures; it is an architectural expression of the accumulation of religious ideas especially marked among the people of diverse origins in South India.

Right: THE INDO-CHINESE PENINSULA

A Burmese pagoda. Buddhism means much to the Burmans and many pilgrims visit the sacred pagodas, whose gorgeous gilded or white towers satisfy also the love of display common to the Burmese people. The transitional cultural character of the region is suggested in this pagoda by the Chinese-like upturned roofs associated with an abundance of decoration recalling that of the Hindu temples.

THE EAST INDIES

[R. A. L. Janssen

Malay houses are commonly built on piles along the coasts and by rivers, whether over water or on normally dry ground as here. Simply constructed of poles and leaf-thatch, they suggest a simple and easy-going mode of life. The house shown belongs to well-to-do people, is unusually well built and has a rice store on the right ; in the background are coconut trees.

NEGRO AFRICA

[South African Railways

The Queen Mother's Krall in Swaziland exhibits a refinement of the simpler huts common over much of Negro Africa. It comprises about 30 dwellings, groups of them protected by fences made of stakes, grass, and ropes of twisted stalks as shown on the left. Huts in the left middle-distance reveal their construction of saplings bent into semi-circular form, crossed to form a dome, and then thatched with grass.

ABORIGINAL SOUTH AMERICA

An Indian hut in Brazil. The site is a sandy stretch in a wide river valley in the Campos region. The Indian belongs to a tribe of fishers who find this situation useful for their work and also if flight by river may be necessary when attacked by a warlike tribe. Also the site is liable to flood during the rainy summer and the reed hut is therefore a temporary structure.

LATIN AMERICA

The great bay of Rio de Janeiro is protected by ridges like that in the background, and has a number of side inlets with such residential suburbs as that shown here. Founded in the 16th Century, Rio has early Portuguese buildings, as well as those of the sky-scraper type— not a response to overcrowding.

however, take less willingly to laborious work in agriculture, though some have settled inland as rice-growers, living in houses built on piles above the flood-plains (see opposite p. 356). Malays are generally easy-going people, and in the Malay Peninsula they tend to be displaced by the more enterprising and industrious Chinese and Indian immigrants ; on a number of the islands, also, Chinese workers, traders and money-lenders form important minorities.

The Papuans of New Guinea are at a relatively low stage of cultural development ; their occupations are of the simple hunting and collecting type, except in some coastal districts where they have been affected by contacts with Malay and other migrants, or where European plantations have been established. Their languages are of a different family from those of the Malays, and their religious ideas and customs have not risen above the animistic stage.

Long ago, traders from India introduced into the East Indies various cultural developments, including the Hindu religion— though this has now almost entirely disappeared. At a later date, Arab invasions imposed the Islamic religion at least as a veneer over earlier beliefs, and they set up numerous small Muslim States. These in turn gave way before European conquerors ; much of the East Indies came under the political control of the Netherlands and Britain, and in the latter half of the nineteenth century Western influences brought about great economic and social changes.

European plantations became numerous and very productive, and in many parts of the East Indies region there are now flourishing enterprises, European and Native, with a wide range of products. Moreover, the mineral resources are also varied : tin and oil may be specially mentioned. The export of local productions gives rise to much commerce, and the cross-roads position of Singapore has made it one of the greatest entrepôt ports in the world.

Partly because of its resources and their development, the East Indies region has shown greater cultural advances than the other equatorial regions. This distinction is to be attributed in part, also, to the easy accessibility of the area to enterprising peoples from other lands, and to the climate which allows these peoples to work under better physical conditions than almost anywhere else in similar latitudes. In particular, the sea-winds which blow over the coastal districts and the relatively low temperature on the highlands of the interior areas have permitted European settlers to make their permanent homes in the islands. Moreover, as there is no marked colour bar felt by the Dutch, there has been fairly close association and even inter-marriage between them and the Indonesians, with the result that the general standard of civilization has been considerably raised on some of the islands, though elsewhere in the region the native peoples have remained at a much lower level.

As in Asia, the Japanese occupation increased nationalist feelings and gave opportunity for revolt from Dutch domination. This resulted in the formation of a federal " United States of Indonesia," which has a voluntary association with Holland and the smaller areas of the Kingdom of the Netherlands, and thus becomes part of a Netherlands-Indonesian Union of the " Commonwealth " pattern.

The Philippine Islands are in some respects exceptional in this region, for their conquest by the Spaniards was essentially missionary in character, with the result that nearly all the Filipinos are Christians. After the defeat of Spain by the United States at the end of the nineteenth century the Philippines passed into the hands of the latter Power ; at the close of the Second World War the islands were granted independence subject only to an arrangement for U.S. troops to be stationed there for the protection of the new Republic and the peace of the Pacific area. Economic development has gone farther in the Philippines than in the more backward islands of the eastern part of the Malay Archipelago, but not so far as in Java. The Filipinos have for long been agriculturists ; rice is their staple food, and plantations give a variety of products for export, especially sugar. The valuable mineral resources of these islands, however, are capable of greater utilization.

The *Pacific Islands* differ in their human geography from those of the East Indian Archipelago in a number of ways, but because of their small areas and populations they can scarcely be regarded as one of the major cultural regions of the world.

CHAPTER XXI
CULTURAL REGIONS (2)

9. Negro Africa.—Before Columbus started the "geographical revolution," the Old World was shut in by the ocean save in Africa, and here the Sahara was the frontier of civilization. It was not until the latter part of the nineteenth century that the White man effectively circumvented this barrier of the desert and seized the new world to the south. There lies Negro Africa, comprising that large part of the continent in which the population is almost entirely of Negro or Negroid descent.

The Bantu languages have spread practically everywhere, the chief exception being the Hausa tongue in the Niger Basin. Various forms of animistic belief developed, and even yet have very much influence on the customs and daily life of the people. These beliefs are now giving way before the advance of Christianity and European ideas, especially in the more southerly areas, and before Islam, which is making still more converts, mainly in the north. In this part, south of the Sahara, Hamitic invasions have modified the religious beliefs, racial characters, economic methods and social organizations to such an extent that the northern savanna lands form a transitional belt overlapping Negro Africa and the Muslim Lands.

In the main, entry to Negro Africa was barred either by deserts or by coastal zones with mangrove swamps and with waterfalls which hindered access by the rivers. The climate, too, was in many parts unsuitable for people from other lands. Hence until quite recently the age-long modes of life had been little changed by outside interference. The Negro peoples are physically adapted to the climatic conditions and have adjusted their ways to their environments. Although the Negroes have adopted cultural achievements brought by immigrants, they appear to have made no noteworthy advances of their own. In many areas they have been handicapped by habits of living for the moment, or of intermittent rather than continuous work, but they have been helped to support difficult times by good nature and a cheerful disposition, and by a marked feeling for music and a keen sense of rhythm.

The Negro and Negroid peoples are at various levels of culture. In the least favourable and least accessible parts of the equatorial forests, small numbers of the descendants of very early inhabitants maintain a precarious existence by hunting and collecting. In most of the forested areas is a sparse population living mainly on the products of shifting agriculture. In those savanna lands which have a sufficient rainfall, fixed cultivation provides a higher standard of living for a denser population. These more advanced farmers have a correspondingly advanced social system and have been influenced to a greater extent by the European Powers which now govern their territories. In the drier savanna lands the Negro tribes have an economy that is mainly pastoral. On the cooler East African plateaus they carry on both agriculture and cattle-rearing, and here again they have been markedly affected by the European occupation.

Over much of Negro Africa, indeed, partition among alien Powers and the opening of the interior to overseas commerce and new forms of production have markedly modified the native ways of life and the tribal institutions ; in some parts the changes were so rapid that adjustments were impossible and there set in a period of economic and social chaos.

Hence, an assessment of the present conditions in the cultural region of Negro Africa must give much weight to the effects of foreign intervention ; this is shown even in Liberia, established as a colony for freed American slaves and now forming an independent Republic. With this exception all Negro Africa is directly held as dependent territories, the greatest part by Britain, France, Portugal and Belgium, while Egyptian influence extends into the Nile portion of the Sudan, and Spain holds relatively small coastal districts.

These Powers have different systems of governing their territories and have had divergent influences on the political and economic circumstances of their Negro subjects. Moreover, these influences have been exercised upon native peoples who had previously reached very different stages of advance, as was illustrated in an earlier chapter from the case of the British dependency of Nigeria. Further, diverse geographical conditions have affected the policies and actions of the controlling

States. For example, on the high plateaus of East Africa where White settlement is possible, there is an incentive to give or sell land to White farmers and to induce or to compel Negroes to become workers. Again, where valuable minerals have been discovered a similar procedure has been followed. On the other hand, in the coastal districts of West Africa and in the hot, moist equatorial regions, Europeans may allow Native retention of land but may take direct or indirect means of aiding the Natives to grow crops for sale to White purchasers.

Because of all these and other factors, there is now a wide range in the conditions of the Negroes. In the political sphere may be seen contrasts between a condition of practical subjection and one with considerable self-government. Bound up with these political contrasts are differences in the degree of education to which the peoples have attained ; in a few colonies the advance is now becoming fairly general and " mass education " is being attempted, while in other territories very few individuals have received any instruction. The Second World War had an influence in some parts, notably in the British dependencies in East Africa and West Africa, for native recruits went overseas and many became proficient in new skills ; in various ways their mental horizons were widened and they returned to Africa bearing the leaven of enlightenment and even unrest. With the stimulus of these developments, some of the colonial territories have received revised constitutions allowing the Native peoples a greater share in the administrations.

Varying degrees of economic freedom are also marked ; virtual servitude in some areas may be contrasted with the opportunity in other colonies for commercial enterprises or the exercise of learned professions. In this connection, again, differences in native tradition on the one hand, and on the other hand foreign encouragement and assistance, play their parts. Diversity is similarly shown in health conditions. In these, geographical circumstances are obviously important ; so, too, are the measures, or the lack thereof, taken by the authorities both to improve nutrition and also to combat disease. In some parts, as in East Africa, such improvements and the prevention of tribal warfare have allowed an increase in the numbers of the people, and thus raised the problem of over-population of the available farming land—already reduced by soil erosion. The

Negroes' desire for more land to cultivate is now a factor in stimulating political and economic developments.

As the combined result of all the political, economic, social and geographical factors, the standards of living have considerable variations. Taken as a whole, Negro Africa is still far down in the scale ; only in exceptional cases has a marked increase been achieved.

With the developments of recent years the question has arisen regarding the future of the Negro peoples. Although in the past they have lacked technical advances, many have now shown their ability to utilize the mechanical devices of the White men, while in some parts, e.g. in Uganda and West Africa, they have successfully adopted the new methods of production and have entered into world commerce. Indeed, it is probable that when disease and malnutrition have ceased to be such heavy handicaps, and when geographical and social isolation no longer cut off the bulk of the population from the knowledge which long ago spread through much of the world, the Negro race, and not only certain individuals or groups as now, may make its contribution to the development of mankind. At the present time, however, the relations between the Negro population of Africa and the White peoples, both in Africa and elsewhere, form one of the great problems before the world.

Two exceptional areas of Africa must be excluded from this cultural region. One is the almost uninhabited part of Southwest Africa in which a decreasing number of Bushmen and Hottentots still retain their simple and primitive modes of life. The other exceptional area is the relatively densely populated highland of Ethiopia where the people are mainly engaged in subsistence farming ; most of them are of Hamitic origin, the languages are both Hamitic and Semitic, and the religious faiths include Christianity, Islam and Judaism.

Madagascar must also be excluded from Negro Africa, for Bantu, Hova and other influences combine to determine the racial and cultural conditions ; indeed, the eastern side of the island may perhaps be regarded as more closely related to the cultural region of the East Indies than to Negro Africa.

10. Aboriginal South America.—By this name we denote the region in which the inhabitants, very few in number, are of pure, or almost pure, Amerind descent. It includes most of the Amazon Basin, except in the immediate neighbourhood of the rivers, and extends northward into the interior of the Guiana Highlands and southward over the less accessible parts of the Campos and Chaco areas.

The region has remained largely unaffected by White penetration for three reasons : its climate is repellent ; for the early European invaders it lacked the attraction of easily won treasure ; it remains scarcely accessible even to the collectors of forest products, except along the courses of the great waterways. Hence the aboriginal peoples still retain their primitive languages, beliefs and customs. They exist under wretched conditions : some live in small groups by fishing, collecting or hunting ; others practise shifting tillage in the limited areas suitable for agriculture either in the forests or on the adjoining Highlands, Campos and Chaco areas. Especially in the hot, wet lowlands, diseases take a very heavy toll of health and life, for many Indians are not so well adapted to their environment as are the Negroes of equatorial Africa.

In its human geography, Aboriginal South America shows marked contrasts with the East Indies and even with Negro Africa in the same latitudes. Its climate, little relieved by high altitudes or by sea-winds, and its relative isolation from the Old World have given it a different racial history in the past, hindered its development in the present, and created difficult problems for its future.

11. Latin America.—Latin America stretches from the northern frontier of Mexico to the tip of South America. Despite its name the greater part is not a " White man's land," for a large proportion of the inhabitants are of Amerind or Mestizo (i.e. mixed European and Amerind) origin, while there are many people of Negro or partly Negro descent, and Asiatic immigrants have also contributed to the present make-up of the population. The exceptional area where people of European descent form the majority of the population is the extra-tropical part of South America (marked " 11a ") in Chile, Argentina and Uruguay and on the adjoining upland of southern Brazil.

The region is " Latin " since, apart from some islands and the British, Dutch and French colonies of Guiana, it was conquered and held for a long period by Spain or Portugal ; hence the official language of the larger States is Spanish, except in Brazil where it is Portuguese. Nevertheless, aboriginal tongues are still spoken in many districts. Similarly the religion is nominally Roman Catholic, though numbers of the natives retain their pre-Christian beliefs either little modified or as an element in their form of the Catholic faith.

The nature of the Spanish and Portuguese conquests determined several features of the present-day human geography of Latin America which distinguish it from English-speaking North America. The immediate search for gold and silver treasure, or for easy wealth in sugar plantations, attracted soldiers and adventurers who came without wives and families and mingled with the aborigines, thus giving rise to the Mestizo population. The governments of Spain and Portugal ruled the territories in their own interests, preventing any economic developments which seemed likely to injure those at home, and by prohibiting trade which would have been remunerative to the settlers tempted them to law-breaking and smuggling.

The wars of independence began in the early nineteenth century when Spain was invaded by Napoleon. The colonists had had no experience in self-government ; after they had gained their freedom they retained their habits of conflict with authority, and for a considerable time the new States had a troublous existence with frequent revolutions. The very varied descent of the peoples, and the low stage of cultural advance in which many of them remained, also hindered the establishment of stable and democratic governments. For these reasons, the number of States in Latin America and the clashes between them have shown a marked contrast with the political situation in English-speaking America, where the early settlements have consolidated into two main federations between which there has been no conflict for well over a century.

Economic development in Latin America was also handicapped by the origins of the population and by the early political conditions. Many of the European settlers long persisted in the tradition of wishing to acquire wealth without work, and over large areas this attitude was encouraged by climatic hindrances to continuous activity of any kind ; to add to the difficulties the native labour was generally unfitted for the work required by the colonists. As a result, the States of Latin America showed little economic advance for some decades after their formation.

Assistance was eventually gained, however, from United States and European capitalists, business men, and engineers, but this brought two results regretted by many people in the

Latin American States. First, there was the payment of interest, profits and salaries to people of other nationalities; second, control of many important enterprises was in the hands of foreigners, who therefore gained great influence in a number of ways. Consequently a movement grew up in Latin America to achieve economic freedom. This movement was aided, among other things, by opportunities for industrial development during the wars in Europe of 1914–18 and 1939–45, and by the " good neighbour " policy which the U.S.A. adopted just before the second of these wars. In recent years, therefore, the twenty States of Latin America have made marked progress towards economic independence and the fuller utilization of their natural resources.

There are, however, considerable differences between some parts of Latin America and others, and four areas deserve special mention. (i) The highlands of the Mexican Plateau and the broader parts of the Andes have a relatively temperate climate which does not hinder human advance. Hence the Amerind peoples of these highlands long ago practised irrigation, worked metals, developed various arts and crafts, built roads, bridges and cities. When the Spanish treasure seekers came they found, and destroyed, the Aztec realm in the Mexican area and the Empire of the Incas in the Andes. In these regions both Indian and Mestizo people now form a numerically large, and economically important, part of the population.

(ii) Other areas which early attracted Europeans were the hot, moist coast-lands, where they established sugar plantations. Here they forced Indians to work for them, and when this source of labour proved inadequate they imported slaves from Africa; hence it is in these districts that there is a noteworthy Negro element in the population, and the Europeans in these areas still draw a good part of their livelihood from plantation agriculture.

(iii) In the West Indies, near the Tropic and with sea-winds reaching all parts, the climate made settlement and even manual work by Europeans more possible; few Indians have survived and the present population is mainly of White and Negro descent in various proportions. Besides Spain and Portugal, other European States, especially Britain and France, took part in the occupation of the West Indies; the political conditions of the islands have changed a good deal, but while some parts are still under foreign suzerainty, others have attained independence. The economic development and the stage of culture also vary from island to island.

(iv) The extra-tropical part of South America and the upland of southern Brazil just within the Tropic (marked " 11a " on the map) is a " White man's land " ; the relatively few nomadic Indians were almost exterminated and the present population is mainly of European descent. The Spanish and Portuguese conquests led to this area becoming part of Latin America, but later immigrations of considerable numbers of industrious Italians and Germans have contributed to development.

On the tropical Brazilian upland, plantations of coffee, fruit and other products are of great importance, but over the rest of the region sub-tropical forms of agriculture and the mixed farming of mid-latitudes are the main economic resources. Around the exporting districts of southern Brazil, the Plate Estuary and central Chile, industries and commerce have developed and there are areas of moderately dense or even dense population. Reference to the map on p. 310 shows that on the average the standard of living in Argentina and Uruguay is marked as moderately high ; Brazil is classed as medium in this respect, though there is no doubt that if southern Brazil were separated from the rest of the State it would come into a higher category. The remaining States of Latin America, however, have but a low standard of living.

As a whole, this sub-region (" 11a ") is much more progressive and has advanced farther in cultural development than the remainder of Latin America.

12. English-speaking America.—This cultural region extends from the Mexican border into the sub-arctic forests in which it becomes transitional to the Arctic Margins region. Two geographical facts have been fundamental in influencing its human developments. The first is its situation on the other side of the " Midland " Ocean from Europe and in about the same latitudes ; hence its relatively easy accessibility from a number of European States. The second is its extent, viz. across the whole width of the continent and almost from the Tropic to the Arctic Circle ; hence its variety in the environments and modes of life of the people.

As a result of its situation people of European descent form the great majority of its population, the only noteworthy exceptions being the considerable Negro element, especially in the south-east of the United States, small numbers of Indians in the Reserves and on the northern margin, and some settlers of Chinese and Japanese origin near the Pacific coasts. The White population has come from all parts of Europe, but the English language has spread almost throughout, partly because of the large number of early immigrants from the British Isles and partly because the English-speaking groups gradually gained political control. The only considerable exception is in eastern Canada where the French language is spoken by a majority of the people ; elsewhere only small communities have retained the speech of their mother countries. Corresponding to the varied origin of the immigrants, a number of religious denominations are represented in the region, but collectively the Protestant churches have most adherents.

Some of the differences between Latin America and English-speaking America have already been mentioned. It may here be emphasized that it was mainly Spanish and Portuguese from southern Europe who went to the inter-tropical parts of the New World, seeking fortune as military adventurers, whereas it was British, French, Dutch, Germans and others from north-western and central Europe who went to extra-tropical North America in much greater numbers and in many cases as families intending to earn their own livelihood.

For the most part they formed compact colonies near the Atlantic coasts, and these colonies were allowed much freedom in their economic activities and even in self-government. Before the end of the eighteenth century the colonies south of Canada shook off British rule and formed themselves into the United States of America. Their previous measure of freedom proved a good foundation for further advance, and the people of the U.S.A. have extended their territory and increased their numbers until they now form one of the two greatest States of the world. Canada has also extended across the continent, but its less productive lands support a smaller population.

The second geographical fact, the extent and consequent variety of environments within the two great States of English-speaking America, may be illustrated by drawing attention to a few outstanding differences in the cultural conditions of seven sub-regions ; these may be broadly related to the climate regions shown on the map on p. 74.

(1) Within the present *North-eastern States* of the U.S.A. lies the coastal strip upon which the first settlements were made ; this area was relatively easy of access from north-western Europe, which in its physical conditions it broadly resembled and from which its settlers were largely drawn. It is the eastern part of the climate region of the mid-latitude, rainy-summer type whose products allowed the early colonists to be practically self-supporting ; later, with commerce fostered by the maritime position and with the rise of large-scale manufacturing, this sub-region became predominantly urban and very densely populated. It has also been distinguished by its cultural advances founded upon European traditions.

Settlements of similar character spread slowly across the Appalachian barrier, and with the aid of easy access to coal and iron took industrial developments to the eastern shores of the Great Lakes. The North-eastern States, taken as a whole, have been and still are those most in touch with Europe.

(2) The *Middle West* occupies the part of the same climate region beyond the Ohio river. It was settled much later, primarily as an agricultural land producing grain crops and supporting great numbers of animals, while cities grew up as trading and industrial centres. As compared with the North-eastern States, the Middle West was remote from foreign contacts, and was for long characterized by " isolationist " tendencies, especially in international affairs. Now, however, it is culturally as well as geographically in a central position, and its political and social ideas influence both the Atlantic and the Pacific regions of the United States.

(3) The *South* of the United States has the sub-tropical, rainy-summer type of climate where plantations of tobacco and cotton encouraged a land-owning, aristocratic class of settlers who depended upon the labour of Negro slaves. After the abolition of slavery and the break-up of the large estates, small farms were largely worked by share-croppers, Negroes or " poor Whites " with a low or very low standard of living. To some extent these conditions still persist, although large-scale, mechanized farming is now bringing agriculture more into line with that in other parts of the States, while more towns and cities are being industrialized and higher wages are paid.

The most striking cultural characteristic of the South lies in the fact that here live almost three-quarters of the total Negro population of the U.S.A. ; this large number of coloured folk together with the heritage of the past still make this problem of a "plural society" particularly acute. Discrimination by Whites against people of Negro or part-Negro descent shows itself in many forms : e.g. it is only slowly that the coloured people have become free to exercise their right to vote, as restrictive poll-taxes have been abolished ; economic freedom is still infringed by limitations upon the class of work permitted to Negroes and by lower rates of pay ; social inequality is another serious disability, especially in the poorer educational and other facilities provided for Negroes, and it is emphasized by compelling them to travel in separate compartments in public conveyances.

Resentment against such conditions is increasingly felt by the coloured people, and a considerable number took the opportunity of a shortage of labour in both World Wars to migrate northward, especially to the great cities ; here, although occasional clashes have occurred, racial ill-feeling is less marked than in the South. As the proportion of Negroes in the total population of the States has in recent years remained almost constant at about 10 per cent., and only relatively small mitigations of their condition have been brought about, no solution of the problem is yet in sight.

(4) *The eastern part of the " short-summer " climate area* of mid-latitudes overlaps the boundary between the United States and Canada. Within it, the St. Lawrence river and the Great Lakes have given entry to several groups of immigrants, and on both sides of the frontier the descendants of the French settlers have retained their language, religion, and distinctive culture. As a whole, this sub-region is less productive and therefore less populated than the more southerly ones ; during the Second World War, however, the Canadian portion made considerable advances in mining, utilization of water-power and industrial development.

(5) *The Great Plains of the United States and the Prairies of Canada* lie between the Rocky Mountains and the sub-regions already indicated ; as the rainfall is normally light and also subject to much variation, this sub-region has already seen great changes in its development. In the latter part of the nineteenth century it was an area of rapid settlement, but in the second quarter of the present century a succession of droughts

brought disaster. From the western plains many ruined farmers fled either back to the East or onward to the West, but their inexperienced attempts left a legacy of soil erosion which will heavily handicap the future. In cooler Canada the droughts were less catastrophic, but the Census of 1941 for the first time showed a set-back in the growth of the Prairie Provinces. The climatic uncertainty over the whole sub-region has made farming a gamble, the standard of living a see-saw, and political life a scene of unrest and hasty experiment.

(6) The " *Mountain States* " of the U.S.A. and their highland continuation in Canada were for long merely a barrier across the continent, but their irrigable basin lands proved a place of refuge to the Mormon community in the middle of the nineteenth century; there are also other places of refuge—the Indian Reserves. Minerals have been the great attraction to White settlers, and as a consequence of exhaustion of some deposits and discovery of others, there have been violent changes in the distribution and the fortunes of the miners. The earlier lack of law and order was reflected in a slow development of cultural amenities. Recently, great engineering enterprises have supplied water for power, irrigation and human use both within the highland area and to its neighbouring regions.

(7) *The Pacific Coast* affords less resources for a livelihood to the people of Canada than to those of the United States. In California early Spanish missions gave their name to many places whose growth has been due to a considerable extent to mining and irrigation, particularly for fruit-growing, and during the Second World War to ship and aeroplane construction. The clear skies of the desert climate of the southern part, with water from the Cordillera, have been utilized to attract the motion-picture industry and well-to-do seekers after health or pleasure ; hence standards of living, and standards of values in living, show contrasts with those of most parts of North America.

Some characteristics are fairly common to English-speaking America. In new environments many migrants had to strike out along new lines, and hence independence and enterprise became high virtues ; other common features of American life are the habit of thinking and working on a large scale ; the use of mechanical appliances in home and factory ; rapid transit by road, rail and aeroplane. Such characteristics have helped the people of the United States not only to use their own resources but also in the space of a few decades to influence developments in various parts of the world, particularly in Latin America and recently in China. They have also helped to raise the standard of living so that the workers have greater earnings in the United States and Canada than elsewhere. Yet it is not only in material things that there are high standards. For example, a broad view is taken in educational affairs, and facilities for University study are abundant ; again, shrewdness in commerce is balanced by humanitarian feelings and moral idealism.

The United States have been referred to as a " melting-pot " of nationalities because immigrants from so many countries have, within the space of a generation or so after their arrival, learnt a new language and a new loyalty. Even so, in matters of foreign politics, the statesmen of the U.S.A. sometimes have to take into account the special sympathies which groups of citizens feel for the peoples from whom they or their stock originated.

The geographical conditions of Canada have given it certain peculiarities as a Dominion of the British Commonwealth. The Canadian people live in four main groups, viz. those of the Maritime Provinces, the St. Lawrence valley, the Prairies, and the Pacific Coast respectively ; these are widely separated from each other but fairly closely bound up with the adjoining groups in the United States. There are therefore many contacts between the two peoples, and in some matters Canada tends to be linked more closely to its immediate neighbour than to the other members of the Commonwealth. The existence of the large French-speaking community in Canada is also of political importance, for it is conscious of national unity, and has no feeling of allegiance either to France or to Britain ; yet as a practical means of maintaining its culture and individuality, it is willing to keep its position within the Dominion of Canada and therefore within the British Commonwealth.

13. South Africa.—Probably the most outstanding feature of this region is that it has a dual character. On the one hand, political and economic affairs are entirely controlled by people of European descent and their type of culture is at least superficially dominant. On the other hand, about four-fifths of the population are of non-European, largely Negro or Negroid, origin ; also, this proportion is tending to increase although there has been no great change during the present century.

The first comers from overseas were Dutch farmers ; later came Protestant refugees from France ; at the end of the eighteenth century the British conquered Cape Colony and British settlers followed. In consequence of numerous griev- ances against the British, the Boers " trekked " northwards in the thirties of the nineteenth century, first crossed the Orange river and then pressed on across the Vaal river ; in these areas they formed pastoral communities under the names of the Orange Free State and the Transvaal State.

While the Europeans settled in the south of the continent and worked northward, tribes of Bantu warriors fought their way southward killing, displacing or enslaving other Negro tribes and Hottentots. Thus came the inevitable and bloody clashes between Whites and Blacks, including those of the British with Kosas (Kaffirs) in the Cape Colony and Zulus in Natal, and those of the Boers with Kosas, Zulus, Matabele, Basutos and others in the interior. Eventually the White men won and reduced their opponents to a state of subjection, but on both sides the warfare left a legacy of hate and fear to many of their successors.

Thus relations between British, Boers and Natives were for a long time complicated and often bitter, and towards the end of the nineteenth century came another cause of conflict. This was the discovery of gold in the " Rand " of the Transvaal, which stimulated a migration into Boer lands of British and other miners and speculators, and finally resulted in all South Africa being taken by the British. The bitterness of the Boers was partly assuaged when in the early part of the present century the British government proposed a union of the Trans- vaal and the Orange Free State colonies with the Cape Colony and Natal, and granted to the " Union of South Africa " the status of a self-governing Dominion of the Commonwealth. In this Union the people of Dutch descent, adopting the name Afrikaners, had a majority of about 60 per cent. of the White population, as compared with the British 40 per cent.

Since that time the old antagonism has slowly decreased, though in the main the two groups retain their own languages— English and Afrikaans—and they belong to different religious denominations. Differences in political matters also persist ;

ENGLISH-SPEAKING NORTH AMERICA (1)

Behind the water-front of New York is a striking group of sky-scrapers. Their development was stimulated by the restricted space on Manhattan Island and achieved by the skill of United States architects and engineers. That many are largely occupied by financiers is due to New York being the monetary capital of the world, and its concentration of multifarious business activities is linked with the production and consumption of goods over immense areas.

ENGLISH-SPEAKING NORTH AMERICA (II)

This section of a Canadian grain elevator indicates another aspect of North American development. It shows a modern, utilitarian, and efficient structure in which this typical western production is stored at the head of navigation on Lake Superior before being poured into the great grain-ships bound for the east. There is not much other traffic, and the Canadian points of transfer are still only small towns.

[South African Official Photograph

SOUTH AFRICA

This part of the city of Johannesburg closely adjoins the gold mines which determined its rise and development. In the background are the white dumps of ore after it has been crushed and treated with cyanide. In this business quarter most of the buildings are of the sky-scraper type, and the rarity of other forms of architecture is an indication of the rapid growth of South Africa's largest city.

[Black Star Pictures

AUSTRALIA

Sydney Harbour. This view shows the extraordinary extent of the potential water-front. The business centre of Sydney lies beyond the left margin and room for further extension is obvious ; yet as its growth has been recent the buildings are largely of the lofty type. A significant feature is the great bridge uniting the southern and northern sections of the coastal railway ; under it could pass the largest ships of the world.

but when at the outbreak of war in 1939 there arose the question whether South Africa should support Britain, a majority of the South African Parliament, which included both Afrikaners and English-speaking members, decided upon war with Germany.

There is a far greater gulf between the European and the non-European peoples. Of the latter the Bantu-speaking Negroes (commonly referred to as the Natives) are by far the most numerous, for they form more than two-thirds of the whole population of South Africa. Their tribal systems are in process of being broken down, and though their various languages are in general maintained, most of the Bantu who live in close touch with the Europeans must make use of " pidgin-English " or a corresponding form of Afrikaans. Their physical heritage is good, and in health they have suffered less from contact with Europeans and from alien ways of life than most of the Native peoples brought under White rule. It has become clear, moreover, that they are by no means lacking in intelligence or educability.

Because of the past warfare between the races, and the present numbers and innate capacity of the Bantu, many of the White population feel it necessary to keep them in a subordinate position. A rigid colour bar prevents intermarriage, gives them practically no political rights, limits them to unskilled labour at wages far below those of White workmen, limits also the neighbourhoods in which they may live and restricts their movements from one district to another. Their standards of living are much lower than those of the Europeans and their educational opportunities are far poorer. The Reserves on which they may carry on their farming are quite inadequate, and they are therefore compelled to add to their income by working for the White people, supplying most of the manual work on the farms, in the industries and in the mines. Although they may, on the whole, be better off than the majority of the inhabitants of " Negro Africa," a growing number feel bitterness about their condition.

As this resentment, like that among other subject peoples, has become greatly intensified by the Second World War, its strength has confirmed many of the Whites in the view that firm subordination of the Black majority is the only possible policy for ensuring peace and civilization in South Africa.

In the Cape Province are the numerous " Coloured " people

who have originated from earlier intermingling of various groups of Europeans and Africans. They have no unity in race, language or social organization ; they speak some form of English or Afrikaans and, though they are not so rigidly subordinated as are the " Natives," they are very dependent upon the White men.

The last racial element of any importance is formed by the Indians who live mainly in Natal, where their predecessors were brought as labourers on sugar plantations. They are now engaged largely in domestic service, farming or trading, and in open competition they can generally undersell the White people. Because of this fact, and the consideration that in Natal they already tend to outnumber the Europeans, their further entry has been barred and their purchase of land and places of residence have been restricted. Their claims to equality of treatment have been supported in India, and in consequence relations between the two governments have been strained.

The economic structure of the region still depends largely upon gold-mining, for agriculture is limited by light or scanty rainfall over large areas and by soil erosion, while industrial development is still in its early stages. Yet gold is an insecure foundation, and the question has been seriously considered in the Union : Should gold-mining cease to be the main economic resource, what could take its place ? The answer which has been put forward by some of the leaders of economic and political thought is that an industrial system must be constructed upon the basis of iron and other minerals, and of the various products of agriculture, utilizing energy from local coal and water-power. The difficulty is realized to be the inadequate amount of skilled labour available in the White population, and it has been urged that the supply must be increased either by considerable European immigration or by a change in the policy towards the Black and Coloured peoples. To make the Natives efficient agents in building up a new and greater industrial structure for South Africa will necessitate their education and the removal of the economic colour bar. This course is urged also by others of the White leaders who think that only by the disappearance of political and social discrimination between the peoples can they eventually live side by side, and this policy is claimed by some of the Europeans as well as by the Africans to be but simple justice.

14. Australia and New Zealand.—The human geography of these two island groups is far simpler than that of South Africa, or indeed than that of most cultural regions.

Australia.—The relative isolation of Australia and Tasmania from the other continents resulted in the aboriginal populations being of a low standard of culture ; they were also numerically weak, for the region was not able to support a large number of people at their stage of economic development. The European settlers therefore had little difficulty in overcoming them ; those of Tasmania have been killed off, some intentionally and others unintentionally, and in Australia only small numbers of aborigines or half-breeds remain in the more remote or less favoured parts of the continent. Yet here as elsewhere the capacities of the Native people are seen to be much greater than was earlier recognized, when the Australian aborigines were regarded as among the lowest racial groups.[1]

Although men of several nationalities shared in the discovery of the continent, the British made the only effective occupation. During the nineteenth century agricultural communities gradually settled in the better-watered and relatively cool southern margins of Australia and in Tasmania, where climatic conditions are not markedly unlike those of Europe. From the middle of the century onward the discovery of gold increased the numbers of people in these areas and also led others into parts of the great arid and semi-arid interior which offers few resources other than minerals and scanty pasture. The gold workings attracted chiefly men of Australian or British birth, and for a time a considerable number of Chinese, but to avoid non-European settlement Restriction Acts were passed to limit further immigration. Though some Chinese have engaged in work elsewhere in Australia, largely as market gardeners, they have generally preferred to return home when their industry had brought them enough money for their future.

In the tropical northern part of the continent, another racial complication was threatened by the introduction of Kanakas, " South Sea Islanders," by the sugar planters of Queensland ;

---

[1] Apart from the now familiar cases of Natives successfully adopting the White man's occupations and modes of life, a striking instance may be quoted in the fact that a full-blooded " Blackfellow," who was educated at a mission school and was shown European paintings, in the first place proved his initiative by attempting to teach himself the art, and later so profited by instruction that his pictures have been bought by the National Gallery of Australia.

later, however, the Commonwealth government adopted the
" White Australia " policy, repatriated the Kanakas, and gave
bounties to the sugar growers to enable them to continue the
industry. Now the plantation labour is entirely supplied by
White men ; some have come from other parts of Australia,
but some are immigrants from Italy or are of Italian descent.

The question has been much debated whether people of
British stock can occupy tropical Australia. In Queensland,
the sea-winds are an advantage, and it is probable that manual
labour is not an hindrance, but a physiological aid, to the
maintenance of fitness. Moreover, it is claimed that children
can be brought up healthily, and that in successive generations
White people can be acclimatized to this north-eastern area. In
the central and western parts of tropical Australia, physical
conditions are somewhat different and the work is at present
largely sheep- and cattle-raising ; European settlement is still
small, and labour both for the pastoral work and for domestic
help is partly got from full-blooded or mixed aboriginal stocks.

Considering Australia as a whole, it may be said that the
population is very largely of British origin, and as a consequence
there is a practically universal use of the English language ;
there is also an absence of religious discord. Politically, there
is a similar simplicity, for at the beginning of the present century
the five mainland colonies and Tasmania formed themselves
into the self-governing " Commonwealth of Australia."

The relatively scanty population of Australia, as contrasted
with its considerable extent, is closely related to its physical
conditions and its type of economy. Early development depended largely upon pastoral work, but this was a weak foundation, for it has been retarded by the slight rainfall over large
areas and by the occasional droughts which have brought
disaster. Mining, especially of gold, is also an insecure and
insufficient basis for numerical growth. Agriculture is of various
types, but only the fertile margins of the continent are available
except where rivers flowing towards the interior or artesian
wells supply water for irrigation. Industries were undertaken
later, but stimulated by war-time needs they have greatly advanced in various directions ; their eventual growth, however,
may be limited by the amount of coal and water-power.

With industrial and commercial developments, and with the
possibility of further agricultural production in the north by

people of White and aboriginal descent, the present population may be doubled or even trebled without a lowering of the high average standard of living.   On the other hand, there seems no prospect of anything like close settlement over the great arid or semi-arid expanses of Australia.

New Zealand.—This much smaller island resembles Australia in the two important respects of the predominance of British stock in its population, and the general type of its economy, together with the associated facts that the population is small and has a high standard of living.   Yet at the same time there are some noteworthy differences between the two Dominions.

In the first place, in contrast to the Australian aborigines, the Maori of New Zealand quite clearly belong to the wavy-haired division of mankind and show physical resemblances to the White racial groups.   They were found by the Europeans at a relatively high level of cultural development, and after a period of strife between the two peoples they have now adapted themselves to the new conditions.   They show undoubted capacity for taking a full share in the life of the community, they have been admitted to seats in the House of Representatives proportionate to their numbers, intermarriage with White people presents no difficulty, and it is quite possible that in course of time they may become an indistinguishable element in the make-up of the New Zealand nation.

In the second place, New Zealand differs from Australia in the fact that it does not extend northward into tropical latitudes, and therefore there has been no plantation system with its dangerous influence in the introduction of cheap Coloured labour, nor is there any difficulty for White settlers to acclimatize themselves to conditions in any part of the country.

Thirdly, New Zealand has a climate with adequate rainfall for its pastoral and agricultural work, still the mainstay of its economy, and it has not had serious set-backs due to drought. Moreover, the fact that high mountains face the prevailing rain-bearing winds gives to this Dominion an abundance of water-power and hence the possibility of industrial development, especially in the processing of food for export and in the production of textiles and other requirements of its own people.

Although this country is geographically the antipodes of the British Isles, and although in political and strategic matters it is particularly concerned with the other States which are situated on the margins of the Pacific Ocean, there is still a remarkably close sympathy between the Mother Country and this farthest distant Dominion of the British Commonwealth.

Conclusion.—Reviewing the major cultural regions of the world one sees great contrasts, and an important question for the geographer is : How are these differences affected by the environments of the respective peoples ?

Climate is certainly one factor. Its influence can be seen in two opposite ways : on the one hand there is a retarding effect observable both in the hot, equatorial regions and also in the cold Arctic Margins ; on the other hand there is the stimulating effect of cyclonic weather on the peoples of Europe, the northern part of the Far East, much of English-speaking America, and the temperate regions of the southern hemisphere to which White settlers have migrated. Yet there is no simple correspondence between the great climate regions of the world and the major cultural regions ; the geographical factors are more complicated.

Of great importance were the physical conditions of the regions in which civilization developed, particularly the Nile, Euphrates and Indus valleys and the plains of China, for their special natural resources played a great part in permitting and encouraging, though not necessarily determining, the advances made by their inhabitants. From these primary centres, cultures of various types spread outwards, the movements helped or hindered by such physical conditions as the relief of the land, with valley-ways contrasted with mountain barriers ; the separation of land areas by narrow seas or by broad oceans ; the kind of natural vegetation or the lack of it. Where conditions were favourable, secondary centres of development arose : among the most noteworthy were the Mediterranean islands and coasts, and at a later date central and western Europe.

In all regions the factors determining the nature of advances have been, on the one hand, the characteristics of the peoples and of their already acquired cultures, and on the other hand, the physical conditions and the resources of new environments.

In conclusion, it must be noted that, although there are relationships between the major cultural regions, each has its own distinctive character ; they do not fall into type-groups as do the climate regions. Hence the human regions have a world-pattern quite unlike that of the physical regions.

PART III

GEOGRAPHICAL SYNTHESES

CHAPTER XXII

HOT REGIONS AND THEIR RHYTHMS

Geographical Regions and their Criteria.—In the preceding chapters it has become increasingly clear that nature and man affect one another in many ways ; indeed, for thousands of years they have been evolving together in mutual relationship. Consequently, in many parts of the world there are no longer natural landscapes, but cultural landscapes, in which appear many results of man's activities.

Similarly, it must be realized that in each region there is a particular association of nature and man ; hence, although in the first part of this book certain *natural regions* were marked out, e.g. on the basis of their climate or their natural vegetation, and in the second part certain *cultural regions*, it is still necessary to consider the regions of the world as they exist with their special physical and human components combined with one another. These areas may be termed *geographical regions* to make it clear that all the geographical elements, physical and human, are taken into account.

In this third part, the synthetic geographical regions are distinguished from one another by employing as criteria the landscapes which compose them—either the natural landscapes, where they still characterize the regions, or the cultural landscapes, where these have replaced the natural ones. The factors which have been most influential in determining the characteristics of landscapes in general are relief, climate and vegetation, while in the cultural landscapes some important human elements, e.g. the nature of the crop-lands or the occurrence of built-up areas, are influenced by other factors such as the special cultural characteristics of the people. Therefore, while the geographical regions broadly correspond with the great relief, climate

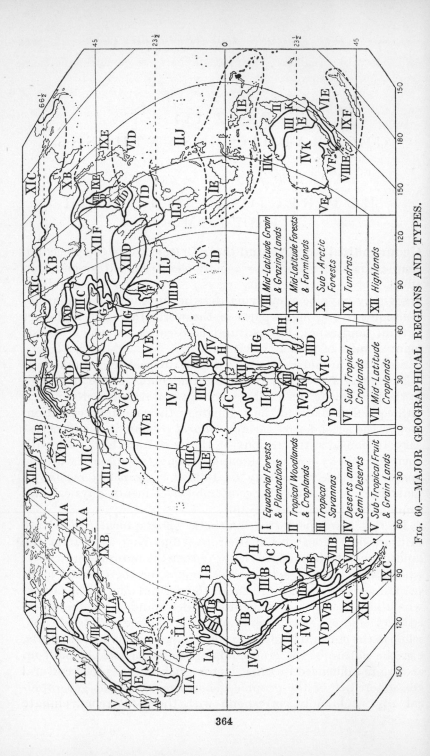

FIG. 60.—MAJOR GEOGRAPHICAL REGIONS AND TYPES.

I Equatorial Forests & Plantations
II Tropical Woodlands & Croplands
III Tropical Savannas
IV Deserts and Semi-Deserts
V Sub-Tropical Fruit & Grain Lands
VI Sub-Tropical Croplands
VII Mid-Latitude Croplands
VIII Mid-Latitude Grain & Grazing Lands
IX Mid-Latitude Forests & Farmlands
X Sub-Arctic Forests
XI Tundras
XII Highlands

and vegetation regions of the world, there are certain deviations from this correspondence.

The map in Fig. 60 is the result of such a synthetic demarcation of the major geographical regions. Like the climate regions, they fall into certain groups or types ; on the map the types are indicated by numbers, the individual regions being distinguished by appended letters. It should be noted that the geographical regions and their types are arranged in a marked pattern over the world.

To state all the features of each type would involve a repetition of facts already given, but this may be partially avoided by a two-fold arrangement : (1) A brief description of the landscapes which are characteristic of the respective regions, with a note indicating to what extent the natural landscapes have been modified by the activities of the people ; (2) A short study of a particular district representing each type of region to show how man adapts himself and his work to the seasonal changes which occur in nature during the course of the year. This study should bring out the characteristic annual *rhythms* in each type of region : i.e. time-sequences of the geographical phenomena.

I. Equatorial Forest and Plantation Regions.—These regions mostly lie within about 10 degrees of the Equator. The outstanding characteristic of the natural landscapes is the dense, evergreen forest which, as a whole, shows little change throughout the year, though particular varieties of trees have their own seasons of leafage, fruiting, etc. The evergreen nature of the forest is related both to the slight annual variation of temperature, and also to the absence of a season of drought. While some regions of this type have an almost steady amount of precipitation during the year, others have most rain near the equinoxes with intermediate drier periods ; the African climate shown in the graphs on p. 367 is unusually dry at one of these periods. As temperatures vary little, the seasons depend upon, and frequently are named after, the rainfall conditions.

There are five major regions of this group, viz. Ia, the *American Isthmus region*, overlapping the northern and southern continents ; Ib, the *Amazon and Guiana Lowlands* ; Ic, the *Congo region* ; Id, *Ceylon* ; Ie, *Malaya and the East Indies*, including the southern part of the Philippine Islands.

Certain parts of the earth's surface with an equatorial climate (type E.H.R.) and the corresponding forest cover are so inimical to man that large areas have had their landscapes little modified; they are true equatorial forest regions. Other areas, however, such as Ceylon and Java, are naturally similar but have been so modified by cultivation or forestry that they are better regarded as equatorial plantation regions.

The *equatorial forest regions* have but few inhabitants, and these are engaged either in the primitive occupations of collecting the products of the trees, hunting and fishing, or in the simplest kind of agriculture ; some tribes combine both modes of life.

Where the seasonal changes of temperature and rainfall are slight, and where also the occupations of the people are most primitive, the mode of life does not vary greatly through the year. Among the Semang gatherers and hunters in Malaya, for example, the annual rhythms are less marked than those in the other types of geographical region. The daily rhythms are repeated with little variation save for the collecting of certain fruits, such as those of the durian tree, at their ripening period. On the other hand, where there are more marked seasons and the people depend to a certain extent on agriculture, the annual rhythms are much more definite ; these are illustrated by the following example.

Negro Collectors and Tillers of Equatorial Africa.—A few miles south of the Equator, the river Ogowe crosses the edge of the African plateau by rapids which have cut deep gorges ; thence it has a broad channel across the coastal lowland, over which it slowly meanders, joined by side streams draining many pools and lakes. Dense forest comes down to the river's edge except where village clearings have been made close to the stream ; only across the wide lower reaches of the river can one see to any distance.

For the most part, the natural landscape is but little modified. The widely scattered settlements are formed of a double row of huts constructed of wood, leaves and lianas ; behind the dwellings are small cultivated patches. From the villages a few paths lead to the main cultivated clearings and temporary camps in the forest. After the clearings have been used for two years, they are abandoned to invasion by the natural vegetation, and in a score of years have again become an almost indistinguishable part of the forest.

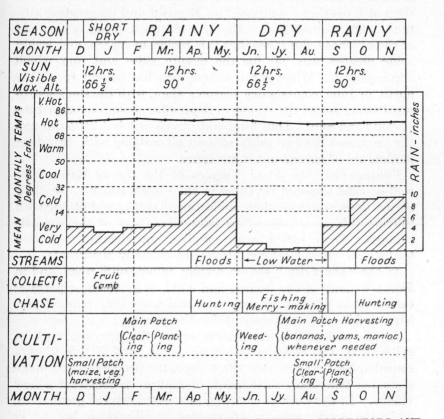

SEASON	SHORT DRY	RAINY				DRY			RAINY		
MONTH	D	J	F	Mr.	Ap.	My.	Jn.	Jy.	Au.	S	O	N

FIG. 61.—RHYTHMS IN AN EQUATORIAL FOREST : COLLECTORS AND TILLERS OF EQUATORIAL AFRICA.

Note.—(1) To assist comparison between the climatic conditions shown in this series of rhythm graphs, the temperature curves and the rainfall columns are printed on the same scale in all the diagrams. (2) At the Equator, at the December solstice the midday sun is $66\frac{1}{4}°$ above the south horizon, at the March equinox it is overhead, at the June solstice it has moved to a position $66\frac{1}{4}°$ above the north horizon, and by the September equinox it has returned to its overhead position.

The seasonal rhythms depend fundamentally upon the course of the sun. With the daytime always lasting twelve hours, the altitude of the midday sun is the dominant factor. In December the sun is overhead south of the Equator and its greatest altitude is 66½ degrees S. ; with the northward swing of the belt of the overhead sun it reaches this region in March, and would bring greater heat but for the cloudy skies and rain which accompany it. When the overhead sun has passed far to the north, in June, comes a dry season ; then, with the sun's southward swing across the region in September, comes another time of cloud and rain. Thus temperatures change but little through the year, and the two rainy seasons alternating with two drier periods are of paramount importance.

Consequently the Fang Negroes of the Ogowe Basin have well-marked seasonal rhythms in their work and life, for their occupations, which combine collecting, hunting and fishing with shifting tillage, are timed to take advantage of the climatic changes. Their varied work involves considerable migration to districts where local conditions are specially favourable.

In the " short dry " season certain edible fruits ripen, and in January many of the women and children go to those parts of the forest in which they may best find what they require, perhaps making an encampment for the purpose.

At the end of this dry season comes the heaviest work of cultivation, viz. clearing the main patch, and if this is at a considerable distance from the village, the people have to make a smaller temporary settlement, or may even construct a new village. In the work of clearing, men cut down the great trees, while the smaller growths are cleared by all and are burnt ; in the ash-strewn soil the women plant yams, manioc and bananas. When the equinoctial season of heavy rains has developed, the lowland streams and lakes flood wide expanses, and the forest animals are trapped on islands of dry ground ; this gives opportunity for the men to go on hunting expeditions. During this rainy season cultivation is impossible, but there is a rapid growth of all kinds of plant life and at the close the women must weed the clearings.

The succeeding dry season means low water ; shallow streams show patches of sand and mud, and lakes and ponds are cut off from the rivers. Now is the opportunity for trapping fish and there is again a migration to suitable spots, almost all the people going to cleared encampments. As the sun is now north of the Equator and the temperatures are somewhat lower, the weather encourages a time of merry-making ; especially in the evenings there are feastings, dancing, singing, and the telling of folk-tales.

Before the second rainy season there is a return to agricultural work. During the dry weather the products of the main patch have ripened, and from now onward the yield of manioc, yams and bananas is gathered whenever it is needed ; storage is generally unnecessary. The gathering and preparation of the food is the work of the women, and the men later utilize the floods of the rainy season for more hunting trips.

Meanwhile, at the beginning of this second rainy period, the smaller patches are cleared and planted with vegetables and maize ; these ripen when the short dry season sets in and are then harvested. Thus the calendar of these people who combine tillage with the simpler modes of life shows definite rhythms even in the equatorial regions where many of the natural changes are less marked than elsewhere in the world.

Equatorial Plantation Regions.—In three main areas the dense evergreen forest has been to a considerable extent cleared for cultivation and the landscapes differ in appearance according to the work of the people as well as to natural conditions. The Guiana coast-lands in region Ib are utilized for plantations of sugar-cane. In Ceylon (Id) there are tea and rubber plantations, while a greater area is cultivated by native farmers for rice and coconuts. In Malaya, Java and elsewhere in the East Indies, the plantations yield sugar, tea, coffee and rubber.

Because plantation production is itself for export, while it usually requires considerable imports, commerce has developed in these regions, ports have grown up and subsidiary occupations may also be carried on. Hence relatively large populations have congregated around some of the ports, and their neighbourhoods have become built-up areas where the landscapes are definitely of the cultural type.

Since the plantations aim at obtaining one commodity, the rhythm of cultivation varies according to the particular kind of production. For example, sugar-growing needs a fairly dry season for the ripening of the cane, and this is followed by a period of intense activity in cutting, carrying and crushing the cane, the boiling down of the juice, and in some cases the refining of the sugar. In the case of rubber, on the contrary, because a dry season would interrupt the flow of the latex a more continuous rainfall is desired ; this allows continuous tapping of the trees, followed by coagulating the latex and exporting the rubber ; indeed, these operations may depend on the world-price of rubber, production being increased when there is a prospect of profit and checked when prices and profits decline.

II. Tropical Woodlands and Crop-lands.—On the northern and southern sides of the equatorial forest regions are found regions of the tropical, rainy-summer type, characterized by high temperatures and by abundant precipitation during a long season, alternating with a shorter one with little rainfall. The natural vegetation varies from forests as dense as those of many equatorial areas, through forests or jungles of less luxuriance, to lighter woodlands and even to growths of thorny scrub. Moreover, the precipitation is generally sufficient for the growing of a number of crops and the planting of useful trees. Consequently, cultivation may support a moderate, or even a great, number of people, and since some of the products are the basis of trade, centres of commerce have grown up in suitable situations. In certain cases, too, considerable industries have been established. Hence, over some areas the natural landscapes have been completely transformed into those of the cultural type.

These various regions, marked by great heat and a long season of heavy rain, tree growth, and at least the possibility of agriculture on a considerable scale, are grouped as Tropical Woodlands and Crop-lands.

In the western hemisphere, the Tropical Woodlands and Crop-lands include the region here named *Central America— Caribbean* (IIa) because it consists of the Central American States on the mainland between North and South America, and of the coastal districts and islands bordering the Caribbean Sea ; in this region the plantations of the West Indies may be specially mentioned. In South America, the *Guiana Highlands* (IIb) are almost uninhabited and the natural landscapes remain virtually unchanged by man. The *Uplands and Coast-lands of Eastern Brazil* (IIc) have been considerably developed in the cooler southern coast-lands, where the plantations are specially renowned for their coffee and the port of Rio de Janeiro is noteworthy. The *Chaco region* (IId) includes various kinds of natural vegetation and there has been little utilization by man.

In Africa, there are two regions of this group, viz. the *Southern part of West Africa* (IIe) and the *East African Coast-lands* (IIg), in both of which forests and woodlands have been considerably changed by plantations in the more easily accessible districts near the sea. The extensive area which may be called the *Angola-Zambezi region* (IIf) is but little utilized and scantily populated. *Eastern Madagascar* (IIh) comprises the larger, better-watered and more developed part of the island.

The great region of the *Southern Monsoon Lands* (IIj), including the greater part of the Philippine Islands, differs essentially from the other regions of this group, because large parts of it have been the homes of civilizations which date back thousands of years. There are still areas of dense forest and jungle, but both in India and in China much of the land has been so thoroughly used that the landscapes are cultural rather than natural. There are many types and many degrees of land utilization : for subsistence agriculture and for commercial cultivation ; for industries and for commerce ; for villages, towns and means of communication. The most productive and the most developed districts are densely populated, and some of the largest cities in the world have grown up on the rivers and by the ocean.

By contrast, the *North-eastern Coast-lands of Australia* (IIk) have few people and little production ; in the cooler south-east is the small plantation area which is of exceptional character as it is worked in conformity with the " White Australia " policy.

The following account of rhythms observed in the Tropical Woodlands and Crop-lands is taken from the *West African Region* (IIe), intermediate in its state of development between the more advanced and less advanced regions of this group.

Yam Growers of Southern Nigeria.—Just beyond the limit of the dense equatorial forest, much of the low African plateau has been utilized for growing yams and other crops. The Negro cultivators whose work is here described live in large permanent villages from which many paths radiate outwards some miles to the boundaries of their territory. On either side of the paths are the patches of farmed ground, those of each household being fairly close to one another ; of these patches, one out of every

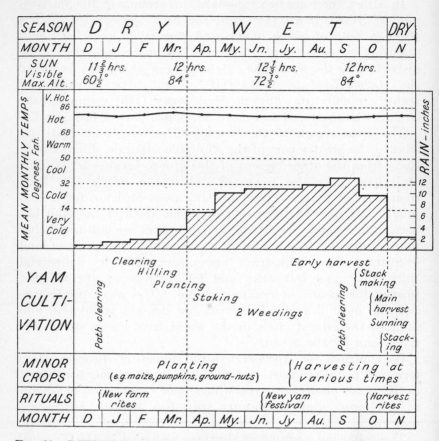

FIG. 62.—RHYTHMS IN A TROPICAL CROP-LAND : YAM GROWERS OF
SOUTHERN NIGERIA—LAT. 6° N.

Note.—The midday sun is 60½° above the south horizon at the December solstice, and 84° above the
south horizon at the March equinox ; at the June solstice its northward course has taken it to a position
72½° above the north horizon, and by the September equinox its southward course has again brought it to
84° above the south horizon.

five is cultivated in a given year and then for four years it is left to become covered with a growth of bush. The farming is thus of the fixed type with a long period of fallow between each crop. Between the paths and behind the cultivated patches are " islands " of natural tropical forest.

With the double swing of the overhead sun across this almost equatorial region, first northward and then southward, the sun is always high at midday even when not overhead. During the season when most of the northern hemisphere has its summer, there is here no marked increase of temperature because of the heavy rainfall, which lasts for more than half the year, from April till October ; the rest of the year is dry and often sunny. It is to this simple climatic rhythm of one wet and one dry season that the Negroes adapt their work ; this also is fairly simple, for it is mainly the growing of yams.

The farming year begins near the middle of the dry season with the clearing of the paths now overgrown ; this is done by parties of men who are related to one another working in co-operation, as they do also in the next task of clearing the farm patches. Before the cultivation of the plots, the priests must perform rites to ensure their fruitfulness. Then, towards the close of the dry season, the soil is hoed up by the women into mounds, or " yam hills," in which small yam tubers are planted. A few minor crops, including pumpkins, maize, ground-nuts and beans, are also planted at about the same time. These give a change from, or a relish to, the yams ; even with this help the diet is so limited that the people may suffer from malnutrition.

As the rainy season advances, the fast-growing yams have to be staked, and later the women must twice weed the patches belonging to their household. Some of the minor crops may be ready for harvesting soon after the middle of the rainy season, but others not until they ripen in the drier weather. Early-ripening yams become available as food well before the main crop, but none may be taken until after the rites of the " new yam " festival have been held and thought to have made the harvest safe. In fact, the climate is not subject to such variation that crop failures and famines are a serious menace.

At the close of the rainy season come the preparations for the main harvest : paths have again to be cleared, and wood-and-cane frameworks, twice the height of a man and about two or three hundred yards in length, have to be built for stacking the yams.   With the dry season comes the heavy work of digging, done by all; then the women wash the yams in streams and dry them in the sun, after which the men tie each yam, about the size and shape of a slender melon, separately on the framework of the stack.   A " harvest thanksgiving " forms the third great village ritual of the year.

Wild products of the forest are also utilized, especially the oil palms.   Some of these are the property of individual farmers and are tapped by their owners to get the sap from which wine is fermented ; others are the common property of a related group of people, and their fruits are gathered to obtain the kernels and oil.   These latter products are sold in towns in exchange for European goods and money.   Hunting is a minor occupation, and domestic animals, chiefly goats and chickens, also make a small addition to the food supply.

III. Tropical Savannas.—The second group of the tropical, rainy-summer regions is that in which from about April to September there is a season with a moderate amount of precipitation causing a minor drop in temperature, followed by a period of long and marked drought.   In consequence the land has relatively little tree growth and grasses are the main constituent of the vegetation cover.   On the natural pastures of the savannas, the wild life now tends to give place to cattle and other recently introduced animals.   Pastoral work, either for subsistence or for the market, is the main occupation of the scanty population, for many forms of cultivation are handicapped for lack of water.

The *Llanos of the Orinoco Basin* (IIIa), the *Campos* (IIIb) on the other side of the Equator in South America, and the *Interior of North-eastern Australia* (IIIe) represent the Savanna Regions where the population is scanty and where the landscapes have as yet been but little modified.   *Western Madagascar* (IIId) has long been occupied by tribes from across the ocean with a wider knowledge of utilizing the possibilities of the region, and as a result of recent developments production has become greater and more diversified.

The greatest advance, however, is shown in the *Sudanese Savannas* (IIIc) north of the Equator in Africa.   These lands have been the scene of repeated immigration by peoples from the north and east, who introduced the arts of cultivation in addition to domesticating animals, and also simple crafts and the organization of trade ; here, therefore, the populations are larger, human activities play a greater part in the region and the cultural elements in the landscapes are considerable. This region is the scene of the following account of geographical rhythms as they are observed in a savanna region a few hundred miles north of the forest area studied in the preceding section.

Pastoral and Agricultural Tribes of Northern Nigeria.—Here, in the broad zone of tropical grassland which stretches through the northern Sudan, is an expanse of fairly level country, varied by some upland areas and by some river valleys cut below the general elevation. The rainfall is such that both pastoral and agricultural work can be carried on, and as a rule some tribes are nomadic and live on the produce of their stock, while others are sedentary cultivators. The appearance of the landscape changes markedly with the seasons.

When the sun is on the opposite side of the Equator, there is the dry and less hot season (see p. 376) ; in December the sun rises at noon only to about 54 degrees and the length of the day is about 11⅓ hours ; the mean temperature is a little over 70° F. The north-east trade-wind blows from the Sahara ; it is known as the Harmattan and is dry and dusty ; the tall grasses die, the leaves fall from the acacias, baobabs and other occasional trees, and the landscapes seem almost barren. The only water-supply is from the larger streams or from wells.

The Fula and other pastoral nomads must now take their cattle to the shores of Lake Chad, to the river valleys, or to exceptional patches which have moister soils and longer periods when pasture is available. They may also take with them animals belonging to the sedentary tribes—a service for which agricultural produce is exchanged. The nomads live mainly, however, on the fresh or sour milk of their cattle.

Meanwhile, during the drought the cultivators, Hausas and others, have been employed in harvesting, threshing and storing their grain ; in the latter part of the dry season they clear the ground for new fields, burning such growths as trunks of scattered trees or thorny shrubs and strewing the ash over the soil. New land for tillage is required by the extensive system of agriculture, for after about three or more seasons the old fields have lost their fertility and must lie fallow for a number of years. During the three years there may be a rotation of crops, but efficient manuring is not common. There is ample room for

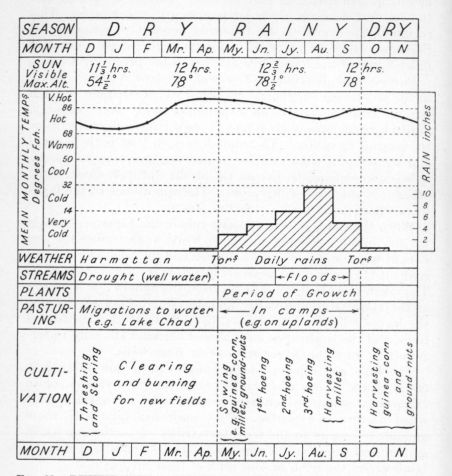

FIG. 63.—RHYTHMS IN A SAVANNA REGION : PASTORAL AND AGRI-
CULTURAL PEOPLES OF NORTHERN NIGERIA—LAT. 12° N.

Note.—At the December solstice the midday sun is 54½° above the south horizon, and at the March and
September equinoxes it is 78° above the south horizon, but at the June solstice its northward course has
taken it to a position 78½° above the north horizon.

new cultivated patches without shifting the villages. These are composed of huts of various forms, a common type being a circular construction of dried or baked mud, protected from rain by a domed or conical roof thatched with Guinea-corn stalks or grass.

After the March equinox, the sun comes north to this region and the heat becomes very great indeed for a month or two. Then tornadoes cross the country, at first bringing only dust storms but later rain storms ; these herald the approach of the season of heavy rains when almost daily downpours occur. At its height, the rainfall and the cloud reduce insolation so that the temperatures fall.

The rainy season establishes itself in May ; the landscapes become green, the grasses rapidly grow to more than the height of a man and the trees put forth their leaves. The small streams fill, and in the latter part of the season the rivers roll in floods.

The pastures are abundant and the herds return ; in some parts they may even be sent to the drier upland areas. The nomads live in semi-permanent encampments, their huts enclosed within a hedge of thorns. At night the cattle are taken within the enclosure, and by day they must be watched, to prevent them damaging the crops of the agriculturists.

For the cultivators the rainy season, i.e. the growing period, is a busy time. In the first weeks the grain is sown, and later on repeated and careful hoeings are necessary. Guinea-corn is the most widely grown cereal, and in the drier areas with it is often sown " bulrush millet " ; from these is made a porridge which forms the staple food of these people. Ground-nuts, often known as pea-nuts or monkey-nuts, are commonly grown both as a foodstuff and for the oil. Peas and maize are less cultivated, and also tobacco ; on the heavier soils cotton is now produced to an increasing extent.

The farming is largely carried on by the family as a unit, women sharing in much of it except the heavier tasks of hoeing and reaping, but when time presses, kinsmen join in co-operative labour. The millet is ready for reaping before the rains cease, and it gives an early food supply. The end, like the beginning, of the rainy season is marked by the occurrence of tornadoes.

The fine weather of the succeeding dry season ripens most of the crops, and first Guinea-corn and then ground-nuts become available. Ceremonies accompany the eating of the first-fruits of each harvest, and rituals commonly precede the clearing of the new fields when the harvests are completed. In the marginal areas towards the semi-deserts, the variability of the rainfall is a serious menace to the farmer, and the due observance of fertility-rites is regarded as a matter of the greatest importance.

IV. Deserts and Semi-deserts.—Stretching along both the Tropics, except where the sea-winds bring rain, and also extending into the interior of continental masses in higher latitudes, are regions of almost constant drought. Without continuous vegetation cover, scattered plant growth gives sustenance to very little animal life ; man has great difficulty in living in these areas, and the typical landscapes have a rocky, stony or sandy aspect. Across the arid regions some trading can be carried on, nomads lead their flocks from one patch of poor pasture to another, or pastoral work may pivot upon some favourable spot, but almost the only places where a completely settled life is possible are either mining camps or where water is found underground or in rivers which penetrate the barren wastes from other regions. Hence, apart from the exploitation of mineral resources (doomed to ultimate extinction), irrigation is the principal basis of man's life in the deserts, and differences in the nature and use of the water-supply are the main reasons for the differences between the several regions of this group.

These may be listed as follows : IVa, the *Californian Gulf Region*, by the western coast of North America ; IVb, the *Lower Rio Grande Region*, on the east side of the Cordillera ; IVc, the *Peru-Atacama Desert*, by the west coast of South America ; IVd, the *Desert of Western Argentina*, on the east side of the Andean Cordillera ; IVe, the *Saharan-Arabian Deserts*, and IVf, their extension in *Arid North-western India* ; IVg, the *Caspian-Turkistan Desert*, in the heart of Eurasia ; IVh, the *Somali Desert* (which includes more of eastern Africa than the political territory of Somaliland) ; IVj, *Arid South-west Africa* ; IVk, *North-western and Central Australia*.

In the desert and semi-desert regions, it is the river valleys with an oasis type of cultivation that have been the most significant from the human aspect, and in these the geographical rhythms are highly developed. Therefore an irrigated area in Lower Egypt is selected for a special study.

Fellahin of the Nile Delta.—In one sense it is true that " Egypt is the gift of the Nile," but man has changed the gift almost out of recognition. Instead of the mud-flats of the Delta, at flood season covered with water but for most of the year showing vast expanses of dried and cracked clay or stretches of sand deposited by the river or the sea, there is now a densely populated, fertile plain over which the water of the Nile is so distributed that throughout the year the ground yields its crops and irrigated Egypt has become " a green land."

The landscape is almost entirely a cultural one ; the slight relief of the land consists of little more than the banks of the river channels—banks formed by the streams but strengthened to prevent break-through or overflow—together with lower banks of innumerable canals which afford perennial irrigation for most of the surface. Above the normal flood-level rise small " islands " of land which frequently show up because of the villages which are crowded upon them and because of the trees which have been planted near the houses.

Most of the Egyptian peasants, the fellahin, live in large villages formed by low, clay-built houses which also shelter their animals. From the villages go out each day thousands of men, women and children to work in the fields with almost unremitting labour. Much of the work is done by the hoe, though buffaloes and donkeys are used for ploughing and harrowing.

By the Islamic law, a man's land is divided among his children and hence the holdings have become extremely small ; two-thirds of the fellahin have plots amounting in all to less than one acre. On the other hand, a few rich men have managed to acquire very large estates, worked at a miserable wage by landless peasants or by those whose holdings are too small to support their families. Pressure upon the cultivable space, together with the possibility of irrigating the land at any period, has led to the almost invariable system of two harvests each year. The crops are arranged to follow each other on the same plots so as to form a two- or three-year rotation, and the land seldom lies fallow.

The rhythm graph shows that in winter occurs the very slight rainfall, but this is of no value to agriculture. Far more important is the fact that the temperatures of this season are warm enough for the growth of a number of crops. One of

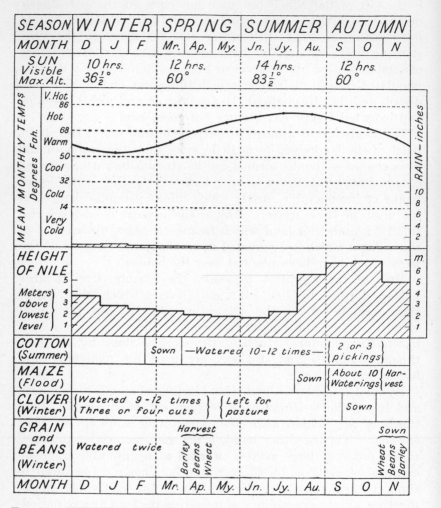

SEASON	WINTER			SPRING			SUMMER			AUTUMN		
MONTH	D	J	F	Mr.	Ap.	My.	Jn.	Jy.	Au.	S	O	N
SUN Visible Max. Alt.	10 hrs. 36½°			12 hrs. 60°			14 hrs. 83½°			12 hrs. 60°		
MEAN MONTHLY TEMPS. Degrees Fah. — V. Hot 86 / Hot 68 / Warm 50 / Cool 32 / Cold 14 / Very Cold											RAIN — inches 10 8 6 4 2		
HEIGHT OF NILE Meters above lowest level — 5 4 3 2 1											m. 6 5 4 3 2 1		
COTTON (Summer)				Sown	—Watered 10–12 times—					{ 2 or 3 } { pickings }		
MAIZE (Flood)									Sown	About 10 { Waterings }	Har-vest	
CLOVER (Winter)	{ Watered 9–12 times } { Three or four cuts }				{ Left for } { pasture }					Sown		
GRAIN and BEANS (Winter)	Watered twice			Harvest Barley Beans Wheat						Sown Wheat Beans Barley		
MONTH	D	J	F	Mr.	Ap.	My.	Jn.	Jy.	Au.	S	O	N

FIG. 64.—RHYTHMS UNDER PERENNIAL IRRIGATION : FELLAHIN OF
THE NILE DELTA—LAT. 30° N.

Note.—At this place, and at all other places between the Tropic of Cancer and the Arctic circle, the midday
sun is always above the south horizon.

these is clover which, besides providing food for the animals, contributes to the fertility of the soil on which such heavy demands are made. The clover is sown in autumn that it may be ready for growing through the winter and early spring ; during this period it is cut three or four times and needs frequent watering. While the Nile is low, a barrage near Cairo diverts the water from the main branches of the river, which becomes almost dry, to the smaller channels and the countless irrigation canals and ditches. From these the water is raised to the fields by men using shadufs, by buffaloes or donkeys turning water-wheels or, to an increasing extent, by pumps worked by engines and belonging to companies which charge for this supply. Wheat also is grown in the winter, as a cash-crop to be sold to foreigners in Egypt or abroad, and smaller amounts of barley and beans for home use ; these crops, of course, have to be watered, though much less than the clover.

The spring is marked by a rapid rise of temperature, frequently intensified by the Khamsin wind from the south which brings burning air from the desert laden with so much dust that it may even obscure the sun. In this season the clover is cut for the last time, and the winter grain and beans are harvested.

Yet even earlier, preparations are made for the summer crops, by far the most important being cotton, which is sown in early spring as it needs a long period for growth and ripening. As summer advances, the midday sun climbs nearly to the zenith and the trade-winds blow steadily from the north-east. The heat becomes great, and transpiration from the plants is so rapid that very large quantities of water must be put upon the fields. At the end of the summer the first cotton bolls open, and the heavy work of picking is then begun, to be repeated over a period of several weeks until the plants are completely stripped. The prosperity of all Egypt depends largely upon the cotton, but its success may be endangered by cotton-worm and boll-worm pests and also by fluctuations of market price. Rice is another summer crop, grown on much smaller areas.

Overlapping the work on the summer crops is that of the third farming period of the year, viz. the " flood season." This depends upon the summer rains in Abyssinia, and in Lower Egypt it lasts from the late summer over the whole of the autumn. At this season the high water-level in the rivers and canals allows the water to be distributed over the fields without

being raised by mechanical means. The land now gets the
" red water," so named because of its reddish-brown colour
due to the load of fertilizing silt containing valuable chemical
compounds, coarser sand which improves the physical conditions of the soil, and bacteria, also of great importance. The
chief crop of the flood season is maize, which forms the main
food-supply of the Egyptian people, its leaves affording fodder
for the animals and the tall stems being used as fuel. The
maize does not require so long a time of growth as the cotton,
but it needs to be watered about as many times, and the flood
season is a busy one.

It must be remembered, too, that because of the quick and
overlapping succession of a number of crops there is at all times
of the year much work to be done, including the threshing of
the cereals and the packing of the cotton after the harvests.
Hence in this region, with almost continuous heat and a supply
of water always available, there is a possibility of constant
activity, and this is enforced upon the fellahin by the great
density of the population and the consequent poverty of the
great majority of the people.

CHAPTER XXIII

WARM REGIONS AND THEIR
RHYTHMS

V. Sub-tropical Fruit- and Grain-lands.—The regions
which are situated outside the tropics on the western sides
of land-masses and consequently have the " Mediterranean "
type of climate, with rain in the warm winters and drought in
the hot summers, are six in number : viz. Va, *Central California* ;
Vb, *Central Chile* ; Vc, the *Mediterranean Lands,* which include
Portugal on the Atlantic coast and part of the shores of the
Black Sea ; Vd, the *" Cape Region "* of *South Africa* ; Ve,
South-western Australia ; Vf, the *" Adelaide Region "* of *Australia.*

The regions of this group were in large part clothed with
woods or scrub with thick-skinned evergreen leaves, but they
have by now lost much of their natural vegetation. Those
hard-leaved trees which are economically valuable, e.g. the
olive and the cork oak, remain in their original homes and also
have been transplanted to other lands of the same group, and
the same is true of the vine which, although deciduous, is
native to the Mediterranean area. In addition, cultivated
plants, notably citrus fruit trees, have been brought from
regions with other types of climate. Certain grain crops,
especially wheat, are also valuable products of the Mediterranean
type of region. Hence the term " fruit- and grain-lands " may
suitably indicate the dominant, though by no means the only,
forms of cultivation.

To supplement the natural water-supply, irrigation, which has
long been practised in the lands around the Mediterranean Sea,
is now adopted in all regions of this group. Moreover, their
coastal position facilitates commerce in the surplus products,
and as various other occupations have been added to agriculture,
moderately dense populations are the rule. Great cities have
grown up as ports and as centres of government.

Large parts of these regions are situated where mountains or

383

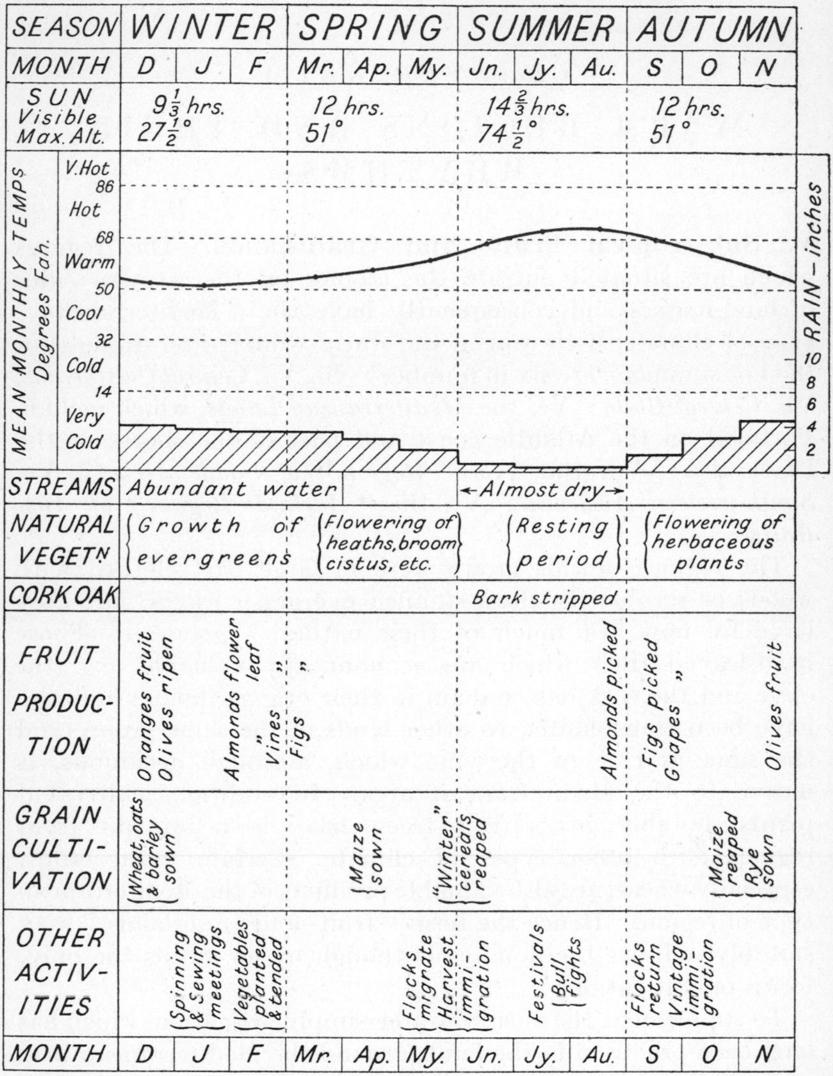

SEASON	WINTER			SPRING			SUMMER			AUTUMN		
MONTH	D	J	F	Mr.	Ap.	My.	Jn.	Jy.	Au.	S	O	N
SUN Visible Max. Alt.	$9\frac{1}{3}$ hrs. $27\frac{1}{2}°$			12 hrs. 51°			$14\frac{2}{3}$ hrs. $74\frac{1}{2}°$			12 hrs. 51°		

MEAN MONTHLY TEMPS Degrees Fah. — V.Hot 86 / Hot 68 / Warm 50 / Cool 32 / Cold 14 / Very Cold

RAIN—inches — 10 8 6 4 2

STREAMS	Abundant water					←Almost dry→						
NATURAL VEGETN	(Growth of evergreens)			(Flowering of heaths, broom cistus, etc.)			(Resting period)			(Flowering of herbaceous plants)		
CORK OAK							Bark stripped					
FRUIT PRODUC- TION	Oranges fruit / Olives ripen	Almonds flower / leaf / Vines " / Figs "							Almonds picked	Figs picked / Grapes "	Olives fruit	
GRAIN CULTI- VATION	Wheat, oats & barley sown			Maize sown		"Winter" cereals reaped				Maize reaped / Rye sown		
OTHER ACTIV- ITIES	Spinning & Sewing meetings	Vegetables planted & tended			Flocks migrate / Harvest / immi- gration		Festivals / Bull fights			Flocks return / Vintage immi- gration		
MONTH	D	J	F	Mr.	Ap.	My.	Jn.	Jy.	Au.	S	O	N

Fig. 65.—RHYTHMS IN A SUB-TROPICAL FRUIT- AND GRAIN-LAND: FRUIT AND GRAIN GROWERS OF PORTUGAL—Lat. 39° N.

plateaus descend to the sea, and the country-sides show marked relief ; the slopes are frequently terraced, and in many respects the landscapes have assumed cultural aspects. The seasonal rhythms of a region of this type are illustrated by considering those experienced in the European area near Lisbon.

Fruit and Grain Growers of Portugal.—The district is not far from the Atlantic Ocean ; it is hilly, and the rainfall is sufficient to allow a considerable variety in the vegetation. Cultivation has spread over practically all the lowland areas and up the lower slopes of the hills. Vineyards and olive-yards occupy considerable areas, and below the olive trees are planted cereals and vegetables. The slopes are terraced, and water is frequently led down by ditches from terrace to terrace to supplement the rainfall. Small-holdings are the rule, and intensive hoe cultivation supports a moderately dense agricultural population. The people live in small houses, grouped into hamlets or villages often perched on hilltops or ridges. Along the roads and by the houses eucalyptus trees have been planted, and there are many orchards of fruit trees.

Above the level of cultivation, the uplands bear zones of woodland and small areas of pasture ; the cork-oak and the evergreen-oak are common, and at higher levels pines are characteristic. On the poorer upland soils, especially on limestone areas which are too dry for trees, are evergreen thickets of the maquis type composed of bush-like plants such as heaths, juniper and myrtle. Still poorer " garrigue " growths, often thorny and aromatic, and including broom, sage, thyme and cistus, form a scanty cover to stony soil.

In this latitude, at mid-winter the day lasts about 9 hours and the sun rises only to about 27 degrees above the horizon ; nevertheless, the prevailing westerly winds keep the mean temperature above 50° F. The travelling " lows " of winter give an adequate amount of rain, and the natural vegetation continues its growth with little change in its appearance. Visible alterations in the landscape are provided by the cultural elements, for at the beginning of the winter men sow the grain, chiefly wheat, oats and barley, the fruit appears upon the orange trees and the olives begin to mature. The oranges and olives are picked as they ripen during the winter ; the oranges are sent abroad, and the olives either stored for eating or pressed for oil.

In the winter there is little field-work, and in the villages the women collect to work at their spinning and sewing, while in the evenings the men may join them for dancing. Towards the end of the winter, farming is resumed ; vegetables are planted and have to be tended until they are pulled or dug at various times during the spring and summer. Almond trees put forth their blossoms and as spring approaches vine shoots become green and leaves appear upon the fig trees.

Spring is the season when the greatest change is seen in the natural vegetation. While there is still a fair rainfall, with the rising temperatures the evergreen plants of the maquis and garrigue blossom and may make the dull-looking landscape bright for a short time. In the same season, the people hoe up the maize plots and sow the seed for its summer growth. Also, the animals are sent up to the higher lands for the coming hot season ; the flocks consist mainly of sheep and goats which can feed on the poor pastures or on the shrubs of the maquis and garrigues. Then, at the end of spring, the winter cereals ripen and are reaped. This work is more than can be carried out in the time available by the villagers, and there is an immigration from the uplands which are less productive and have a surplus of labour ; the migrant workers come in large bands, set up encampments, rapidly complete the harvest in each district and move on to the next.

During the summer, the high temperatures and very slight rainfall cause a drought which checks the growth of almost all vegetation except those cultivated plants, chiefly maize and vegetables, which have water supplied to them by irrigation. The evergreen trees and shrubs have a dull, lifeless look, and when the sap is no longer rising in the cork-oaks the bark can be safely stripped from them—an operation which is carried out every nine or ten years. As the fruits of the cultivated trees are not yet ready for gathering, there is less work and the peasants can take a welcome break, the " sesta " (" siesta " in Spain), for a couple of hours in the midday heat. Now, too, is a convenient time for the holding of religious and social festivals, and in some parts of Portugal bull-fights are organized.

After the first autumn rains, there is a renewal of plant and human activity. There is a " second spring " in the flowering of the herbaceous wild plants, e.g. anemones, crocuses, asphodels and narcissi. Young grasses also spring up and give a tinge of green to the ground, and the animals may now return to the lowlands.   Almonds and figs are picked, and then comes the gathering of the grapes ; where vineyards are most extensive the vintage needs so much labour that there is a second immigration of workers from the uplands.   Next, the maize is reaped and the autumn closes with the sowing of rye, the first of the winter cereals, while the fruit begins to form upon the olive trees.

VI. Sub-tropical Crop-lands.—In about the same latitudes as the sub-tropical fruit- and grain-lands, but on the opposite side of the continents, are the sub-tropical crop-lands which have more rainfall and receive the greater part of it in the summer.   The regions of this group are in the main identical with the climate regions of the sub-tropical, rainy-summer type ; they comprise : VIa, the *South-eastern United States*, commonly known as the " Southern States " in North America ; VIb, the *South Brazil–North Uruguay Region*, so termed because most of it overlaps those two States of South America ; VIc, the *South-east African Coastlands*, in Natal and part of the Cape Province ; VId, the *Central China–South Japan Region*, including the southern part of Korea ; VIe, the *New South Wales Coastlands*, reaching into the southernmost corner of Queensland.

The term " crop-lands " has been applied to this group of regions for two reasons : (i) it suggests that in general the natural conditions are thoroughly utilized or even transformed for farming ; (ii) it implies that the production is not distinguished by one or two special forms as in the case of the " sub-tropical fruit- and grain-lands," but is so varied that the general term of " crop-lands " is most suitable—provided that it is realized that usually a part of the crops is for livestock.

Because the natural water-supply comes at the time when temperatures are high, many useful plants have favourable conditions.   The variety of production is therefore great, and in these regions are obtained large supplies of rice, maize and other cereals, many kinds of fruit and vegetables, tea, cotton, silk, cattle and pigs.

Except in the South American area, as yet little developed, cultivation and the keeping of livestock have extended widely over these regions, and large numbers of people have made them their homes and satisfy many of their needs directly from them ; in addition, the production is in part exported, com-

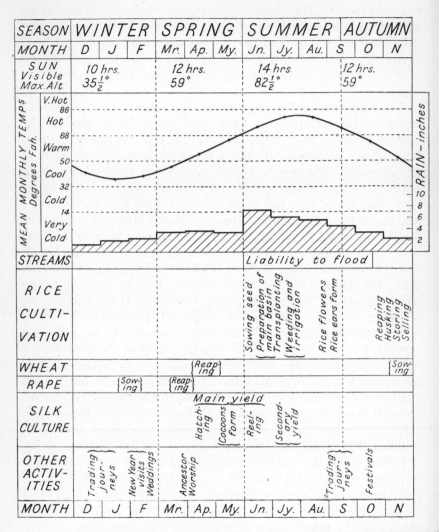

FIG. 66.—RHYTHMS IN A SUB-TROPICAL CROP-LAND : RICE GROWERS
OF CENTRAL CHINA—LAT. 31° N.

munications have been established and large commercial centres have grown up. The landscapes have thus tended to become of the cultural type ; this process has gone farthest in the Chinese area, because of its long period of civilization, and in the southern United States, where the settlement and use of the land have been carried on systematically during the past two or three centuries.

The study of geographical rhythms is taken from a region which shows an Oriental form of the development of a sub-tropical crop-land.

Rice Cultivators of Central China.—Rather more than a hundred miles west of Shanghai, the delta formed by the Yangtze Kiang and other rivers once had a landscape in which the main features were streams, some large lakes, numerous ponds and low ground covered with swamp vegetation. Long ago the country was reclaimed, and now shows a cultural landscape of farmland consisting chiefly of basins, perhaps below the level of the streams and lakes, surrounded by dykes ; on the dykes are the roads bordered by rows of mulberry trees, and the houses built of earthen bricks and thatched with straw. Another feature of the landscape is formed by the grave-mounds ; on these, grass is grown as fodder for water-buffaloes which the people keep to help in ploughing the rice-fields if their holdings are large enough.

Two essential conditions for rice cultivation are that nature must give the possibility of regulating the water-supply, and that the people must provide the considerable amount of skill and labour required. Each year the land has to be drained for the preparatory work on the soil ; then the water has to be let in and constantly maintained at the correct height or the plants would be either dried up or drowned. Water can be let into the basins from the streams when they are high, but when they are low it is pumped in by each farmer and his family working a treadmill which pulls up small wooden buckets on a continuous chain and tips the water on the plots. To drain the farm basins, a common trench runs along the deepest part of a series of plots of ground belonging to different farmers who together operate a larger drainage pump.

The farmers' year begins at the time of the Chinese New Year—February 5th of the European calendar. This is one of several festivals whose dates are fixed at times of relative

leisure ; wedding ceremonies are arranged for this period and all
the people visit their relations—a compulsory duty in this country where family ties are so important.

In spring come the first moderately heavy rains and a rapid
rise of temperature, which allows the ripening of wheat and rape,
previously sown on patches of non-irrigated land ; these crops
are reaped about the end of March and in April. The oil
from rape seed is specially valuable in a diet which lacks
animal fats. Just before the annual work of silk culture come
festival rites devoted to the worship of ancestors and to visits to
their tombs.

For many centuries silk culture has been highly esteemed in
China ; the women have the duty of looking after the silkworms, supplying them with mulberry leaves and reeling the
silk threads. Recently, however, this domestic industry has
declined, partly because factories do the work more efficiently
and partly because of the lower prices which are offered since the
use of artificial silk. Hence the money which was got from
the sale of silk has now to be obtained from other sources. In
the village whose work is here described the women rear and sell
a few sheep ; these are kept in huts close to their houses ; they
feed them in summer on grass collected by the children from
under the mulberry trees, by the streams or on burial grounds,
and in winter on dried mulberry leaves.

The main resource of the people is rice grown by each family-
group almost entirely for its own needs. The early summer
is a time when men, women and children all work to their utmost
in the various operations severally allotted to them : sowing the
seed in the " nursery beds," preparing the paddy-fields, trans-
planting the young shoots, keeping the water at the right level,
repeatedly weeding the crop and manuring it after the unwanted growths have been removed. In late summer the plants
flower and the grain forms ; while the rice ripens, many of the
farmers of this district take the opportunity to row their
boats by the small streams either to the larger rivers or even to
the coast and there to earn some money as carriers or as trading
agents. The cash thus obtained is spent on clothing and other
necessities, and perhaps on cigarettes and a very few other
luxuries.

In autumn the rice is ready for cutting ; festival rites now
usher in the labours of reaping, carrying and threshing the

paddy, husking and storing the grain, and possibly selling a part of the harvest for use in towns of the neighbourhood.

While the last of this work is being carried out, wheat or some other winter-growing crop is sown. Then during the winter itself comes a time of relative leisure ; the men may again go on trading journeys while the women have time for making good the wear and tear to clothing and to household gear.

The well-being of the people is dependent upon the regular recurrence of the climatic rhythms, especially the rainfall. In this delta region, there is no difficulty about the river having sufficient water for irrigation, but there may be a danger of heavy summer rains in upstream areas causing the flooding of the paddy-fields and even the destruction of dykes, roads and houses.

Regional Types in Mid-latitudes.—In dividing the lands of mid-latitudes into regions on a climatic basis in Chapter V, the distinction between them was in most cases made according to their rainfall, and in one group according to the length of the summer. Now that the regions are considered from the broader geographical point of view and human factors are also taken into account, the climatic boundaries will be to some extent superseded and the grouping of the regions somewhat altered.

In the " mid-latitude dry " climate regions, man has made little change in the more arid parts and these drier areas have already been dealt with among the geographical regions of the " desert and semi-desert " type. In the other mid-latitude regions, however, man's occupation and use of the land are so important that two allied criteria are taken as determining the classification of the geographical regions and their limits : (*a*) the extent to which the natural landscapes have been transformed ; (*b*) the chief types of farming, since farming is the most common and widespread work, and it is to this occupation that the cultural aspects of the landscapes are mainly due.

Thus, apart from the arid regions, a useful classification of the mid-latitude geographical regions may be made and labelled as follows : (i) " Crop-lands " in which, because of favourable climatic and other conditions, most of the land has been taken into use and a considerable variety of crops is produced ; (ii) " Grain- and grazing-lands " where, because of a smaller rainfall, farming is generally restricted either to the growing of relatively drought-resistant varieties of grain or to the grazing of animals, usually upon natural pastures ; (iii) " Forest and farmlands " where, generally, owing either to mountainous relief with heavy rainfall or to a short summer, much of the land remains under forest and the farming is limited both in the area it occupies and in the range and yield of its products.

VII. **Mid-latitude Crop-lands.**—These regions in which thorough use has been made of the land are four in number: viz. VIIa, *Central and Eastern North America* ; VIIb, the *La Plata region of South America*, including the plain of the lower Parana river ; VIIc, the *Central Belt of Europe*, stretching from the Atlantic Ocean almost to the Ural Mountains and the Caspian Sea ; VIId, *North-eastern China and the Manchurian Plain.*

In North and South America and in Asia, these crop-lands correspond in the main to the mid-latitude, rainy-summer climate regions, and in Europe to a considerable extent to the mid-latitude, rainy climate region, where cultivation found the most favourable conditions. In two continents, however, the area of crop-lands has extended notably beyond these limits : in North America it has spread northwards into the St. Lawrence lowlands and part of the Prairie region ; in Europe it has been developed in the U.S.S.R. to include both a relatively small area with the short-summer type of climate and also a larger area in that part of the light-rain climate region which is least handicapped by lack of water. These extensions beyond the optimum climatic conditions have been due to several factors : e.g. the enterprise of the peoples concerned ; the existence of means of communication facilitating the spread of farming communities and also the transport of the products of cultivation ; a local demand for food by a population attracted to special areas by other means of livelihood such as mining, manufacturing, trade and the functions of government.

A general idea of the nature and the broad-based productivity of these regions has been given in the account of mid-latitude plough farming in Chapter XV, and it will have been realized that there is a fairly dense rural population. When it is also remembered that these crop-lands are the scene of much other activity, as is indicated by the maps showing mineral workings, industrial regions and commerce, it is evident that the crop-lands include areas of exceptionally dense population and contain many of the world's greatest cities. Consequently both in town and country the landscapes have been more completely transformed than in almost any other type of region.

Yet, while there are similarities between the regions of this group, there are also differences. On the whole, the European and the North American mid-latitude crop-lands show the most marked likeness in their human aspects, in spite of the more equable temperatures in the western part of the European region. Much the same kind of production has spread over these two great regions : maize and wheat are the most widely cultivated grains ; root crops and hay are obtained as feed for cattle and other livestock ; a similar range of vegetables and fruit is grown ; crops such as tobacco, beet and flax are closely associated with industrial development. Moreover, very large deposits of coal, iron and other minerals are worked and are the basis of manufactures, while the two regions are linked by the most important ocean trade-route in the world. In both regions, too, the modes of life of the people are essentially alike, though modified in detail.

The La Plata region of South America is broadly similar to the mid latitude crop lands area of North America in its agri cultural conditions, but it lacks mineral wealth and has not had a corresponding development in industries and commerce.

The Far Eastern region of north-east China and the Manchurian Lowland has closer similarities in its climatic conditions with the North American area than with any of the others of this group, but it displays marked differences from them all in its human geography. Because its civilization developed to a considerable extent in isolation from that of Europe until quite recently, its modes of life display contrasts in many respects. To some extent its products are those of the other mid-latitude crop-lands, e.g. wheat is one of the most important grains, having been introduced from the West in very early times, and maize came from America soon after the discovery of that continent, but a great deal of land is devoted to millets and to a sorghum called kaoliang. A recent development which has brought the regions of the group into closer similarity in their farming products has been the widespread adoption from this region of the nutritious soya bean into the other mid-latitude crop-lands, especially the U.S.S.R. and the " corn belt " of the United States. In China, cattle-rearing is not important as in the remaining regions of the group, partly because of the relatively restricted area of cultivable land, and the farming is generally of a more intensive character than in the West.

Coal, iron and other minerals exist in the Asiatic region in very considerable amounts, but they have not been worked on a large scale until recently and industries based upon them are still in an early stage of development ; foreign trade likewise has not advanced as it has done in the European and North American counterparts of north-eastern China and the Manchurian Lowland. Hence in Asia the dense populations are still supported to a greater extent by the cultivation of the soil, and alternations of relative prosperity and distress are more directly due to the variability of the Monsoon system than to industrial and financial " booms and slumps " as experienced in the West.

Because of the differences between the mid-latitude crop-land regions, two studies of geographical rhythms are given, relating to northern China and western Europe respectively, but it must be pointed out that these represent somewhat extreme contrasts, and also that the tendency is for human activities to become more alike in so far as physical factors allow.

Grain Growers of North China.—On the northern side of the Tsinling Mountains, which form part of the boundary between central and northern China, is the broad valley of the Wei Ho just above its junction with the Hwang Ho. It is a generally level plain, its fertile soils formed partly from loess blown from the north-west and partly from alluvium brought down by the Wei Ho.

The climate of the Wei Ho valley differs from that of the Yangtze delta in having less rain and much colder winters ; hence the growing period of plants is restricted. The landscape therefore gives an impression of verdure only for about six months, while for the rest of the year the prevailing colour is brown. Here in northern China farming depends almost entirely upon the direct rainfall, for irrigation is but little employed, and there is a more noticeable seasonal change in the activity of men, considerably less in winter than in summer.

About three-quarters of the cultivated land produces wheat, millet, or kaoliang, which constitute the chief foodstuffs of the people, together with vegetables. Soya beans and rape are the source of fat, taking the place of butter, lard and margarine in other mid-latitude regions. Rice is rather a luxury ; so,

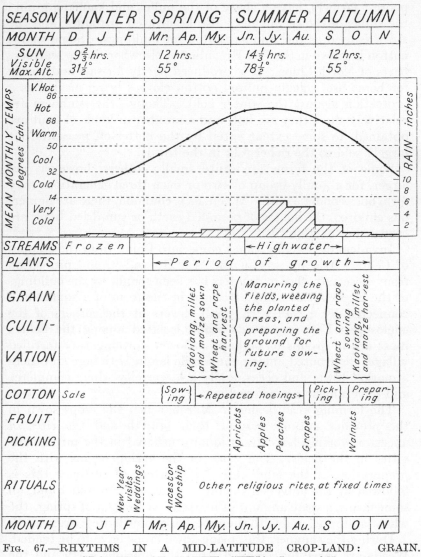

Fig. 67.—RHYTHMS IN A MID-LATITUDE CROP-LAND: GRAIN. GROWERS OF NORTH CHINA—Lat. 35° N.

too, is the meat of pigs and poultry.   The oxen, donkeys or mules, used for ploughing and drawing carts by all except the poorest farmers, have a share of the millet and kaoliang grain ; the stalks of the cereals may also be utilized as fodder, and the straw is used as fuel and as thatch for buildings.   Some coarse cotton is grown in the Wei Ho valley as elsewhere in the warmest parts of North China ; it is produced partly for sale and partly for home use, thickly quilted cotton clothes being needed as a protection against the winter cold.   Though the summers are relatively short they are hot, and a number of kinds of fruit are obtained, to some extent eaten by the better-off peasants but largely sold to the richer folk in the towns.

Some of the farms are quite small ; others, however, are larger, for a family-group of two or even three generations may form one economic unit.   When, as is common, there are numerous children, the houses of pounded earth or sun-dried brick are crowded or overcrowded.

Invaders have many times come into China from the steppes of Central Asia by way of the Wei Ho valley, and protection from these and other marauders has been sought by the buildings of the larger farms being arranged in the form of a square and connected by a wall with small towers at the corners of the enclosure.   Few farmsteads stand isolated among the fields ; most are in groups of perhaps a dozen, forming tiny fortified villages distributed among the fertile lands, with here and there a market town, and occasionally a larger city where commerce and government are centred.

The farming year begins in March, when the crops sown in the previous autumn resume their growth and the rites of ancestor worship have traditionally ushered in the men's activities in the fields.   The work of the spring begins with the preparation of the land and the planting of cotton ; this is followed by the universal sowing of kaoliang and millet and, on some farms, a small amount of maize.   At the end of spring, the wheat and rape, and with them perhaps some barley, are reaped.

During the summer, the spring-sown crops have to be tended. Weeds are carefully removed from the precious earth and the process of hoeing the cotton and thinning out the plants has to be repeated several times.   Moreover, all the cultivated ground needs to be manured to maintain its fertility under its intensive use.   Now, too, the fields which have already yielded their harvest must be got ready for the next sowing. Work is required also for the gathering of the successively maturing fruits, e.g. apricots, apples, peaches and grapes.

The autumn harvests begin in September with the repeated pickings of the cotton plants as the bolls ripen, and this is followed in October by the reaping of the millet, kaoliang and maize, and by the gathering of walnuts. Between these operations the wheat and barley are sown in good time for their early growth before the onset of winter. The last of the autumn tasks is the preparation of the cotton for sale or use —work which makes a considerable demand for labour as machinery is here little employed, in contrast to its use in the United States.

Most of the outdoor work, lasting from spring to autumn, is done by men and boys, though at the busiest times women and girls have to give their help in the fields. Winter, however, allows a considerable respite to the men ; they draw water, tend the few animals to the extent that this is necessary, and they may weave cotton or grass-cloth, yet they have leisure for meeting and gossiping and the favourite recreations of telling and listening to tales or playing on an instrument like a one-stringed violin. The women have a busier time than the men in winter ; in addition to the constant work in the house, they spin the cotton, make most of the clothes for the family and even make and mend the rope shoes.

The rhythms of life in this region are subject to interruptions which spell disaster. The monsoon rains may fail, especially in this part of China bordering the semi-arid interior of Asia, or they may come too late for the crops to ripen during the relatively brief heat of summer. On the other hand, the farms on low-lying land by the rivers may suffer from floods when exceptionally heavy rains fall on the surrounding mountains. The Wei Ho valley has on several occasions experienced an additional catastrophe—that of earthquake—for it adjoins the line of faults along which the Tsinling Mountains have been upraised ; it is recorded that this line of weakness in the earth's crust was the scene of the greatest single disaster in the history of mankind when, in 1556 A.D., 800,000 people lost their lives. Hardship and tragedy as well as a laborious life are here the price of man's occupation of the region and his acceptance of the opportunities it offers.

Industrial-crop and Livestock Farmers of Flanders.—The European region is the largest and most populous of the mid-latitude crop-land group, and one of its chief characteristics is that it has become largely industrialized. An example of a landscape and its associated rhythms is therefore selected from the Maritime Plain of French Flanders where the farming has become closely interrelated with the local industries. This district is the French tip of the polder lands of the Low Countries, overlooked by the higher area of the Franco-Belgian coalfields and manufacturing cities.

The lowland stands but a few feet above the sea, from which it is partially protected by a narrow stretch of dunes. It has been reclaimed by means of a close network of ditches and canals by which the water is drained from the land and discharged into the sea through sluice-gates in the dune-belt.

The climate is distinctly maritime, for although the total annual precipitation is not great, rain falls on nearly half the days of the year and a marked feature is the almost constant humidity of the air. It is this humidity which, in spite of the moderate annual range of temperature, makes the winters feel " raw cold " and the summers enervating. The humidity of the air is increased by evaporation from the innumerable ditches and the often wet surface of the land, and the sky is frequently grey and overcast. The level landscape has an open appearance, for there are few trees and these are low and bent towards the east by the strong sea-winds.

The soils have been developed from recent marine deposits of clays and sands, and although they are generally light in texture they need systematic draining. The ground water is always near the surface, and in winter its level rises and floods may occur. Much of the fertility of this polder land is due to man's work in draining, unusually deep ploughing and digging, and to the addition to the soil of various constituents : chalk from the adjoining uplands, animal manures, mud and vegetable matter cleared from the ditches and canals, waste from the neighbouring factories, including soot, refuse from oil-seeds, beetroots and bones.

Effective use of the soil is made by the alternation of wheat, which has relatively shallow and widespreading roots, with beet and chicory, which have long tap-roots reaching a lower level. In this district wheat has an exceptionally heavy yield,

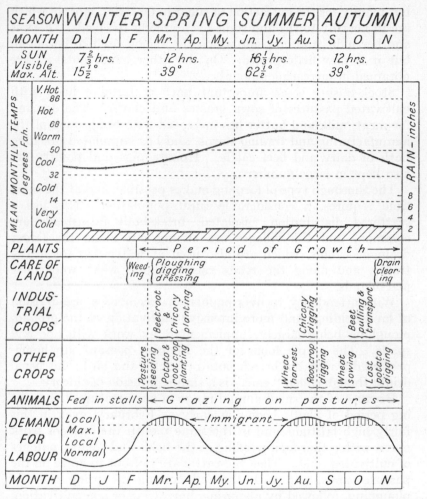

SEASON	WINTER			SPRING			SUMMER			AUTUMN		
MONTH	D	J	F	Mr.	Ap.	My.	Jn.	Jy.	Au.	S	O	N
SUN Visible Max. Alt.	7⅔ hrs. 15½°			12 hrs. 39°			16⅓ hrs. 62½°			12 hrs. 39°		

Fig. 68.—RHYTHMS IN A MID-LATITUDE CROP-LAND: INDUSTRIAL-CROP AND LIVESTOCK FARMERS OF FLANDERS—Lat. 51° N.

but its cultivation is decreasing as a result of greater demands for the products of cattle-raising. The characteristic crop of the area is beet, to some extent used for the distillation of alcohol but mainly for the extraction of sugar in factories, most of which are in near-by towns and some even among the fields. Flax is another industrial crop for which the region used to be noted, but it is now little grown. On the other hand, potatoes are obtained in increasing amounts.

Stock-raising is an important part of farming here, with cultivated pastures of sown grasses and clover. The demand for meat, milk and butter has increased with the growth of the manufacturing and trading towns, and has stimulated breeding both of dairy and beef cattle. Horses, pigs and poultry are also kept in large numbers.

The thorough type of farming makes possible, and at the same time requires, a considerable rural population. This has a scattered distribution ; isolated, brick-built farmsteads are common, and the villages are strung out along the larger drainage canals, which are also used as waterways for heavy traffic, and along the roads raised above what were once marshlands.

With a tendency to over-population occurred a sub-division of land-holdings and more intensive cultivation of the ground, ploughing being largely supplemented by work with hoe and spade. The staple foods of the Flemish peasant are home-produced : wheaten bread, potatoes, milk and lard ; his usual drink, though called " café," is a simple infusion of chicory.

Because of the small annual range of temperature, the growing period of plants begins as early as February, even in this fairly high latitude, and in the same month the outdoor work opens with a thorough weeding of the fields and smaller patches of cultivated land. Then the cattle are put out to graze on the pasture lands, and with the full coming of spring there is ploughing, followed by manuring, harrowing or hoe cultivation. The pastures are seeded, and the crop-lands are planted with beet, chicory, other root-crops and potatoes.

With so much to be crowded into a few weeks, there is such a demand for labour that the need cannot be met by the workers living on the farms, even though employed for the full time that the light permits. The supply has therefore to be increased by immigrant labour from the industrial towns of Flanders, and to some extent even from the coal-mines to the south and the fishing-villages to the north.

In late spring and the first part of the summer, there is a slack period when the immigrants return to their other work, and for a time even the local labour has less than the normal demand upon it ; some of the countrymen may find employment in towns and others take the opportunity for making visits or attending village fêtes and fairs.   The dairy-farming, however, still needs milkers and butter-makers and those who prepare and market the various products of cattle, pigs and poultry.

In the latter part of the summer there is a return to full activity with the preparations for harvesting the ripening crops.   The wheat is reaped as early and as quickly as possible to take advantage of dry spells in this season when the rainfall is approaching its maximum, and also to get the wheat in before the first root-crops are lifted and taken to farmsteads or factories. So great is the need for labour at the harvesting that another wave of immigration floods the country-side.

At the beginning of autumn comes a slight relaxation, but the urgency of the work is soon renewed by the sowing of the wheat, and by the very heavy labour of the beet pulling and stacking and its transport to the factories.   The harvest period comes to an end with the digging of the last potatoes.   Meanwhile the final work of autumn has begun : ditches and canals are cleared of weeds and of the silt that the rains have washed from the fields.

In winter the animals are taken indoors.   Here they are fed partly on the direct produce of the farms, e.g. hay, fodder roots and the above-ground parts of the industrial crops, and partly on refuse returned from the factories, especially beet pulp. Little work can be done on the wet land, and for about three months the demand for labour is small.   Hence the factories, which have now their full supply of raw material, draw upon the farming population for workers, and thus winter shows another link between agriculture and industry.

VIII.—Mid-latitude Grain- and Grazing-lands.—In general, these regions are limited in the use of their land by a comparative lack of water ; hence they correspond broadly to the climate regions of the mid-latitude, light-rain type.   As a consequence of extensive, as opposed to intensive, utilization, their populations are usually rather scanty and scattered, and over large areas landscapes are still to a considerable extent natural.   In some respects, however, exceptions to these general rules occur and will be noted as the individual regions are indicated.

The mid-latitude grain- and grazing-lands are five in number. VIIIᴀ is the " *Western Plains* " *of North America*, and it covers the greater part of the light-rain region.   The growing of grains, of which wheat is the most important, has spread over the better-watered eastern edge and the cooler northern portion of the area, while for the rest the main occupation is the grazing of cattle and sheep on natural pastures.   But rivers from the Rocky Mountains bring water, used at certain places for irrigation and producing food either for livestock or for man. VIIIʙ is the *Pampa-Patagonia region of South America*.   In the Pampa area this overlaps the rainy-summer climate region where wheat and alfalfa are grown, while in Patagonia, where the climate is of the light-rain or even dry type, the grazing of sheep is the main use made of the poor pastures.

In Eurasia, the U.S.S.R. includes two areas which, although contiguous and having similar light-rain climates, may be distinguished as distinct regions of this group.   VIIIᴄ is the *Volga-Irtish Steppe*, so-called to indicate that it extends into the basins of these two rivers ; here, as in North America, wheat-growing and the rearing of sheep and cattle are the chief occupations.   VIIIᴅ is the *Turkistan Foothills region* where, from the mountains of Central Asia, rivers bring water to a belt of loess ; here, long ago, ran a great trade-route between China and Europe marked by a string of trading centres at oases, e.g. Samarkand and Tashkent.   Although, until recently, pastoral work was the chief use made of most of the region, irrigation has now been so widely extended that it is the basis of the cultivation, not only of various kinds of grain and fruit, but also of cotton and other raw materials for manufactures.   Hence industries have developed, large numbers of people have settled here, and some of the ancient towns have become great modernized cities.

Indeed, in the Turkistan Foothills Region the forms of production are so varied, and over much of the area the landscapes have so changed their character, that this region seems to be nearing a condition when it might be more useful to regard it no longer as one of the mid-latitude grain- and grazing-lands but as

a mid-latitude crop-land region. In that case it would be necessary to point out that it differs from the others of the mid-
latitude crop-lands type as having oasis cultivation as one of its
basic characters. This instance of the Turkistan Foothills
Region is a reminder of the fact that regional characters, and
therefore regional grouping, are subject to change.

The Australian region of the grain and grazing group is the
Murray-Darling Grassland (VIIIᴇ), which resembles the North
American region in the character of its land utilization.

The special study relating to mid-latitude grain- and grazing-
lands is drawn from the productive and relatively well-popu-
lated northern part of the North American area where grain-
growing is the chief concern of the farmers. Here the seasonal
rhythms show differences from those of other types of region
previously studied, but it must be pointed out that they are also
unlike those of the drier parts of these regions where grazing is
almost the only occupation.

Grain-growers of the Canadian Prairie.—A belt of country,
with a natural growth of tall prairie grass or of grass interspersed with small woods or belts of trees, stretches obliquely
through the so-called " Prairie Provinces " of Canada, between
the coniferous forests in the north-east and the drier steppe-like
area in the south-west of these provinces. In this true prairie
belt the wide landscapes had by nature a monotonous appearance, and their cultural successors have not made as great a
transformation as in many regions, for the typical occupation
of the present time is grain-growing on an extensive scale.
The generally level character of the relief of the land facilitates
the use of tractor-drawn machinery, and with its assistance the
land-holdings can be large and the settlements therefore
scattered. Most of these consist of a small group of farm
buildings constructed of stone, brick or wood ; they are linked
by few roads to the towns which have grown up at the railway
stations from which grain, the chief produce of the region, is sent
away.

The climate is one of extremes, with a range from a mean of
about 0° F. in January to over 60° F. in July and August ; the
winter lasts at least five months, with mean temperatures below
freezing-point. The period of plant growth, during which the
temperatures are above 42° F. and there is also an adequate
rainfall, is short, and the agricultural activities are crowded into

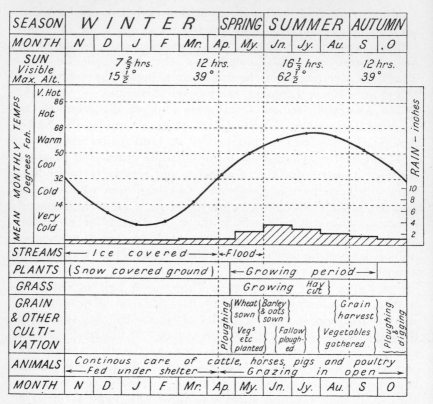

SEASON	W I N T E R					SPRING	S U M M E R			AUTUMN
MONTH	N	D	J	F	Mr.	Ap.	My.	Jn.	Jy.	Au.	S	.O

| SUN Visible Max. Alt. | 7⅔ hrs. 15½° | 12 hrs. 39° | 16⅓ hrs. 62½° | 12 hrs. 39° |

MEAN MONTHLY TEMPS Degrees Fah.

V. Hot 86 / Hot / 68 / Warm / 50 / Cool / 32 / Cold / 14 / Very Cold

RAIN – inches / 10 / 8 / 6 / 4 / 2

STREAMS	←— I c e c o v e r e d —→ ←Flood→
PLANTS	(Snow covered ground) ←—Growing period—→
GRASS	Growing {Hay cut}
GRAIN & OTHER CULTI-VATION	Ploughing {Wheat sown} {Barley & oats sown} {Grain harvest} Ploughing & digging / {Veg⁵ etc planted} {Fallow plough-ed} {Vegetables gathered}
ANIMALS	Continous care of cattle, horses, pigs and poultry ←—Fed under shelter—→ ←— Grazing in open —→
MONTH	N	D	J	F	Mr.	Ap.	My.	Jn.	Jy.	Au.	S	O

Fig. 69.—RHYTHMS IN A MID-LATITUDE GRAIN- AND GRAZING-LAND : GROWERS OF HARDY GRAIN IN CANADA—Lat. 51° N.

a brief spring, a three-months' summer and a short autumn. As a consequence of the extreme climate, the rhythms show a simple annual cycle of strong contrasts.

During the long winter of intense cold, the precipitation is in the form of snow which accumulates to make a cover on the land, while the surface of the streams is ice-bound. The landscape lies under an almost unbroken sheet of white, save for some dark patches of woodland or small orchards, or for lines of trees along the roadsides or planted as wind-breaks against blizzards. The livestock commonly includes a few horses, cattle raised either for dairy produce or for beef, some pigs and a number of poultry. At this season the animals must be kept under shelter, and to supply them with food from the preceding harvest gives a limited amount of work to the men, but it is a period of comparative leisure. The women continue their work in the house, and the children attend their schools which may be at a considerable distance from their homes.

With the rapid rise of temperature in spring, the snow-cover melts and the water floods the ice-free streams ; the growing grass supplies pasturage for the animals, now turned out to graze, and the men begin their busy time of work on the fields. As soon as the soil is sufficiently dry after the thaw the ground is ploughed, if this could not be done at the end of the autumn, then harrowed and rolled, and finally drilled and seeded. The greater part of the land is given to wheat produced as a cash crop for export ; it is sown as early as possible, and hardy varieties have been specially bred to ripen quickly before the autumn frosts. After the wheat, potatoes and other vegetables for home consumption are planted whenever opportunity offers.

At the end of the brief springtime, men turn to the sowing of hardy varieties of oats and barley, which grow even more quickly than wheat does during the short but fairly hot summer ; these grains occupy smaller areas than the main crop and there are other minor crops, such as rye and flax, suited to the severe climate. A rotation system is common by which wheat is followed by one of the other cereals, and then the land is ploughed and left fallow during the next summer. When all the crops are above the ground, the landscape is largely green—the light green of newly growing grass, and the varied greens of the wheat, oats and barley—while the small vegetable patches have different colours.

By this time the summer is well advanced, and the farmers are sometimes anxious about the prospects of their harvests ; one danger is that of sudden hailstorms which may beat down the crops. The first cutting is that of hay to be stored as winter feed for the animals, and in the later parts of the summer some of the vegetables are dug up. As autumn approaches comes the maturing and harvesting of the grain. This is the time when the landscape is most varied and colourful. The great expanses of wheat turn to a rich golden-brown, while the oat-fields and the smaller areas under barley add different shades of brown or buff ; then, when the grain is reaped, the stubble-fields become patches of brown or yellow.

So much work has to be accomplished in the short time

between the ripening of the crops and the onset of the killing frosts which occur in late autumn, that men, women and children all have to labour in whatever ways they can, while in many cases temporary farm-workers have to be brought in from cities or from forest camps. On the larger and best-equipped farms, both labour and time are saved by the use of huge " combine-harvesters," which reap and thresh the wheat, and drop bags of grain and heaps of straw in rows on the stubble. As rapidly as possible, the grain is hauled to the elevators at the nearest railway station and from these it is poured into the trucks.

The last part of the autumn is utilized to begin the ploughing of the stubble-fields. Turned up by the plough, the prairie soils now show their characteristic dark-brown colour which gives the landscape a deeper hue than it had worn during the preceding seasons of growth, and affords a transient and most striking contrast with the whiteness of the winter which quickly follows.

CHAPTER XXIV

COOLER AND COLD REGIONS
AND THEIR RHYTHMS

IX. Mid-latitude Forests and Farmlands.—These are the forest regions in which man has settled by making clearings of various extent and carrying on farming, often under difficult conditions and sometimes on the very margin of cultivation. Beyond the occupied areas, the forests may be used for cutting timber, but in the regions as a whole the landscapes still show much of their natural appearance. As pioneer settlements have pushed in various directions, different types of climate and natural vegetation are represented in areas of this kind, but the production shows much similarity. The populations are generally scanty, but there are a number of commercial centres of various sizes and a few large seats of government where States have been formed in these regions.

Region IXA comprises the *North-west American Coast-lands*. They are largely mountainous, with the mid-latitude, rainy climate, and they are clothed with coniferous or mixed forests ; settlements are limited to the valleys, where pastures and hay feed livestock, some grain is grown and the more favoured districts produce the hardier kinds of fruit. From the other side of the continent, Region IXB, the *North American Short-summer Belt*, stretches far inland, mainly in Canada but overlapping into the United States ; the natural vegetation is either mixed forest or wooded prairie, and the farming products are broadly similar to those of the North-western region. On the west side of South America, Region IXc is *Southern Chile*, comparable in most respects to its counterpart in North America but with less lowland and much less economic development.

The largest and by far most populous of the group is region IXD, the *European–West Siberian Short-summer Belt*. This name is a concise but not quite complete label, for the widespread region includes the mid-latitude, rainy climate areas of south-western Iceland and western Norway in addition to the short-summer areas of south-eastern Scandinavia, south-western Finland, a broad belt of Russia in Europe and a narrower belt in western Siberia; moreover, man has pushed his farming northward into the marginal part of the sub-arctic climate region.   Indeed, if the scope of this book allowed subdivisions of the major geographical regions, the " Atlantic Margins " minor region of western Europe, including the oceanic parts of the British Isles with Brittany and north-western Spain, might be associated with this mid-latitude forest and farmlands region, for some of their natural conditions and modes of life show marked similarities.[1]

With the varieties of climate represented in the European and West Siberian short-summer region, the forests vary and include both deciduous and coniferous types, while in some parts marshes and heathlands represent the natural vegetation.

Green pastures and hay for dairy and other cattle occupy much of the farmlands; oats, barley and rye are the commonest grain crops; root crops and vegetables are also grown; apples are the most widespread of the hardy fruits.   It is in this region of the group that the forests have been encroached upon to the greatest extent, and that human activities in general have gone farthest; in some areas mining has become the basis of industries, and there are capital cities of the States whose territories overlap the geographical region.   Also, here as in other regions of the mid-latitude forest and farmlands, the neighbouring seas form great fishing-grounds and many of the coastal settlements combine farming and fishing.

Region IXE, the *Eastern Asia Short-summer Belt*, consists of south-eastern Siberia with adjoining areas in Manchuria, Korea and Japan; in its climate, types of forest and production it is broadly similar to its counterpart in eastern North America.

The last region of the group, IXF, is *South-east Australia and New Zealand*; it is situated on each side of the Tasman Sea and comprises part of the Australian mainland and Tasmania with the distant islands of New Zealand.   Like the north-western region of North America, it has a relatively mild climate and in the non-wooded lowlands it has the same group of agricultural products.   In New Zealand, however, the pastoral industry is

---

[1] These similarities are brought out in the preceding books of this series : see the chapters on " Regions and Peoples of Britain " in Vol. I—The British Isles, and on " Geographical Regions " in Vol. II—Europe.

dominant, with great numbers of cattle and sheep and with its natural pastures largely replaced by sown grasses.

The special study of rhythms in the mid-latitude forests and farmlands is taken from the northern edge of the European short-summer region.

Hay-and-Dairy Farmers of Central Sweden.—From the culti-vated area of what was originally the mixed forest region of central Sweden, fingers of settled land stretch north-westward up the valleys of the Dal river system into the coniferous forests. Here for many centuries man has won a living from the soil on the margin of cultivation, subsisting on the " hay-and-dairy " variety of mixed farming adapted to these northern conditions— less than 6 degrees from the Arctic Circle.

Opportunity for this northward advance was given by the waterways and, more particularly, by the deposits which were laid down in the ice age along the banks of the glacial streams and lakes and which consist of sand and silt offering favourable soil conditions. These narrow strips of almost horizontal and potentially fertile ground penetrate, and contrast with, the surrounding glaciated country with its hummocks, swamps and areas of bare rock. The sandy soils are obviously more easily worked, being level, dry and free from boulders ; they have the additional value of allowing the water from the melting snow of spring to drain away rapidly and the vegetation to take prompt advantage of the rise of temperature, while in summer they respond quickly to the warmth of the sun.

As a consequence of man's utilization of his opportunities the relatively monotonous natural landscape of the coniferous forest is now broken by winding belts of a much more varied cultural landscape. In these belts the waters are bounded by fields of grass or grain, set with villages and dotted with barns, while near the settlements small orchards of apple and pear trees have been planted.

The summers, moderately warm and wet, allow a better growth of grass than of grain ; the land is therefore used for food for cattle rather than for the direct sustenance of the people. As the winters are long and cold, the livestock have to be fed and kept under shelter for several months and much of the grass must be stored ; hence hay-and-dairy farming is a re-sponse to the climatic conditions of this marginal area.

Moreover, the available soil, restricted as it is, has its fertility

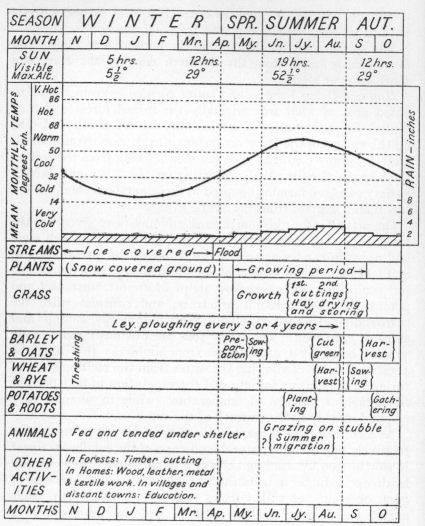

SEASON	WINTER					SPR.	SUMMER			AUT.	
MONTH	N	D	J	F	Mr.	Ap.	My.	Jn.	Jy.	Au.	S	O
SUN Visible Max.Alt.	5 hrs. 5½°			12 hrs. 29°			19 hrs. 52½°			12 hrs. 29°	

Fig. 70.—RHYTHMS IN A MID-LATITUDE FOREST AND FARMLAND: HAY-AND-DAIRY FARMERS OF SWEDEN—Lat. 61° N.

maintained by a system of ley farming in which sown grasslands are ploughed up every three or four years and put under a rotation of grain or root crops for three years. Permanent pastures are rare in this part of central Sweden, and the grasses are sown from productive strains which have proved their suitability to the local conditions.

The legal system by which lands are divided among a man's heirs tends to make the individual holdings both small and scattered, but this process has been checked from becoming a serious handicap by agreements to combine small plots, and also by the migration of many of the younger people to the growing industrial districts of Sweden or to America. Nevertheless, the average farmer has but a small acreage and on it he keeps a few cattle, a horse, and perhaps a couple of pigs and some poultry. Grain crops occupy less than half the cultivated area ; they include oats as the main foodstuff for the people, less barley, and small amounts of rye and wheat—the last being a recent innovation, in part due to the introduction of quick-ripening varieties from Canada.

Part of the dairy produce is sent away, the development of co-operative societies and the use of mechanical milk-separators having greatly aided this branch of the industry ; the rest of the milk, butter and cheese is used locally, together with other products such as meat and leather.

Recent increases of production on the farms are one reason for the decline of an ancient system of summer migration of cattle to patches of natural but poor pasture within the forest ; also there are nowadays not enough young people to accompany the animals to these relatively distant pastures, and the scattered huts which still remain in the small forest clearings find their chief use in the accommodation of holiday-makers from the towns.

Most of the farmsteads are situated close to the rivers or lakes and, for mutual protection in past times, are grouped into fairly compact villages. For the same reason, and particularly as a traditional precaution against the depredations of wolves and bears, each farmstead is constructed in the form of a quadrangle, the farm buildings opening to a central courtyard in which is the well. The living-house is usually on the north side of the yard in order that its windows may face the south ; the relatively low altitudes of the midday sun in this latitude are given in the rhythm-diagram. Timber is naturally the chief material used in building.

The long winter necessitates the safe keeping of food, other stores, fuel and farm implements ; hence, adjoining the accommodation for the livestock are barns and various other sheds. while still more barns are scattered over the neighbouring fields.

The construction of a cellar for the dairy produce and other food shows an adaptation to the climate, for to maintain it at as even a temperature as possible it is dug deep into the solid rock and covered with a roof of earth and stone.

Outdoor work on the farm has to be crowded into less than half the year. At the beginning of May, as soon as the land is free of the winter frost and the spring thaw, work starts with the preparation of the ground and the sowing of the chief grain crops—barley and oats. At the same time the grass and the autumn-sown wheat and rye resume their growth.

At the beginning of summer the livestock are either sent to the forest clearings, if the practice of transhumance still persists, or they are turned out on the stubble- or grazing-fields. The main use of the grass is, however, for hay; the leys are well kept and manured, the selected varieties of grass grow quickly, and the first cutting may come at the end of June, a second in August and perhaps a third in September if the weather has been favourable. The yield of each ley begins to fall off after three or four years; it is then ploughed up after the August cutting and remains fallow for one winter before being sown with grain. After the hay is cut, it is thoroughly dried by spreading over wooden racks, a process which, in the rainy summer of this region, is necessary and may take some time; then it is hauled to the lofts or barns. Additional feed for the animals is got from some mixed crops of oats and barley, cut green about the time of the second hay harvest. Meanwhile, the potatoes and the small amount of root-crops have been planted, while at the end of this season occurs the reaping of the wheat and rye.

At the beginning of autumn the next year's crops of wheat and rye are sown, to take advantage of the last of the warm weather for germination and early growth before the young shoots are covered by the blanket of snow, thick enough to protect them from the winter frost. The part of the barley and oats destined for human consumption needs in this climate a relatively long period of growth; sown in the spring, it does not ripen till well into autumn and the harvest may extend into October. Then, like the grass, the grain needs to be well dried in the fields before it is carried to the farm. The year's production ends with the digging of the last root-crops, potatoes and other vegetables.

The winter may be considered to begin in November, when the mean temperature falls below freezing-point and the bulk of the work of the farm must be carried on indoors. The grain is threshed and stored, and for quite six months the animals must be tended and fed in their byres. This season, however, gives leisure for additional occupations. There is the felling of trees in the forest, with the sawing of logs for building or carpentry and the cutting of smaller timber for fuel. In the houses the farm workers of the summer take up their winter rôles of skilled craftsmen in wood, leather and metal, while the women weave, knit, and make and mend clothes. The high standard of education in this country is kept up by the attendance, not only of children in the village schools, but of more advanced students in winter sessions of technical, art and academic institutions in the larger towns of Sweden.

Thus, in the none-too-favourable natural conditions of this marginal region of cultivation, men have made their homes and in their ways of life have learnt to combine physical well-being and cultural development.

X. Sub-arctic Forests.—These regions, sometimes known as the Boreal Forests, occupy enormous areas near, or to the south of, the Arctic Circle ; region Xa is the *Northern Forest of Canada and Newfoundland,* and region Xb is the *Northern Forest of Eurasia,* stretching from Norway to eastern Siberia. Because of their high latitude and the consequent seasonal differences in the amount of insolation, there are marked contrasts between the brief, warm summers and the long and very cold winters. The forests, mainly of coniferous trees, provide the characteristic features of the landscapes, with a rather sombre appearance in summer and a cover of snow in winter. In these regions, men are few in number and have made very little change in the natural landscapes.

In the past, the main occupations were hunting and trapping the wild creatures, and in Eurasia the keeping of domesticated reindeer, and the marked seasonal changes necessitated migrations of animals and man. More recently, mining has become important in certain spots and trade in general has increased ; in particular, the aeroplane has made possible rapid communications into otherwise almost inaccessible areas. Farming is still very restricted both in extent and in kind ; the chief areas are in the Peace River district of Canada, the middle basin of the Lena River in Siberia, and a narrow belt along the course of the Trans-Siberian railway linking the mid-latitude forest and farmlands of the east with those of the west of the U.S.S.R. Hay and root-crops for cattle are the main aims of such agriculture as is possible, with vegetables and the hardiest grains as food for man. Settlements are few and generally small ; as a rule they are either by the rivers which aid communications, or near the southern margin of the region where the climate is less severe and where lumbering and commerce with more favoured lands is relatively easy.

It is from a Canadian district of this marginal kind that a special study of rhythms in the sub-arctic forests is taken.

Lumbermen and Hunters of Eastern Canada.—In the area which extends across the water-parting between the St. Lawrence river and the streams flowing to James Bay, the southern portion of Hudson Bay, conifers predominate, spruces being the most common, together with pines, firs and larches ; there are also some deciduous trees, including poplars and birches found mainly in the wetter parts. Compared with those of warmer climates, the trees have a relatively small girth and are not of great height ; their trunks rise straight and are clear of undergrowth and of low branches, but their upper branches shut out much of the light and the forests give the impression of sombreness or even of gloom.

Below is spread a carpet of fallen needle-leaves, in some parts covering a thin layer of poor soil and in others exposing patches of rock laid bare by the heavy glaciation of the past. Innumerable rock-basins have been hollowed by ice ; many are occupied by " muskegs," bogs formed of marsh vegetation such as sphagnum moss, and others have become lakes of all sizes. Streams draining from these have irregular and often tangled courses, interrupted by rapids and falls. Boulders emerge from the waters and marshes, and may make obstacles to movement between the trees of the forest. Over most of the country the natural landscape still remains, rarely broken by the clearings of the lumbermen, the settlements of miners and the fur-trading posts of the Hudson Bay Company.

The white men have extended their activities into this region, but their occupation of it is sparse and, like the Indians who still form a noteworthy part of the population, they must as a rule adopt a migratory way of life. Almost the only exceptions

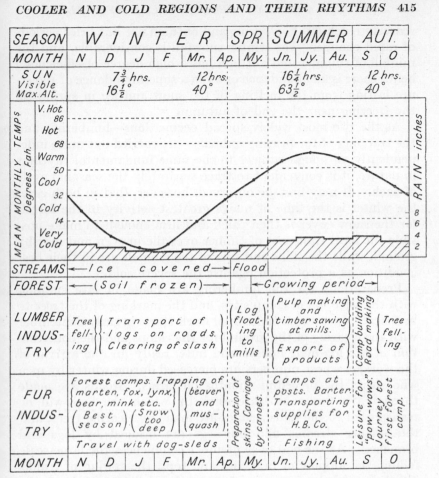

Fig. 71.—RHYTHMS IN A SUB-ARCTIC FOREST : LUMBERMEN AND
HUNTERS OF CANADA—Lat. 50° N.

are at the mines, the few stations on the railroads, the trading-
posts on the older routes through the forest, and in the " clay
belt " where a glacial lake-bed gives better soil conditions and
makes possible a restricted amount of farming.

The extreme severity of the climate is shown by the temperature graph. If the winter is reckoned merely as the period
during which the mean temperatures are below freezing-point
it nevertheless extends to about six months, while for some
weeks the average readings are below 0° F. The summer is
very short, and in the warmest month the mean temperatures

scarcely reach 60° F.; spring and autumn are but brief periods of rapid change. The winter snowfall is considerable, and the rainfall of summer and autumn has a high degree of efficiency; hence there is an abundance or even a superabundance of moisture lasting from the melting of the snow and ice in spring till the freezing near the end of autumn.

As the two most widely spread occupations—lumbering and the trapping of fur-bearing animals—are carried out quite independently, although subject to the same fundamental rhythms in nature, it is convenient to trace separately the seasonal cycle of each. It may first be observed, however, that in both cases the winter is the time of man's greatest activity in the forest, for the snow cover is then thick and firm enough to make possible the local transport of timber over the uneven and marshy ground, while the skins and furs of the animals are in their best condition as a protection against the severe cold.

Preparations for the lumbering are made in late summer with the selection of camp sites, and the marking of the trees to be felled. In autumn the actual work starts in early September with the clearing of the ground for the camps and the construction of the log-built houses and huts, ready for the arrival of the workers whose numbers are increased during winter by men who spend the preceding months on farms. Roads are made through the forest to waterways by which the logs will be transported to the mills; lanes are made by clearing trees, and the smaller streams and muskegs are bridged by logs and branches. At the end of September commences the large-scale felling, the lopping of branches and tops, the sawing of trunks into logs, and the dumping of timber by the sides of the roads. This work continues into winter, and by the beginning of December the snow is sufficiently deep and hard to allow the lumber to be hauled along the roads on sledges drawn by tractors or teams of horses, and to be piled high by the sides of the streams. The small, unusable " slash " has, by law, to be carefully burned to remove inflammable material which in the past has allowed fires to destroy enormous areas of valuable forest.

Spring comes about mid-April, when the mean temperatures rise above freezing-point, the snow melts from the ground and the water floods the lakes and streams freed of ice. Before long the forest shows signs of renewed life; small, light-green needles appear on the dark conifers, and the poplars and birches are clothed with new leaves. Meanwhile the lumbermen have begun the next stage of their work. The logs are levered into the swollen, fast-running streams and manœuvred over rapids and falls to the larger rivers ; there they are built into rafts and towed down to the mills on the shores of the St. Lawrence and its tributaries.

During the summer the main part of the lumber industry is carried on in the mills, which are strung out along the whole southern edge of this forest belt and continue to receive material from the more distant areas of the interior even in autumn. Timber for building purposes is sawn and prepared from logs from the most suitable varieties of trees, among which pines rank high in this eastern region of Canada. In recent years, after much of the large timber in the more accessible districts has been utilized, saw mills have been surpassed in importance by pulp mills, which can use smaller stuff as well as logs from spruce, poplar and birch trees. The pulp industry has increased also because of the still-growing variety of uses to which wood-pulp is put, including the making of many paper products (e.g. newsprint and cardboard containers), rayon, and even chemicals, from what was formerly waste.

The fur industry is carried on by the very small number of white traders at the Hudson Bay Company's posts or at " fur-towns " at the side of the few railroads which penetrate the region, and by the larger number of trappers who, apart from some white men, are " Woods Indians " or half-breeds.

The year's work begins in autumn when the trappers set out for their forest camp ; the journey may occupy several weeks, and each Indian family or family-group has for its hunting-ground a recognized area within the tribal territory. The Indians use birch-bark canoes to transport themselves and their equipment ; rapids are skilfully navigated, but where one stream has to be left for another a " portage " of canoes and cargo has to be made. Shelter is provided by conical " tepees " made of rolls of birch-bark, which are carried in the canoes and spread over poles cut in the forest as required.

The first part of the winter is the best season for trapping, when martens, foxes, lynxes, bears, minks and other forest animals are caught. The Indians can tell from tracks in the snow where the game is to be found, and as the yield in one district gets less the camp is moved to another which promises better results ; the people use snowshoes, and their goods are carried on dog-sleds which can travel over the ice-covered rivers and lakes. At the winter camps, huts of logs and fir branches may be made. As the winter goes on, the amount of snow may become so great that it may cover the traps and hinder the work, but when the break-up of the ice begins at the end of the season comes the time for trapping the musk-rat, or musquash, and beaver which live by the sides of the streams. The animals have to be skinned, and the skins cleaned, stretched and made into bales to be carried easily and without injury.

Spring, for the trappers as for the lumbermen, is the season when the products of their winter's labour are transported by water. The valuable furs, however, unlike the heavy logs, can be taken northward to trading-posts from which they are exported by the sea-route through Hudson Bay, as well as southward to those in the basin of the St. Lawrence river.

During the summer large groups of tents are set up around the trading-posts, where furs and skins are bartered for a variety of manufactured articles : cloth ; steel traps ; rifles and ammunition ; kettles, matches and stoves ; tea, flour and tobacco. The Hudson Bay Company's traders are, however, not allowed to sell alcoholic liquor to the Indians. Some members of the trapping communities earn money from the Company by conveying furs and trade goods to and from the centres of shipment, and others add to the food-supply by catching trout and other fish, shooting wildfowl and gathering berries.

Autumn gives a short period of comparative leisure, and " pow-wows " are held at tribal gatherings held near the con-fluences of the waterways, before dispersal into the forest for next season's work.

It must be added that the boreal forest as a basis for the fur industry gives an example of the changing values of geographical factors. On the one hand, the forest animals have been reduced in number by the demands of distant lands for furs and by the increased effectiveness of modern equipment such as steel traps and rifles. On the other hand, there has recently arisen a new branch of the industry which is competing success-fully with the trapping of wild animals ; this is the keeping of " fur farms," in which the much-valued silver foxes and other fur-bearing animals are bred in captivity, on the margins of the region near the main waterways of Ontario and Quebec as well as in the Maritime Provinces of Canada.

XI. Tundra Lands.—These lands adjoin the North Polar Seas on each side of the Arctic Circle. They comprise three regions : XIA, the *American Tundra* ; XIB, the *Greenland Coasts* and *Northern Iceland* ; XIc, the *Eurasian Tundra*, with the Scandinavian Highlands. With the Arctic type of climate, and in still higher latitudes than the sub-arctic forests, the tundras have even greater contrasts between their light but short and cool summers and their dark, very long and very cold winters. (At the top of the diagram on p. 421 is the graph showing the periods of light, twilight and total darkness at Lat. 77 degrees N., and it is worth careful examination because it shows facts which are fundamental to an understanding of these regions.) In the tundra landscapes, the varied colour, life and movement of summer make a complete contrast to the white shroud of winter ; off the coasts, too, the often stormy summer seas give place in winter to motionless expanses of ice.

The lives of the few inhabitants show equally great seasonal changes. The reindeer herders of Eurasia, like the hunters of caribou in America and of various other animals in both continents, must migrate with the animals from which they get their living. So, also, must the people who depend upon fish and other marine forms of life and who dwell by the shores and even, for brief periods, upon the frozen sea. Not only do their locality and environment change, but their homes—houses, tents or snow-huts—must be different according to the seasons, and corresponding variations affect their ways of life.

Subsistence production is still the rule to a considerable extent, but barter or sale of the products of the tundra or the seas for goods from industrial regions is becoming increasingly important. As in the sub-arctic forests, the development of air communications with the South is one factor in this change and another is the recent advance in navigation in the polar seas. The long-sought north-east and north-west passages from the Atlantic to the Pacific Ocean have been mastered, and more significant in the modifications in human life in the polar area has been the increase of coastwise summer traffic to the settlements scattered along the Arctic shores.

It must be pointed out that among the tundra dwellers there are very considerable differences in the modes of life ; these are due in part to local differences in such matters as the character of the tundra or the nature of the ice off the coast, and in part to other peoples transforming their primitive conditions.

One interesting generalization may be made about the life of the people living within the Arctic Circle : seasonal rhythms are extraordinarily marked, but for that very reason the daily rhythms are weaker than in lower latitudes. While, for weeks or months, there is continuous darkness in winter and continuous light in summer, at those times the distinctions between day and night largely disappear ; human activity may remain almost continuous throughout the twenty-four hours when circumstances demand it in summer, and there may be correspondingly long periods of inactivity in winter.

The following study of geographical rhythms in these regions is taken from those of the people of north-western Greenland. Although only a small group, they are of special interest because they have been the least changed by recent contacts and because they live nearer the Pole than any other community, with the exception of the coal-miners of Spitsbergen—whose mode of life is, of course, quite different from that of the other inhabitants of the Arctic regions.

Seal-hunting " Polar " Eskimo of Greenland.—The small settlement in the north-west salient of Greenland can exist in this remote situation, half-way between the Arctic Circle and the Pole, because the environment has an unusual combination of conditions necessary for human life. The counter-clockwise currents around Baffin Bay take relatively warm waters northward along the west coast of Greenland far into polar latitudes, leaving the shores free of ice in summer, and bringing fish and the all-important marine animals—seal, walrus and whale— within reach of the " polar " Eskimo. Moreover, the high plateau of Greenland here leaves patches of lowland by the coast, and between the glaciers which work down from the interior to the sea are areas of tundra. At these places houses may be built, and land animals and birds may be caught when the ground is free of snow and ice. The houses of stone and sods are few in number, small and mostly scattered ; though inconspicuous they are the only permanent cultural elements in the landscape.

Here, as indeed over most of the world, it is not possible to make a definite dividing line between the seasons, but the

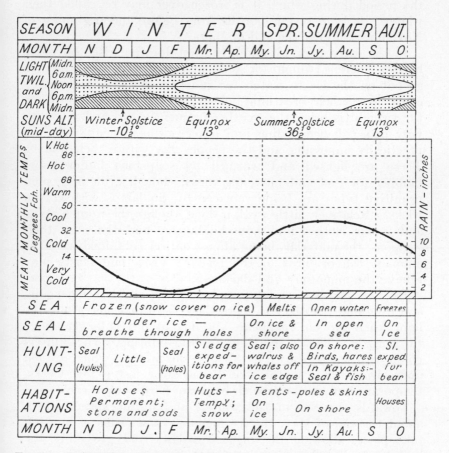

FIG. 72.—RHYTHMS IN THE TUNDRA : SEAL-HUNTING ESKIMOS OF
GREENLAND—LAT. 77° N.

Note.—In the graph near the top of the diagram, the periods of total darkness are shaded by lines, those
of twilight by dots, and those of light are left white.   The line enclosing the light period marks the length of
time during which the sun is above the horizon ; this period is measured horizontally according to the time
of year, and vertically according to the time of day.   For example, by reading along the line marked noon,
one can see that the sun is invisible at that hour from near the end of October till the middle of February,
i.e. at this latitude the " polar night " lasts for about 3½ months.   Similarly, by reading along the line
marked midnight, one can see that the " midnight sun " is visible from the end of April till near the middle
of August—a period of 3½ months.   Also, by reading vertically downwards at the December solstice, it can
be seen that even when the sun is invisible at mid-winter there is twilight from about 9 a.m. till about 3 p.m. ;
again, at the equinoxes, when the sun rises at 6 a.m. and sets at 6 p.m., there is twilight during the whole of
the remaining 12 hours.
Note also that the sun is 10½° below the horizon at noon on December 21st.

condition of the sea is so important to the polar Eskimo that the period during which it is frozen over may be called their winter ; it lasts seven months from before the beginning of November till near the end of May.

In the early part, although the sun does not rise above the horizon, there is twilight for some hours around noon ; the men go out on the ice to watch for and harpoon seals when they come up at their breathing-holes. In December and January the twilight is brief, the weather frequently bad and visibility very poor ; hence sealing and other outdoor occupations are practically impossible and the people stay within their houses. These are lighted and warmed by soapstone lamps using blubber for fuel and moss for wicks, though even here such primitive types are being replaced by tin lamps with cotton wicks. Relatively little work is done, though the women make and repair clothes and household gear, and the men their weapons, the materials being almost entirely obtained from the animals, fish or birds of the region. Visits and feasts may relieve the monotony and darkness.

By February it is light enough to allow seal-hunting again, and from mid-February to April there is a rapid increase in the light when the sun reappears and day by day is longer above the horizon. This is the time for bear-hunting. The hunters go off with sledges drawn by about a dozen dogs, which are fed upon dried fish ; as the expeditions may last a few weeks, temporary huts are built with blocks of hard-packed snow.

Towards the end of the winter, and in the spring when, about the end of May, the ice melts, several forms of hunting take place, allowing the biggest catches and providing the bulk of food and equipment for the coming year. The seal gather and are slaughtered in considerable numbers, first on the ice and then on breeding-grounds on shore ; at the same time walrus, and whales migrating northward, are caught off the edge of the ice. At this season the winter-houses are left empty and the roofs taken off for much-needed airing. Tents are constructed by the women ; they are made of sealskins stretched over wooden poles, and are set up on the ice, until this melts, and then on the land.

Summer is the season of open water, and lasts from July until the latter part of September, though even during this period the mean temperatures are not many degrees above freezing-point.

The men now fish and hunt the seal in the sea, each man paddling his kayak, a canoe made of skins stretched over a wooden framework and light enough to be carried over ice. On shore foxes are caught in stone traps and hares are snared ; gulls are taken by baited hooks and guillemots in nets. This season is the busiest one, for besides the fishing, hunting and trapping, largely the work of the men, the women have to prepare the skins and plumage for later making-up into clothes, tent and boat covers, and also dry the flesh for winter use.

With the beginning of ice-formation along the shore towards the end of September, the short summer gives place to a still shorter autumn. The men now go again on bear-hunting journeys with dogs and sledges ; meanwhile the women collect the slow-ripening crowberries, almost the only vegetable food, from beneath the snow, and they re-roof the houses and put the supplies needed for the coming winter into safe and cold storage outside.

Among the polar Eskimo, trading is small though essential. They barter to traders the surplus skins and blubber, and ivory from the tusks of the walrus and the small Arctic whale known as the narwhal. In return they must obtain wood for tents, kayaks and sledges, and some metal parts for utensils and weapons, e.g. the blades of harpoons. They do not, however, use rifles—weapons which have been sold to more southerly Eskimo and in some cases have caused the destruction of such numbers of the animals that the whole economy of these communities has been endangered.

The small group of polar Eskimo has so completely adapted its mode of life to its environment, and so successfully acquired habits and skills necessary both for its work and for withstanding the rigours of the climate, that it has been able to maintain itself far from the peoples of other regions. This isolation has hitherto preserved it from the alien influences and dangers which have changed or exterminated many other simple communities, but the question suggests itself : Can these polar Eskimo retain their characteristics, or perhaps even their existence, in face of the easier contacts now made possible by aircraft and motor boats ?

XII. Highlands.—A number of highlands stand out so markedly from the adjoining areas that they must be regarded as distinct geographical regions. Two consequences of their great elevations may be emphasized. First, within them physical conditions vary considerably, as has already been indicated when some of them were classed as distinct climate regions ; similarly their vegetation is of varied character so that on the map of natural vegetation some areas could be shown only as " highland zones." Second, as a consequence, the modes of life of their inhabitants differ from place to place within each region, and in a number of cases the people migrate to take advantage of the possibilities, or to avoid the disabilities, which the seasons bring first to one district and then to another. In general, agriculture is very restricted and pastoral work cannot support many people ; in some of the regions mining is an additional resource. Commerce is hindered by the relief, and on the whole the populations are small.

Although no simple classification adequately covers all the highland regions, the following grouping may help in realizing their more outstanding characteristics.

(1) *The Ice-cap Regions* : XIIA, the *Greenland Plateau* and XIIB, the *Antarctic Plateau.* These are very cold everywhere, and are practically incapable of supporting human life.

(2) *The Culminating Highlands of the Earth's Surface* : XIIc, the *Andean Cordillera* and XIID, the *Tibet-Pamir Plateaus* with ranges extending outwards from the western area. These regions show a great variety in their conditions, but considerable parts are characterized by extreme altitude and even larger areas by their great cold ; these regions have few inhabitants.

(3) *The Dry-Basin Highlands* : XIIE, the *North American Cordillera* ; XIIF, the *Sinkiang-Mongolian Highlands* ; XIIG, the *Anatolia-Baluchistan Highlands.* Although the North American Cordillera in its more northerly part is notably cold, and in that area is not distinguished from the adjoining sub-arctic climate region in the map on p. 74, most of the highland region is of the relatively dry type. Broadly similar in its physical conditions is the Asiatic region which includes Sinkiang and the Mongolian Plateaus. The region in south-western Asia, which extends from the Anatolian Plateau in the west through Iran to Afghanistan and Baluchistan in the east, is another in which arid or semi-arid climates are very important factors in affecting the modes of life.

(4) *The Temperate Highlands* : XIIH, the *Abyssinian Highlands* ; XIIJ, the *East African Highlands* ; XIIK, the *South*

African Plateaus. Although these regions are in equatorial or tropical latitudes the effect of their altitude is to give them physical conditions approximating to those of mid-latitudes ; hence, especially in the more southerly areas, they have attracted European and other settlers to what was originally "Negro Africa." To this group of temperate highlands may perhaps be added XIIL, the *Alpine Region,* in which great contrasts occur within a small area ; indeed, its extent is so limited that the question arises whether the Alpine area is better regarded as an independent major region or as a minor region of special character within the mid-latitude crop-lands of Europe.

The following study of geographical rhythms is taken from an interior basin of the North American Cordillera, to show how people with a migratory mode of life make use of a semi-arid region and also take advantage of the differences in temperature of adjoining higher altitudes.

Migratory Indians of the Colorado Plateau.—The Colorado Plateau gives examples of markedly different conditions at successive elevations which occur within a relatively short distance from one another, and of the consequently different natural rhythms which man can utilize. Here are large "reservations," totalling about 20,000 square miles, set apart by the government of the United States for the Navajo Indians ; these number about 40,000 persons, and they are actually increasing in numbers as well as maintaining a culture of their own in spite of slow modifications in their ways of life. Important factors aiding their survival are the natural unattractiveness of the region to the White man, its isolation by the surrounding mountains, and the difficulty of communications within it because of the deep valleys and cañons of the Colorado and its tributaries. There are few other residents : missionaries, teachers, government officials and traders.

The Navajo Indians form the only native community of the New World which depends mainly on pastoral work, excepting those who carry on cattle- and sheep-rearing in connection with enterprises first begun by White men. These Navajo Indians were nomadic hunters and collectors before the Spaniards introduced domesticated animals ; they now keep sheep, with smaller numbers of goats and a few cattle, and use the flesh of the animals for food, and their wool, skins and hides for blankets and other articles, yet they do not make use of the milk as do

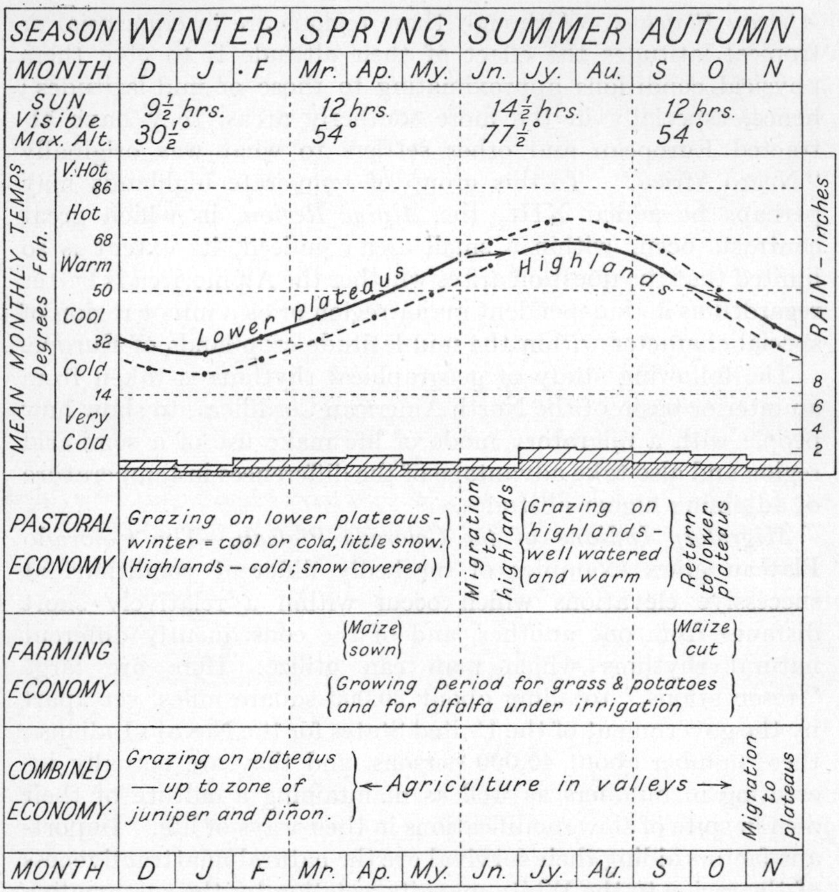

SEASON	WINTER			SPRING			SUMMER			AUTUMN		
MONTH	D	J	·F	Mr.	Ap.	My.	Jn.	Jy.	Au.	S	O	N
SUN Visible Max. Alt.	$9\frac{1}{2}$ hrs. $30\frac{1}{2}°$			12 hrs. 54°			$14\frac{1}{2}$ hrs. $77\frac{1}{2}°$			12 hrs. 54°		

MEAN MONTHLY TEMPS. Degrees Fah.

V. Hot 86 / Hot / 68 / Warm / 50 / Cool 32 / Cold / 14 / Very Cold

Lower plateaus — Highlands

RAIN – inches : 8 6 4 2

PASTORAL ECONOMY	Grazing on lower plateaus— winter = cool or cold, little snow. (Highlands — cold; snow covered)	Migration to highlands	Grazing on highlands— well watered and warm	Return to lower plateaus

FARMING ECONOMY		(Maize sown)	Growing period for grass & potatoes and for alfalfa under irrigation	(Maize cut)

COMBINED ECONOMY	Grazing on plateaus — up to zone of juniper and piñon.	←Agriculture in valleys →	Migration to plateaus

MONTH	D	J	F	Mr.	Ap.	My.	Jn.	Jy.	Au.	S	O	N

Fig. 73.—RHYTHMS IN A DRY-BASIN HIGHLAND : MIGRATORY INDIANS OF THE COLORADO PLATEAU—Lat. 36° N.

Note.—(1) The continuous, thicker lines along the temperature graphs, joined by arrows, show the normal conditions experienced by the pastoralists as a result of their migration from the lower plateaus to the highlands. (2) The smaller, more darkly shaded, rainfall columns show the amounts received on the lower plateaus ; the larger columns show the amounts received on the highlands—approximately twice as great.

the pastoralists of the Old World. While most of the Navajo Indians depend upon their animals and have a nomadic way of life, a small but increasing number are farmers with permanent settlements. Moreover, some combine farming with pastoral work, carrying on agriculture in the valleys during summer and migrating with their flocks to the plateaus for the winter. Thus three types of economy, each with its own series of rhythms, coexist in the same region.

The Navajo reservations are in the eastern part of the upraised Colorado Plateau, which is formed from almost horizontal strata and is dissected by rivers coming from the Rocky Mountains. Hence the main area is composed of plateaus standing nearly a mile above sea-level, from which rise greater heights, some reaching about 9,000 feet, while there are deep valleys, including veritable cañons, lying hundreds of feet below the general level.

Enclosed by high mountain ranges, most of the region has a slight rainfall of rather less than 10 inches a year, occurring mainly in summer and early autumn, though the higher parts have considerably greater amounts. In the valleys, the scanty water-supply from direct rainfall may be supplemented by irrigation from the rivers ; also, adjoining the steep rises both in the valleys and on the lower plateaus are springs and wells which have been improved and increased in number by the U.S. government. The plateaus, shut off from sea-winds, have rather extreme temperature conditions, while in the deep valleys the summer heat is often very great indeed, and frosts may be severe in winter.

Corresponding to the differences of altitude and climate are different types of natural vegetation. In the lowest and driest parts are only desert plants—scattered cacti and tufts of grass growing after the scanty rains. At about 5,000 feet are wide stretches characterized by sage brush and rabbit brush, and including areas of better grass which affords pasture and gives a meadow-like appearance to the country where it occurs. At rather higher levels is a sparse growth of trees, especially juniper and piñon, which bears edible seeds and is therefore known as the nut pine. Above 7,000 feet are relatively well-watered, high plateaus and ridges with open forests of yellow pine rising from a grassy floor.

For more than half the year the pastoral groups of the Navajos live on the lower plateaus feeding their flocks on the grassy areas. Even in winter, grazing is possible beneath the low, spreading branches of the juniper and piñon trees, which hold the light falls of snow and protect the animals sheltering beneath them. The low shrubs and trees supply fuel to the shepherds, and huts are built with a framework of poles or logs, covered with boughs or bark and plastered with earth.

At the close of spring there is a gradual migration, commonly involving journeys of only about twenty miles, to the higher plateaus and ridges.   Because of their changes of location the people and their animals are exposed to no great contrasts of temperature during a large part of the year ; also, their pasturage is increased in two ways : on the lower plateaus the heat and rain of summer allow the grass and shrubs to recover from past grazing, while the higher meadows give good pasture after a short period of growth in spring following the melting of the winter snow.   During the summer the Indians on the highlands need to provide themselves with little shelter, perhaps a frame of pine poles covered with boughs, or merely a rough stone wall as protection from the occasional strong winds.

During the autumn they return to the lower plateau levels, and some take advantage of two additional sources of food-supply : the gathering of the seeds of piñon trees, and the barter of some of their meat for fresh peaches and dried fruits grown by Hopi Indians who carry on cultivation in a neighbouring reserve.   The Navajos make blankets from wool coloured by simple vegetable dyes, and sell them, as well as hides, skins and live animals, to White traders.   For their seasonal migrations and for their visits to the few trading-stations, they have pack-horses and ponies ; wagons are little used in this almost road-less country.

The small permanent settlements of farming communities are on fertile alluvial soils in the valleys, where cultivation is largely of the oasis type, water being supplied either from wells or springs or by a simple system of diversion from the rivers. The extreme climate limits the work to the period between the middle of spring and the middle of autumn.   Maize and potatoes are the chief food products and pasture grasses are grown for local use ; a relatively prosperous group of farmers raises alfalfa for sale outside the region.

Although these comparatively intensive and remunerative forms of cultivation are the main support of some of the Navajo Indians, a larger number depend on a combination of agriculture with migratory pastoral work.   The form varies according to local conditions, but in general there is an annual rhythm including (1) farming in the valleys or at specially suitable places on the lowest plateau areas during the warmer part of the year, (2) an upward migration in the latter part of the autumn, (3) winter grazing on plateaus of moderate elevation as far as the zone of meadow grass, juniper and piñon, and (4) a return to the lower lands at the opening of the period of plant growth.

The use of the naturally poor pastures of the greater part of the region is subject to two handicaps : the first is the variability of the rainfall, especially in the critical summer months when the heat is greatest ; the second is over-grazing, for in addition to their flocks some of the Indians keep large numbers of ponies, although many of them are not used at all but wander about and consume far more grass than the same number of valuable sheep. For these reasons the adjustment which must exist between the habits of the people and their environment is endangered, and the normal rhythms of plant, animal and human life are subject to serious, if temporary, interruption.

CHAPTER XXV
"ONE WORLD"

In this third section of the book a partial synthesis of the various physical and human factors has been made by seeing how they work together and constitute geographical regions; now the synthesis must be completed by considering to what extent these geographical regions affect one another and constitute a unity—one world of nature-and-man. But it must be noted that unity does not imply uniformity. Taking an analogy from the human body, it is clear that its various parts differ in structure and function; there is not uniformity, but nevertheless there is a unity which expresses itself in the interdependence and interaction between the constituent parts.

Considering the world from this point of view, there is certainly a unity in its physical geography. The planet is obviously one, although the geological history of the earth's crust has resulted in differences of relief and structure in its various parts. Its movements in relation to the Sun bring different climates to these parts, but a broad pattern shows itself in the distribution of the types of climate over the globe. Moreover, variations from the normal climate of any region are transmitted to other regions by the movements of the great currents of air and water.

Similarly the plant and animal geography shows both differences and interactions. The living creatures on the planet have characteristic modes of life closely related to the physical geography; also, changes which occur in the distribution of particular species affect species in other regions, as when insect pests are carried to distant areas and there attack and possibly destroy other animals or plants.

Man, too, has evolved in association with his environments, both living and non-living, and since he became a thinking being and his desires and ideas influenced his actions, he has become a considerable factor in affecting the conditions of the regions into which he has spread. Hence, because it is from the human aspect that this final survey is undertaken, there arises the question : How far has Man, by interrelating the geographical regions of the globe with one another, brought about a world unity ?

Economic Interactions between Regions.—In this connection two branches of human activities merit special attention : economic and political ; the economic aspect will be first considered. Until about two centuries ago, the difficulties of communication were so great that the world was divided into regions almost isolated from one another in respect of production and exchange of commodities ; each was in the main self-sufficing, and there was certainly no economic unity in the world of that time. But improved and new means of transport allowed cheap, speedy and large-scale exchange of goods, together with very rapid postal and telegraphic commercial and financial transactions, and thus the geographical regions were brought into close touch. These processes have been so greatly accelerated and extended during the last few years that now there is an appreciable approach towards unity in economic affairs over very large parts of the world, though obviously this man-made unity has not yet been fully attained. Moreover, if it were attained it would not necessarily make this a perfect world, for men's actions may be " good " or " bad " and a unified world would suffer throughout its extent by " bad " actions in any part. (To return to the analogy of the human body, the imperfect functioning of any organ has its effects elsewhere, and perfect health depends on the efficient functioning as well as the harmonious interaction of all the parts.)

Some of the effects of economic interdependence and interaction between the regions of the world may be appreciated if one considers the normal peace-time conditions of the food-supply of western Europe. As this area is largely industrial, its home production of food has to be supplemented from abroad. Grain and animal products come from a number of regions of the mid-latitude crop-lands type, or the mid-latitude grain- and grazing-lands type ; further, if weather conditions diminish the supply from certain of these, the lack may be offset by larger imports from others. Fruit and wine come, with a similar compensatory adjustment, from half a dozen sub-tropical sources, while rice, tapioca, tea, coffee, etc., are supplied from several tropical and inter-tropical regions.

There is usually a fairly smooth working of the system, and a shortage of food would probably be due, not to a lack of production, but to the inability of the people of western Europe to pay for what they need.   Such a situation might occur as a result of the inefficient functioning of the industrial and financial system of the importing region ; the break-down would be most serious when an industrial depression became world-wide, as it has tended to do in the " slump " periods which have alternated with " booms."   Thus, the normal feeding of western Europe illustrates the beneficial results, while its break-down may show the regrettable results, of the present degree of development of economic unity on a world scale.

Political Interactions between Regions.—How present-day political factors may affect political interrelations between regions is brought out by the phrase : " world war."   The ideas of nations, the clash of their ambitions or hopes, their needs or fears, may determine their policies and may lead to war, which once started may spread to every continent and almost every State.   Peace is indivisible ; war is indivisible.   Into such a war practically every activity of mankind is drawn, and many branches of human geography in many regions are changed.

The present stage of world unity in both economic and political affairs can be illustrated, first by a brief analysis of the main causes of the post-war " world famine " which became serious in 1946 and brought the threat of starvation to people of many regions, especially in Europe and the Far East, and secondly by the international action on a world-wide scale which was needed to avert its most tragic effects.

Food production had been reduced in the first place by the political factor—war ; the overrunning or devastation of agricultural land prevented farmers from producing the requisite supply of grain for human consumption and from raising animals and obtaining meat and dairy products ; much of Europe was affected in this way and also China, the Indo-Chinese Peninsula and the East Indies.   In addition, there had been a shortage of labour which had extended over years, together with an accumulated lack of fertilizers, animal feeding-stuffs and agricultural machinery.   Then, in 1945, climatic conditions greatly augmented the trouble ; an extraordinary coincidence of droughts affected several of the large grain-producing regions : in the southern hemisphere the wheat and maize areas in Argentina,

South Africa and Australia all suffered heavily ; in the northern
hemisphere the rice-fields of India lacked winter monsoon rains,
and drought greatly reduced the yield of the wheat and barley
harvests of the Mediterranean region of Europe and north-west
Africa.

During the years of war, the normal stocks held in importing
countries had been reduced or even exhausted, and therefore
what supplies were now available in the producing regions
should, to avoid catastrophe, have been distributed with more
than usual efficiency. But here again devastation had occurred :
transport had suffered, for ships and barges, wagons and lorries,
had been destroyed, while ports, railways and roads had been
damaged. Further, purely political difficulties cropped up ;
e.g. international pooling and organizing of the available means
of transport was hampered, and the entry of material into particular districts was even barred. Moreover, before the actual
transfer of commodities there are normally commercial and
financial arrangements, and these also had been interrupted :
the vast expenditures on war materials had broken down the
usual system of credits and payments, and thus additional
difficulties had to be met to allow prompt distribution of foodstuffs from and to the States concerned.

In many countries piecemeal attempts to deal with the
situation were made in the early months of 1946, but it became
apparent that the efforts of individual States needed to be co-
ordinated by international planning, and in May of that year
the Food and Agricultural Organization of the United Nations
proposed an International Emergency Food Council representing twenty States to advise their governments upon the
necessary action.

Emergency measures included the extension of bread ration-
ing and the raising of extraction rates in milling grain ; the
substitution of potatoes and barley in place of wheat ; the
restriction of the use of grain in making beer and spirits, and in
feeding animals ; the diversion of supplies from the less needy
countries to those where the situation was desperate ; arrangements to make immediately available the stocks still held in
North America, where the harvest of 1945 had been good.

A longer-term international policy had to be devised to extend
over four or five years during which shortages were expected.
Besides a continuance of some of the emergency measures, it

included plans for increasing the acreages under the desired
kinds of grain by using the available land and labour in the
various countries in the most effective way ; to enable farmers
to carry out the plans, combined arrangements for fixing prices
had to be made. Also, because during the time of greatest
scarcity there had been restrictions in using grain as cattle feed,
there was now required a system of building-up herds to produce the animal products necessary for full nutrition. Further,
as most of the consuming States were poverty-stricken, they
needed special financial arrangements to assure them requisite
credits or means of payment.

The United Nations (U.N.).—The famine-relief proposals
of the Food and Agricultural Organization were one of the early
practical results of the United Nations Organization (U.N.O.).
The United Nations comprised fifty governments, which in 1945
replaced the League of Nations formed at the close of the First
World War. The U.N.O. is planned to have more definite,
and also wider, powers than those given to the former association, and in its Charter Article 1 sets forth its purposes as
follows :

" 1. To maintain international peace and security, and to that
end : to take effective collective measures for the prevention
and removal of threats to the peace and for the suppression
of acts of aggression. . . .

" 2. To develop friendly relations among nations based on
respect for the principle of equal rights and self-determination
of peoples. . . .

" 3. To achieve international co-operation in solving international problems of an economic, social, cultural, or humanitarian character, and in promoting and encouraging respect for
human rights and for fundamental freedoms for all without
distinction as to race, sex, language, or religion ; and

" 4. To be a centre for harmonizing the actions of nations in
the attainment of these common ends."

It will be observed that the first purpose of the United
Nations may be thought of as negative—to prevent conflict,
while the other purposes are positive—to promote co-operation
in improving the conditions of peoples. To achieve these aims
the Charter set up the following organs :

The General Assembly.—This body consists of representatives
from all the Member-States. Its functions are wide, viz. to

discuss, and in some cases to make recommendations upon, matters relating to the maintenance of international peace and security ; also to initiate studies and to make recommendations to further the aims of the United Nations and to elect and supervise appropriate bodies to carry them out.

The Security Council.—This very important and powerful body is composed of five permanent members, viz. the " Big Five " States of China, France, the U.S.S.R., the U.S.A. and the United Kingdom of Great Britain and Northern Ireland, with six other Member-States elected by the General Assembly, each serving for two years. As the name " Security Council " implies, its special function is the settlement of disputes. This may be done by various pacific means, e.g. by investigating problems at issue ; by recommending measures such as arbitration or reference to the International Court of Justice ; by requiring the parties to a dispute to refrain from certain actions ; by calling Member-States of the United Nations to break off economic or diplomatic relations with any State. Should all peaceful settlement fail, the Security Council may require military action to be taken by some or all Member-States ; for that purpose the Member States have undertaken to hold specific forces at the disposal of the Security Council, and the Council will have available a Military Staff Committee furnished by the States forming its permanent membership.

Decisions of the Security Council will need the approval of seven out of the eleven members and will require also the agreement of all the permanent members ; in other words, any one of the " Big Five " has a power of veto. It may be noted that this provision, and others in the Charter, are not to the liking of all the members of the United Nations, particularly the " middle " or " small " States, but objections were waived to allow the establishment of the United Nations as a working organization.

The International Court of Justice.—This is the "principal judicial organ," empowered to decide upon international disputes capable of legal interpretation which are voluntarily brought to it by Member-States, who undertake to comply with its decisions; it may also be called upon to give an advisory opinion on any legal question submitted to it by the General Assembly or the Security Council. The Court is composed of fifteen judges elected by the General Assembly and the Security Council.

To secure impartiality, it is laid down that the judges must be elected " regardless of their nationality from among persons of high moral character " as well as for their expert knowledge of international law ; also, no two judges may be nationals of any one State. The Court sits at The Hague.

The Economic and Social Council.—This body consists of eighteen representatives of the United Nations elected by the General Assembly. Its duty is to " make or initiate studies and reports with respect to international, economic, social, cultural, educational, health and related matters," and to make recommendations to the General Assembly, or to the Member-States, or to special agencies dealing with subjects within its competence. It may also make " recommendations for the purpose of promoting respect for, and observance of, human rights and fundamental freedoms for all." With such a wide scope, the potentialities of its work are great, but it must be remembered that, while the Council can give advice to States and may influence public opinion by calling conferences and in other ways, it remains for the individual governments either to give effect to the recommendations in whatever way they think fit or to ignore them entirely.

The Trusteeship Council.—In Chapter XVIII, the " Declaration regarding Non-Self-Governing Territories " from the Charter of the United Nations was quoted to show the present-day conception of how colonial dependencies should be administered. To bring practice into line with precept, U.N. has established a Trusteeship Council with authority to supervise " trust territories " which include some, but not necessarily all, of the colonies governed by Member-States. The trust territories consist of three groups : (*a*) those entrusted to particular States after the First World War under a mandate from the League of Nations ; (*b*) those detached from enemy States as a result of the Second World War ; (*c*) those voluntarily placed under the trusteeship system of U.N. by States already responsible for their government. Agreements may be made by Colonial Powers as to which of their dependencies they may be willing to include in the system, and upon what terms.

The General Assembly and, under its authority, the Trusteeship Council may ask the administering States for detailed reports upon the execution of their duties, as the Mandates Commission of the League of Nations had formerly done ;

further, they have additional powers, for they may provide for periodic visits to be paid to the territories and may accept and examine petitions from the inhabitants. For fair consideration of the views of all parties concerned, the Trusteeship Council is composed of representatives of the " Big Five " States, of all Member-States which administer trust territories, and of as many others as may be necessary to balance administering States by those without direct responsibility.

The Secretariat.—A Secretary-General and a staff are appointed to organize the meetings and to carry out the instructions of the organs of the United Nations. The seat of U.N. is in the United States of America, but the international character of the Secretariat is emphasized by the following rules : " In the performance of their duties the Secretary-General and the staff shall not seek or receive instructions from any Government or from any other authority external to the organization. . . . Due regard shall be paid to the importance of recruiting the staff on as wide a geographical basis as possible."

Subsidiary Organs and *Specialized Agencies* are provided for under the Charter, e.g. the *World Health Organization*, the *International Labour Office* (I.L.O.), and the *Food and Agricultural Organization* (F.A.O.). The work of the F.A.O. has a special interest from the geographical point of view. Its objective is permanent collaboration between governments in food-planning based upon world needs. Negatively, it seeks to prevent not only famines, but also the state of affairs in which even in normal times there has been over-production and destruction of a particular food in one area while elsewhere people were suffering from malnutrition because they had not the means of payment.

In its positive aspects, the work of the F.A.O. is based upon scientific knowledge, and one of its chief functions will be to collect information and bring it to the attention of the people by whom it should be applied. It will obtain the facts as to world requirements for diets adequate in kind and amount, and will balance these against normal production, and when necessary take into account forecasts of fluctuations due to weather conditions in the individual producing areas. It can then advise government or other agencies as to the most efficient methods of obtaining the necessary foodstuffs. It is clear, however, that not only must the authorities and the

farmers of the producing countries be willing to take measures
to obtain the desired results, but also the peoples of the consuming countries must be able to pay for the imports at such
prices as will remunerate the producers.

Hence, in 1947, the representatives on the F.A.O. of the
States principally concerned proposed an international scheme
to " iron out " violent fluctuations of prices and supplies.
Under this plan, " ceiling and floor prices " would be fixed for a
few years in advance, and when necessary the governments of
the large producing States would purchase their own farmers'
surplus stocks and sell them to needy countries at prices these
could afford to pay.   The States represented on the F.A.O.,
however, would not empower the World Food Council, the
governing body of the F.A.O., to take such drastic action ; its
function must be only to advise Governments.

The F.A.O. has to deal with all forms of cultivation and
pastoral work, and also with the provision of food by fishing
and whaling ; in addition, because the use of land by farmers
must be related to the growing of trees, forestry comes within
its purview.   It therefore has a wide scope for aiding man to
make the most of nature.

U.N.E.S.C.O.—This is another of the specialized organizations of U.N.   The meaning of the initials and the aims of
the organization are explained in the following extract from its
Preamble.   " The Governments of the States declare that since
wars begin in the minds of men, it is in the minds of men that
the defences of peace must be constructed ; that ignorance of
each other's ways and lives has been a common cause, throughout the history of mankind, of that suspicion and mistrust
between the peoples of the world through which their differences
have all too often broken into war. . . .   For these reasons the
States hereby create the United Nations Educational, Scientific
and Cultural Organization for the purpose of advancing,
through the educational, scientific, and cultural relations of the
peoples of the world, the objectives of international peace and
of the common welfare of mankind. . . ."

The permanent seat of its international secretariat is in Paris,
an annual General Conference of national representatives is held
in turn in different countries, and the work is continuously
supervised by committees dealing respectively with the humanities and the sciences ; education ; media of communication ;

libraries, exchanges, publications and special projects. To emphasize the importance of U.N.E.S.C.O. it may be noted that more than half of mankind can neither read nor write, and that the " mass education " which some States have recently undertaken to remedy this fundamental deficiency still needs to be carried out, and extended, in many parts of the world.

One Harmonious World ?—From what has been stated above it appears indisputable that while there is a unity in the physical world, the world of man now shows many forms of interdependence and interaction, but its unity is still incomplete. Moreover, again using the analogy of the human body as an organism whose health depends on the harmonious interaction of its various parts, it may be considered whether the world of man shows development towards the harmonious working of its communities—racial, cultural, economic and political.

Taking a long view, it is seen that there have been advances in this direction. Racial groups have increasingly come into touch with one another as barriers of distance and of hostility have become lessened ; interminglings have multiplied and, in general, the consequent mixed racial types show no disadvantage in their physical or mental constitution, while from the cultural aspect contacts have been of inestimable value to mankind as a whole.

In economic affairs the partial, but increasing, conquest of distance and time has brought about closer communications between the peoples of the world as producers and consumers ; the result has often involved difficulties and perhaps disasters to particular competitive groups, but in the long run it has meant more efficient production of goods and more abundant supply to consumers. Yet the international organization of trade, and of the financial and currency systems by which trade is carried on, are still imperfect and subject to dislocation.

Political factors are at least partly responsible for economic difficulties and breakdowns, and in the matter of national feelings mankind has not yet outgrown manifestations of " the herd instinct." Human communities have indeed become more rational, and they have commonly shown a tendency to expand their limits, as when tribes have become nations, and when small States have joined into federations. Nevertheless, national groups frequently retain feelings of separateness and occasionally of hostility, and although States may form alli-

ances for particular purposes and thus co-operate, they remain
reluctant to give up their sovereign rights in favour of a wider
political association. Thus, although there are now international organizations, there is not yet any super-national
organization which has a right to determine the actions of its
Member-States, except in so far as such actions are the subject
of voluntary agreements defined and limited in advance. A
World-State, in which all mankind would be included, is still
farther from general acceptance.

Indeed, among the sixty or so independent sovereign States,
clashes of feelings and policies are clearly inevitable under
present conditions. Moreover, in this century such clashes
have led to armed conflicts which, aided by modern means of
communication, have developed into world wars.

One is therefore forced to consider the question whether
there is any trend towards improvement in international
political relationships, and an estimate must depend upon one's
view of the bases of national distrust and enmity. On the one
hand it may be argued that the fundamental causes are tendencies in man to gregariousness and belligerence which are
innate and therefore immutable ; against this view it may be
urged that if such tendencies are indeed innate, nevertheless
they can be " sublimated," to use the psychologists' termin-
ology, into useful instead of harmful expression. Again,
another factor is said to be the economic hardships which some
national groups experience ; against this is set the view that
scientific knowledge, both of methods of production and of the
economic working of societies, can eliminate want. Still
another important cause is said to be fear, in one form or
another ; to this, the answer is given that if the other factors
of innate hostility and economic hardship disappear, fear may
be removed by the spread of knowledge and by mutual understanding. It is certainly true that knowledge is increasing in
every way ; education is improving and expanding, while
cables and broadcasting bring all parts of the world into immediate contact.

Perhaps the most important consideration regarding advance
towards the harmonious interaction of human societies is that
the idea of a community between all men has come into being
and into increasing acceptance. It is related to the realization
of the physical unity of the world—a realization which has

become general only recently—and to the now obvious inter-dependence of the peoples of all regions. As a moral force, the conception of the essential relationship of all mankind may have various origins, e.g. in religious beliefs or in humanitarian feelings ; it may find expression in cultural, economic or political planning ; its complete fulfilment may require much time and its organization may involve diversity within unity ; yet this ideal of a world community is now deeply rooted and widespread.

LIST OF BOOKS

A COMPLETE list of books for a world survey would obviously have to comprise all the standard works on geography. Hence the following list is selected from those dealing either with the world as a whole or with general topics. It therefore excludes books on particular regions or States, although these necessarily supply very much of the material needed for a world survey; it also excludes the innumerable useful articles in publications such as *The Geographical Journal, The Geographical Review, Geography, Economic Geography*, etc. Moreover, this list is restricted to works in the English language.

The following books are arranged, as far as practicable, in the order in which their subject-matter is dealt with in the preceding chapters.

V. C. Finch and G. T. Trewartha : *Elements of Geography* (New York, 1936).

H. Mackinder : *Democratic Ideals and Reality* (London, 1919).

E. Huntington : *The Human Habitat* (New York, 1930).

E. Huntington : *The Pulse of Asia* (Boston, 1907).

E. Huntington : *Mainsprings of Civilisation* (New York, 1945).

W. A. Gauld : *Man, Nature and Time* (London, 1946).

S. W. Wooldridge and R. S. Morgan : *The Physical Basis of Geography* (London, 1937).

J. A. Steers : *The Unstable Earth* (London, 1932).

F. E. Zeuner : *Dating the Past* (London, 1946).

W. R. Jones : *Minerals in Industry* (London, 1943).

A. Street and W. Alexander : *Metals in the Service of Man* (London, 1944).

A. A. Miller : *Climatology* (London, 1931).

W. G. Kendrew : *The Climates of the Continents* (Oxford, 1937).

D. Brunt : *Weather Study* (London, 1942).

C. E. P. Brooks : *The Evolution of Climate* (London, 1922).

S. F. Markham : *Climate and the Energy of Nations* (London, 1942).

G. W. Robinson : *Soils* (Murby, 1936).

E. Ramaan : *Evolution and Classification of Soils* (Cambridge, 1928).

M. I. Newbigin : *Plant and Animal Geography* (London, 1936).

R. Hesse : *Ecological Animal Geography* (London, 1937).

M. E. Hardy : *The Geography of Plants* (Oxford, 1920).

A. C. Haddon : *The Races of Man* (Cambridge, 1924).

A. C. Haddon : *The Wanderings of Peoples* (Cambridge, 1911).

H. J. Fleure : *The Races of Mankind* (London, 1927).

J. Huxley and A. C. Haddon : *We Europeans* (London, 1935).

LIST OF BOOKS **443**

R. Benedict : *Race and Racism* (London, 1942).

E. J. Dingwall : *Racial Pride and Prejudice* (London, 1946).

E. Plant : *Man's Unwritten Past* (London, 1942).

V. G. Childe : *Man Makes Himself* (London, 1936).

V. G. Childe : *Progress and Archæology* (London, 1944).

A. G. Price : *White Settlers in the Tropics* (New York, 1939).

E. E. Kellett : *Short History of Religions* (London, 1933).

C. D. Forde : *Habitat, Economy and Society* (London, 1934).

P. W. Bryan : *Man's Adaptation to Nature* (London, 1933).

E. Huntington, F. E. Williams and S. van Valkenburg : *Economic and Social Geography* (New York, 1933).

N. A. Bengtson and W. van Royen : *Fundamentals of Economic Geography* (New York, 1935).

C. F. Jones and G. G. Darkenwald : *Economic Geography* (New York, 1941).

R. H. Whitbeck and V. C. Finch : *Economic Geography—A Regional Survey* (New York, 1941).

R. O. Buchanan : *Economic Geography of the British Empire* (London, 1935).

A. Pim : *Colonial Agricultural Production* (London, 1946).

United States Department of Agriculture Year Books :

1936 : *Better Plants and Animals*, Vol. I.

1937 : *Better Plants and Animals*, Vol. II.

1938 : *Soils and Men.*

1939 : *Food and Life.*

1940 : *Farmers in a Changing World.*

1941 : *Climate and Man.*

G. V. Jacks and R. O. Whyte : *Rape of the Earth ; a World Survey of Soil Erosion* (London, 1939).

J. P. van Rust : *The Geography of Air Transport* (Washington, 1944).

D. Whittlesey : *The Earth and the State* (New York, 1944).

The Statesman's Year Book (London, Annual).

C. B. Fawcett : *Political Geography of the British Empire* (London, 1933).

W. E. Simnett : *The British Colonial Empire* (London, 1942).

E. A. Walker : *The British Empire : Its Structure and Spirit* (London, 1943).

A. M. Carr-Saunders : *World Population* (Oxford, 1936).

W. D. Forsyth : *The Myth of Open Spaces—Australian, British and World Trends of Population and Migration* (Melbourne and London, 1942).

D. Glass : *Population Policies and Movements* (London, 1940).

R. R. Kuczynski : *The New Population Statistics* (London, 1942).

C. Clark : *The Conditions of Economic Progress* (London, 1940).

C. B. Fawcett : *The Bases of a World Commonwealth* (London, 1941).

J. A. C. Brown : *The Evolution of Society* (London, 1947).

L. Dolivet : *The United Nations : A Guide to the new World Organisation* (London, 1946).

INDEX OF GEOGRAPHICAL NAMES